PROGRESS IN SEMICONDUCTORS
VOLUME 7

PROGRESS

IN

SEMICONDUCTORS

VOLUME 7

Editors

ALAN F. GIBSON, B.Sc., Ph.D.

Prof. R. E. BURGESS, B.Sc., F.R.S.C.

NEW YORK

JOHN WILEY & SONS INC.

1963

©

HEYWOOD & COMPANY LTD.
LONDON
1963

PRINTED IN GREAT BRITAIN BY
SPOTTISWOODE, BALLANTYNE AND CO. LTD.,
LONDON AND COLCHESTER

CONTENTS

BISMUTH

W. S. BOYLE, Ph.D.

and

G. E. SMITH, Ph.D.

*Bell Telephone Laboratories, Murray Hill,
N.J., U.S.A.*

MS. received August 1961

BISMUTH

1. INTRODUCTION

If one is interested primarily in the electronic properties of materials one can make a natural division of solids into three classes; metals, semi-metals, and semiconductors. Both semiconductors and semi-metals contain enough valence electrons to fill an energy band completely. In a semiconductor, the next highest band is separated by an energy gap, but in a semi-metal, the next highest band overlaps the lower or valence band, causing some electrons to 'spill' over, leaving an equal number of holes. A metal has only enough electrons to fill its highest occupied band partially. Among the elemental semi-metals bismuth has a relatively small number of free carriers and hence forms a natural bridge to connect the electronic processes in semi-conductors and metals. Indeed the unique properties of the material have led to the discovery of new phenomena which have later been extended into the other systems. The quantum effects typified by de Haas–van Alphen oscillations are a good example.

In addition to a small number of free charge carriers, the effective masses are small and electron lattice relaxations times are long. These characteristics are all closely related and stem from the small band overlap of conduction and valence bands, in semiconductor terminology. This combination of properties has permitted a large number of fundamentally significant experiments to be performed. Indeed, all the techniques that have proved to be so successful in elucidating the band structure of silicon and german-ium, e.g. cyclotron resonance, infra-red studies, and susceptibility measure-ments, have been used on bismuth by several different groups. This is in addition to the oscillatory experiments mentioned above which occur in a degenerate Fermi gas. Unfortunately, apart from some early calculations by Jones, the theoretical band structure calculations have not progressed nearly so far, and in general we have to be satisfied with a phenomenological effective mass approach for the interrelationships between the diverse data. It is clear that this situation will not exist for long and already perturbation techniques such as the **k.p** method are being applied which give consider-ably more insight into the bands. It is indeed the primary purpose of this paper to bring together all the diverse data which are relevant to the elec-tronic band structure to facilitate further advances of this nature. We can also look forward to significant advances in other directions, one of which will be to obtain a better understanding of the plasma interactions in solids; another stems from the fact that the relative number of carriers can be changed by doping and the band structure can be changed by alloying. All are of fundamental interest and have strong device potential.

We have excluded any discussion of thin films since in general their properties are not closely related to the bulk material, e.g. thin films ~ 1,000 Å are superconducting. We have concentrated rather on presenting data from representative work which elucidate the electronic band structure and other properties of the pure material.

We commence with a brief description of the crystal structure and preparation of single crystal specimens. This is followed by a review of the theoretical work that has been carried out on the electron energy bands. The remainder of the paper attempts to introduce the reader to the wide scope of experimental information. The transport and equilibrium properties are discussed first while we leave for the last sections those experiments which are more closely interrelated in their determination of the band structure. We attempt in summary to present a consistent set of values for the parameters describing the Fermi surface of the free carriers.

2. CRYSTAL STRUCTURE AND SAMPLE PREPARATION

Bismuth has a rhombohedral crystal structure which has been described by three different unit cells. The primitive cell contains two atoms and is shown in Figure 1. The axes x, y, and z are called the diad (binary or two-fold), the bisectrix, and the trigonal (or three-fold), respectively. The lattice vectors are $|a_1| = |a_2| = |a_3| = 4 \cdot 74$ Å and are at an angle $\alpha = 57 \cdot 23$ degrees to one another. The atoms are placed at (u, u, u) and $(-u, -u, -u)$ with respect to the lattice vectors where $u = 0 \cdot 234$. The bismuth structure would be simple cubic if $\alpha = 60$ degrees and $u = 0 \cdot 25$ so that one may also consider bismuth as having a slightly distorted cubic lattice. Precise measurements of the lattice parameters have been made at $4 \cdot 2°$ K, $78°$ K, and $300°$ K by Barrett.[1] He finds that the displacement of the lattice from the simple cubic structure increases with temperature. The second unit cell contains eight atoms and can be imagined as an f.c.c. lattice with two atoms at each site, which has been stretched slightly along a body diagonal. A hexagonal unit cell has been used but has the disadvantage of showing a six-fold symmetry about the trigonal axis when only a three-fold symmetry exists in the actual lattice.

The physical properties of bismuth are highly anisotropic and far from what one might expect from an almost cubic structure. It is probable that atoms in a layer perpendicular to the trigonal axis are held together by mostly covalent bonds and that these layers are weakly held together by van der Waals' forces. Single crystals can be cleaved in this plane much more easily than in any other.

Single crystals can be grown by most of the common methods used with metals and semiconductors. The Bridgman technique can be used if a cast rod is first packed in graphite powder to allow for the fact that bismuth expands about $3 \cdot 5$ per cent in volume upon cooling. The pulling technique[2] has been used by many workers even though it is quite difficult to obtain a clean surface on the melt. Sandblasting is the best way to clean the surface of the material before melting but an etch followed by rinsing may be used. Pulling in a vacuum (10^{-5} mm Hg) is the best method of keeping the surface clean once it has melted; however, the scum formed in an argon or hydrogen atmosphere can usually be tolerated. Crystal growth takes place much faster in a direction perpendicular to the trigonal axis than along it, making attempts to grow crystals in the trigonal direction very difficult.

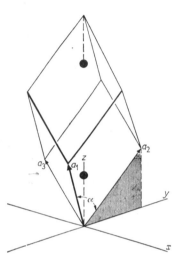

Figure 1. *The rhombohedral unit cell of bismuth containing two atoms. The axes x, y, and z are the diad, bisectrix, and trigonal axes, respectively*
$$|a_1| = |a_2| = |a_3| = 4 \cdot 74 \,\text{Å},$$
$$\alpha = 57 \cdot 23 \text{ degrees, and } u = 0 \cdot 234$$

Another difficulty is the occurrence of many small angle grain boundaries if one pulls faster than about 1 cm/hr. Single crystal seeds cut perpendicular to the trigonal axis may be used but starting polycrystalline growth from the end of a knobbed stainless steel rod is also successful if the growth is necked down for a small distance until a single grain dominates.

Since the material deforms and cleaves easily, care must be taken in cutting samples. A thin, fine grit, high speed abrasive wheel may be used if cutting rates of less than one inch per hour are used, but cutting with an acid string saw is preferable. An abrasive wheel gives deformation into the crystal of about $0 \cdot 010$ in. under the best conditions. Thin flat crystals have been grown between glass slides and thicknesses down to $0 \cdot 001$ in. have been obtained. Also, bars which have been zone refined usually contain large crystallites of high quality.

Many of the experiments on bismuth are performed at low temperatures where impurity scattering dominates, making high purity material desirable. The main impurities in commercially available material are lead, silicon, silver, nickel, and copper. All of these may be segregated successfully by zone refining[3] and impurity contents of 1 p.p.m. are not uncommon.[4]

Several etches and polishes have been developed for bismuth, a few of which we shall describe in detail. A chemical polish[5] is obtained with 6 parts fuming nitric acid, 6 parts glacial acetic acid, and 1 part water. Immersion times of 1–5 min are used and the removal rate is 10^{-3} in.min^{-1}. An etching solution of 1 per cent iodine in methyl alcohol when used after the above polish produces etch pits as shown in Plate I. The etching time is approximately 15 sec. This is also useful for showing grain boundaries in polycrystalline material. An electropolished surface[6] may be obtained with a current density of 1 Acm^{-2} of sample in a solution consisting of 35 g potassium iodide, 1 g iodine, and 10 cm^3 hydrochloric acid dissolved in 200 cm^3 of water. Best results are obtained using polishing periods of 1 min during which approximately 1 mil of material is removed. In all of the above procedures the sample must be dipped in hydrochloric acid to remove a water-insoluble film which accumulates, and then rinsed in distilled water and/or alcohol.

In orienting single crystals of bismuth, a crude determination may be made by cleaving the crystal and etching the cleavage plane. The trigonal axis is then perpendicular to the cleavage plane and the binary axis is parallel to the edge of the triangular etch pits. The binary [10$\bar{1}$] direction is shown in relation to the etch pits in Plate I. The Laue back-reflection X-ray[7] method can be used for more precise determinations.

It is of importance in specifying some physical parameters, such as the tilt of the ellipsoids which comprise the electron Fermi surface, or the sign of the off-diagonal elastic constants, that a convention for aligning cartesian axes with crystalline axes be chosen. The convention most consistently used[6, 8] is that the *positive y* axis be chosen to lie along the projection of one edge of the primitive cell on the plane perpendicular to the [111] direction as shown in Figure 1. To identify the $+y$ axis by Laue photographs, it is sometimes helpful to consider bismuth as an almost simple cubic structure. Then the [111] axis in the simple cubic structure would lie along the trigonal axis in bismuth and the other [111] axes would lie along the basis vectors in the rhombohedral system shown in Plate I. The quadrant formed by the $+y$ and $+z$ axes will then contain one of these 'false' trigonal axes. The quadrant formed by the $-y$ and $+z$ axes contains a 'false' four-fold axis. These points are easily identified on Laue photographs by their apparent symmetry properties and allow a definite identification of the $+y$ direction.

A standard projection for the [111] direction has been published by Salkovitz[9] based on the eight-atom unit cell. This almost face-centred-cubic unit cell is the one from which the Brillouin zone in Figure 2 is constructed.

6

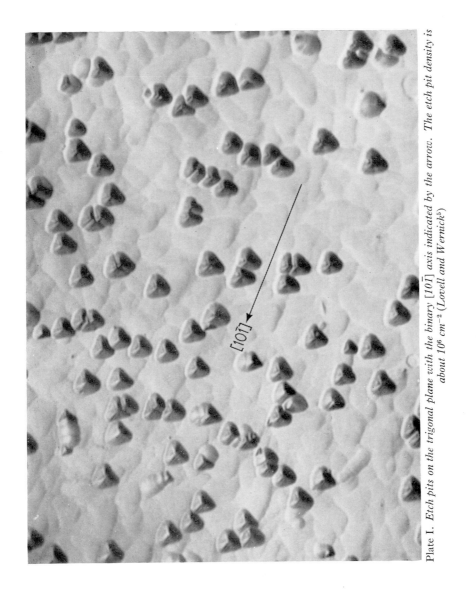

[10Ī]

Plate I. Etch pits on the trigonal plane with the binary [10Ī] axis indicated by the arrow. The etch pit density is about $10^6\ cm^{-2}$ (Lovell and Wernick[5])

[Facing page 6

3. BAND STRUCTURE

To date, the theoretical discussion of the electron bands has mostly been of a phenomenological nature. Specific models of the Fermi surface have been developed in terms of certain experiments and then this information has been used to correlate diverse experimental results. As an increasing number of different experimental techniques have been used to explore the Fermi surface, the model has become more specific, and the parameters more accurately defined. There have indeed been only a few attempts to calculate the electron bands from a knowledge of only the spectroscopic terms of the atom and the lattice constants.

It has long been recognized that the electronic properties must derive from an almost filled Brillouin zone. Jones[10] was one of the first to marshal

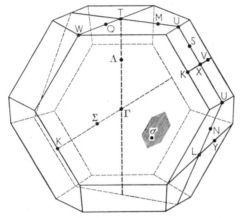

Figure 2. *Brillouin zone and symmetry points for the bismuth structure. The point* Λ *lies on a trigonal axis,* Σ *lies on a binary axis, and* σ *lies in a reflection plane*[16]

evidence for this and he constructed a zone bounded by planes across which a small discontinuity in the energy should occur. His zone was constructed such as to accommodate just exactly the five valence electrons of bismuth. He assumed there was a small overlap in energy between this zone and the next such that small pockets of electrons and holes would be formed. Initially, perhaps, the strongest evidence for the fact that one was dealing with a small number of carriers comes from resistivity measurements. It was found, for example, that the addition of small amounts of tin (four-valence electrons) changed the sign of the temperature coefficient of resistance,[11] indicating that there were at most 10^{-3} conduction electrons per atom.

By symmetry arguments based on the expected location of the overlap, Jones showed that the energy was an even power of the crystal momentum and so could be expressed as $E = (h^2/2m)\alpha_i k_i^2$. An interpretation of the de Haas–van Alphen experiments for electrons showed that the axes of the ellipsoid were not along the principal symmetry axis of the crystal but were tipped out of the trigonal plane by a small angle.[12-14] When expressed in terms of the principal axis of the crystal, the expression for the Fermi surface requires cross terms in the crystal momentum. Recently, cyclotron resonance[14] and de Haas–van Alphen experiments[15] at very low temperatures have developed a correspondingly precise determination of the effective mass parameters for the holes. The holes evidently occupy a position of higher symmetry in the zone since the Fermi surface consists of one or more ellipsoids of revolution about the trigonal axis.

The question of the number or location of the individual elements of the Fermi surface has not been resolved. Symmetry arguments set certain lower limits on the number for particular locations in the zone. The reduced Brillouin zone for the bismuth structure is shown in Figure 2. This zone is similar to that of an f.c.c. lattice except that a distortion has taken place so that there is only one trigonal axis and three binary axes, the distortion being too small to be shown in the Figure. Jones has suggested that the distortion from the simple cubic lattice leads to energy discontinuities across certain planes in the Brillouin zone, which depresses the electron energy and results in a more stable configuration. The various points labelled are points of high symmetry which Cohen[16] has used to determine the possible multiplicities of the Fermi surface and also to fix the constraints on the two-band model (to be discussed below) set by its location in the Brillouin zone. Points of particular interest together with their multiplicity (i) are: Γ (1) the centre of the zone, Λ (2) on the trigonal axis, X (3) centre of rectangular face, L (3) centre of hexagonal face, T (1) centre trigonal face. All other symmetry points a six-fold multiplicity. Points not occupying a symmetry location have twelve- or six-fold multiplicity depending on whether they lie within the zone or on the boundary.

Some indication of the most likely location of the overlap in the Brillouin zone has been obtained from a tight-binding calculation carried out by Mase.[17] In his calculations he makes use of only the p^3 electrons of the $s^2 p^3$ five-valence electrons, considers only nearest neighbours, and neglects overlap integrals. The spin–orbit splitting is introduced as a parameter independent of k. He finds that near the points T and L in Figure 2 there are two bands at each location separated by a small gap of the order of $0 \cdot 1$ eV, each pair lying at approximately the same energy. He suggests, therefore, that these are the most likely regions of overlap. The calculation also shows that at X the bands are all far from the Fermi surface. This is of interest since Jones suggested this as one of the locations of overlap. By treating the spin–orbit splitting as a variable parameter he finds that the lower band at T is much more strongly affected than at the bands at L. In proceeding through the sequence bismuth, antimony, arsenic, the atomic spin–orbit splitting for the p^3 configuration decreases as 1·3, 0·4, and 0·2 eV.[18] It has now been established that alloying antimony with bismuth leads to a behaviour of the resistivity which is similar to that of a semiconductor with a small energy gap when the alloy concentration is 12 per cent antimony.[19] Assuming that the only effects on the energy band arise from the spin–orbit splitting, Mase suggests that this particular dilution of the spin–orbit splitting has lowered the band at T sufficiently to remove the overlap with L.

The energy bands can be represented schematically, as shown in Figure 3. In this diagram **k** has been chosen in such a direction as to intercept the

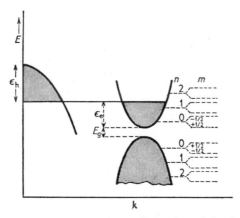

Figure 3. *Schematic representation of band structure showing the Fermi energies* ϵ_h *and* ϵ_e *for holes and electrons, and the direct energy gap* E_g*. The dotted lines on the right show the position of the bottoms of the Landau bands n and the spin splittings m*

minimum of the conduction band, and the region of the overlapping lower band, which gives rise to the holes, is arbitrarily put at the origin. When the effective mass approximation is valid, the energy E_0 near the minimum of the conduction band can be expressed

$$E_0(\mathbf{k}) = \frac{\hbar^2}{2m}\mathbf{k}.\alpha.\mathbf{k} \qquad \ldots (1)$$

The components of the reciprocal effective mass tensor α are given by

$$\alpha_{ij} = \delta_{ij} + m\sum_{rp}{}' \frac{\langle 01|v_i|rp\rangle\langle rp|v_j|01\rangle + \langle 01|v_j|rp\rangle\langle rp|v_i|01\rangle}{(E_0 - E_r)} \qquad \ldots (2)$$

where the summation in general is taken over all bands r, and the two-fold spin degeneracy $p = 1, 2$. The matrix elements of the velocity operation $\langle |v| \rangle$ are expressed in terms of the periodic part of the Bloch function taken at the minimum in the conduction band. The large values of α that are

9

observed for the conduction band suggest that the energy gap E_0–E_r to the next lower lying band is small and that it is the mutual repulsion between the bands that gives rise to the small effective masses. This gap, E_g, has been observed directly in optical experiments,[20, 21] and is indeed found to be only a few hundredths of an electron-volt. Even before this direct confirmation was available, Cohen and Blount[22] suggested that only two bands would be interacting near the conduction band minimum. Not only was the gap expected to be small, but it was also small compared to the spin–orbit splitting. Making use of a one-electron Hamiltonian including spin they found that in the two-band approximation when all three principal components of the inverse effective mass tensor are large, the eigenvalues of the energy in a magnetic field contain a spin-dependent part $\pm \frac{1}{2}g'\beta H$ and is given by

$$E(n, k_z) = (n + \tfrac{1}{2})\hbar\omega_c + \frac{\hbar^2 k_z^2}{2m_z} \pm \tfrac{1}{2}g'\beta H \qquad \ldots (3)$$

where H is the field strength, and $g' = 2m/m^*$. Here m^* is the cyclotron effective mass and is the same mass as that which determines the corresponding orbital level spacing, and g' is the effective spectroscopic splitting factor. This equality only holds under conditions where all the α are large. This is true for the conduction band of bismuth for all those directions of field in which large values of α play an important part; in other words, the orbital and spin splitting should be equal so long the cyclotron effective masses are much less than 1. The dotted lines on the left of Figure 3 show the spin splitting of the orbital levels ($k_z = 0$) when g' is slightly smaller than $2m/m^*$.

A further consequence of the two-band model developed by Lax[23, 24] and Wolff[25] is that the bands should depart rapidly from parabolicity in going away from the band minimum. The analysis of the two-band model proceeds by expanding the periodic part of the Bloch function

$$\Psi'_k(\mathbf{r}) = \exp(i\mathbf{k}.\mathbf{r})u_k(\mathbf{r})$$

in terms of the eigenfunctions, taken at the band edge, of the one-electron Hamiltonian

$$\mathcal{H} = \frac{p^2}{2m} + V + \frac{1}{8}\frac{\hbar^2}{(mc)^2}\nabla^2 V + \frac{\hbar}{2m^2 c^2}(\mathbf{p}.SX\nabla V) \qquad \ldots (4)$$

The four linear equations which determine the expansion coefficients for this basis in terms of the four-band edge functions (i.e. two bands each two-fold spin degenerate) lead to a fourth-order secular equation for the energies. From this secular equation one finds that the energy of the carriers in the conduction band instead of being given by equation (1) is

$$E(k)\left(1 + \frac{E(k)}{E_g}\right) = \frac{\hbar^2}{2m}\mathbf{k}.\alpha.\mathbf{k} \qquad \ldots (5)$$

When a magnetic field is applied, a similar expression holds, given by

$$E(n, k_z)\left(1 + \frac{E(n, k_z)}{E_g}\right) = (n + \tfrac{1}{2})\hbar\omega_c + \frac{\hbar^2 k_z^2}{2m_z} \pm \tfrac{1}{2}g'\beta H \qquad \ldots (6)$$

In the above expressions the components of the inverse effective mass tensor are those at the band edge and are all assumed to be large compared to 1, ω_c is the cyclotron frequency, and n the quantum number for the cyclotron level.

These equations are only valid for the two-band approximation, and Cohen[16] has pointed out that since at least one of the components of α is known to be small, then other bands should be introduced into the expansion. He has generalized equation (5) to include these cases. Moreover, recent results from magneto-optic experiments[26] indicate that the departure from parabolicity is not nearly as large as indicated by equation (6).

The reader is referred to the Appendix for the form of the effective mass tensor for both holes and electrons. Explicit expressions are given to relate the tensor components of the effective mass in the co-ordinates of the principal axes of the crystal to the principal axes of the Fermi ellipsoid. The cyclotron masses for most of the principal crystal directions are also given.

4. TRANSPORT PROPERTIES

Due to the many contributions to the literature concerning transport phenomena in bismuth, we will only discuss a few which are representative of recent work. The categories included are d.c. resistivity, the anomalous skin effect, thermoelectric power, galvanomagnetic effects, and thermal conductivity.

4.1. RESISTIVITY

The resistivity of bismuth shows metallic behaviour in that it decreases almost linearly with decreasing temperature until impurity scattering dominates. With the purest samples (about $99 \cdot 9999$ per cent pure), the residual resistance becomes important at liquid helium temperatures. Resistivity ratios between room temperature and $1 \cdot 2°$ K have been reported[4] to be as high as 400. Unlike metals, the number of carriers in bismuth increases with increasing temperature due to thermal excitation of electrons from the valence band to the conduction band. Galvanomagnetic experiments[27] have shown that the number of electrons increases from $0 \cdot 46 \times 10^{18}$ cm^{-3} at $80°$ K to $2 \cdot 2 \times 10^{18}$ cm^{-3} at $300°$ K. The resistivity at room temperature is $\rho_\parallel \times 1 \cdot 5 \times 10^{-4}\,\Omega$ cm for current flow parallel to the trigonal axis and $\rho_\perp = 1 \cdot 2 \times 10^{-4}\,\Omega$ cm for current flow perpendicular to it.

The mean free path of conduction electrons becomes of the order of 1 mm at liquid helium temperatures, and, if sample dimensions are of comparable size, scattering of carriers from the surface becomes important. Measurements of resistivity in this region have been made by Friedman and Koenig[4] which indicate that scattering from the surface is specular rather than diffuse (diffuse reflection being the case found in other metals). The size effect for specular reflection vanishes if the Fermi surface is spherical, but it has been shown[28] that for a non-spherical surface, as in bismuth, there is an effect when the velocity and momentum have different directions. The resistivity in this case increases as the sample thickness d becomes comparable to the mean free path l, and then reaches a constant value as d/l becomes very small. This is contrasted to the diffuse case where the resistivity continues to increase as d/l decreases.

Another interesting effect seen in the d.c. resistance of bismuth occurs when the cross-sectional area of the sample changes abruptly and the voltage across the transition is measured. It is found[29] that in addition to the normal resistive drop, there is a voltage proportional to the square of the current. This may be explained by considering the electron gas as an incompressible fluid, and making an analogy with the pressure changes which occur in fluid flow due to the Bernoulli effect.†

Bridgman[68] has made measurements of piezoresistance in bismuth and found that the change in resistance under hydrostatic pressure is

$$(\Delta R/R)_{\|} = +2\cdot 45 \times 10^{-5}p$$

parallel to the trigonal axis and

$$(\Delta R/R)_{\perp} = +7\cdot 5 \times 10^{-5}p$$

perpendicular to the trigonal axis, where p is the pressure in kg cm^{-2}. Measurements by Allen[115] of the change in resistance under tension showed that the resistance increased with tension in some crystallographic directions and decreased in others. The above experiments provide values for six linearly independent combinations of the eight components of the piezoresistance tensor necessary to describe a symmetry of bismuth.[114] Measurements of resistance under torque are necessary to provide the additional two quantities needed to determine the piezoresistance tensor completely. Keyes[116] has given a theoretical analysis of the data in terms of a two-carrier model, one of which is multivalleyed. The mechanism for the change in resistance under strain is a shift in the energy minima of one band relative to another and also a relative shift in energy between valleys of the multivalleyed band. This leads to both electron transfer from one energy minima to another and a change in intervalley scattering.

4.2. ANOMALOUS SKIN EFFECT

The r.f. resistance of a metal can be calculated from the d.c. resistance if it is assumed that the mean free path l of the electrons is small compared to the

† It has been brought to the author's attention by S. Koenig that R. Jaggi [*Phys. Rev.* **122,** 444 (1961)] has demonstrated that the 'Bernoulli effect' could be accounted for by a Hall voltage created by the magnetic field of the current in the sample.

skin depth δ. When l becomes comparable to the skin depth the classical formula no longer holds, and one is in the anomalous skin effect region. In the extreme anomalous limit, where $l \gg \delta$, and relaxation effects can be neglected, the surface resistance becomes independent of the relaxation time and depends only on parameters of the Fermi surface.

Pippard and Chambers[30] made measurements of the surface resistance of polycrystalline bismuth rods as a function of temperature and found that extreme anomalous conditions prevailed at liquid helium temperatures and microwave frequencies. Later measurements of surface resistance R in the extreme anomalous region were made by Smith[6] on single crystals, and parameters for the Fermi surface were deduced using Pippard's theory.[31]

For a plane surface, the surface resistance will have the form

$$R = R_x \cos^2 \theta + R_y \sin^2 \theta \qquad \dots (7)$$

where x and y are principal axes of the surface, and θ the angle between the current direction and the x axis. Pippard, assuming that only those electrons travelling nearly parallel to the surface are effective in absorbing energy, derives the expression

$$R_x = b \frac{\sqrt{3}}{2} \left(\frac{\pi \omega^2 h^3}{e^2 c^4 \int |\rho_y| dy} \right)^{1/3} \qquad \dots (8)$$

where ρ_y is the radius of curvature of the Fermi surface in a plane normal to the y axis at the point where the normal to the Fermi surface is parallel to the surface of the metal. The quantities ρ_y and y are expressed in units of momentum. The integration must include summing over all sheets of the Fermi surface when it is not simply connected. A similar expression holds for R_y. The constant b is equal to 8/9 for specular reflection of electrons from the surface of the metal and equal to 1 for diffuse reflection.

It was found experimentally that the surface resistance was much smaller than could be accounted for by the model of the Fermi surface consisting of three electron ellipses having parameters found in other experiments. As a result, it was necessary to assume a six ellipsoid model and also specular reflection in order to reduce the calculated values of R. Parameters for the hole band were also deduced assuming a two ellipsoid model. Since there are an equal number of electrons and holes, they occupy equal volumes in momentum space and therefore give comparable contributions to the surface resistance. Due to the large anisotropy of the Fermi surface, the holes dominate conduction in some orientations and electrons in others, allowing the two contributions to be distinguished.

The quantity $\int |\rho_y| dy$ has the dimensions of a momentum squared, so that the quantities deduced were of the form $\alpha_i \epsilon_e$ and $\beta_i \epsilon_h$, where α_i and β_i are inverse effective mass components for electrons and holes, respectively. The values for α_i and β_i presented in Table 1 were obtained by assuming Shoenberg's[32] value of the electron Fermi energy, $\epsilon_e = 0 \cdot 017$ eV, and a hole

Fermi energy of $\epsilon_h = 0 \cdot 017$ eV deduced in the summary from cyclotron resonance and de Haas–van Alphen data.

Values of the hole Fermi energy have been deduced from specific heat data using both a two[6] and a six[34] ellipsoid model for the hole band, but the resulting values of ϵ_h are too small to be consistent with values derived from other experiments.[14, 97, 102]

TABLE 1. PUBLISHED PARAMETERS FOR THE INVERSE EFFECTIVE MASS TENSORS OF THE ELECTRONS AND HOLES IN BISMUTH (see Appendix)

	α_1	α_2	α_3	α_4	β_1	β_2
Anomalous skin effect[6]	160	1·56	83	6·7	1·7	0·13
de Haas–van Alphen effect[32]	420	0·8	40	4·0		
Cyclotron resonance ‖ field[101]	202	1·67	83·3	8·33		
Cyclotron resonance ⊥ field[14]	114	1·39	108	9·47	14·7	1·07
Sound attenuation[108]	178	1·1	84·5	7·2		
Far infra-red studies[113]	133	1·2	91	6·1		
de Haas–van Alphen effect[97]					20	1·43

4.3. THERMOELECTRIC POWER

The thermoelectric power of single crystal bismuth has been measured between 0° C and the melting point by Chandrasekhar.[35] At room temperature, the Seebeck coefficient along the trigonal axis is

$$S_{\parallel} = -102 \cdot 7 \, \mu\text{V deg. K}^{-1}$$

and perpendicular to the trigonal axis is

$$S_{\perp} = -51 \cdot 4 \, \mu\text{V deg. K}^{-1}$$

This anisotropy can be understood from the expression for S when both electrons and holes are present, which is

$$S_i = \frac{S_e \sigma_{ei} + S_h \sigma_{hi}}{\sigma_{ei} + \sigma_{hi}} \qquad \ldots (9)$$

where S_e and S_h are the partial Seebeck coefficients for electrons and holes, respectively, and σ_{ei} and σ_{hi} are their conductivities in the ith direction. From galvanomagnetic experiments,[27] it is found that $(\sigma_e/\sigma_h)_{\parallel} = 9 \cdot 19$, and $(\sigma_e/\sigma_h)_{\perp} = 2 \cdot 12$ at room temperature, from which $S_e = 125 \cdot 3 \, \mu\text{V deg. K}^{-1}$ and $S_h = +105 \cdot 1 \, \mu\text{V deg. K}^{-1}$ are obtained using equation (9). From the theoretical expressions for S_e and S_h, Fermi energies of $\epsilon_e = 0 \cdot 040$ eV and $\epsilon_h = 0 \cdot 058$ eV are calculated. This results in a band overlap of $0 \cdot 10$ eV, which is at least a factor of 4 larger than the overlap calculated from any low temperature experiment.

Measurements by Sato[36] and by Savornin and Poggi[37] on polycrystalline material do not agree, but it is possible that the samples used in the two sets of experiments had different textures and that the discrepancy could be explained by anisotropy.[35]

Steele and Babiskin[38] measured the thermoelectric power of bismuth at liquid helium temperatures as a function of magnetic field and found S increased to the large value of about $5 \cdot 0$ mV deg. K^{-1} at 10,000 gauss.

4.4. GALVANOMAGNETIC EFFECTS

The galvanomagnetic properties of single crystal bismuth have been studied extensively,[39-44] and an attempt to explain the observed facts in terms of band structure has been made by Jones.[45] Recently, extensive measurements from $77°$ K to $300°$ K and a more complete analysis were carried out by Abeles and Meiboom.[27] To interpret their data, they chose a three-untilted-ellipsoid model for the electrons and a single ellipsoid of revolution for the holes. Two resistivities, two Hall coefficients, and five magnetoresistance coefficients were measured and analysed in terms of the number of carriers and partial mobilities for each carrier ellipsoid. The anisotropies found in both the electron and hole mobility tensors are considerably smaller than those found in Fermi surface measurements at lower temperatures. This may indicate an anisotropic relaxation time. Galvanomagnetic measurements at lower temperatures have been difficult to interpret since the conditions $\omega_c \tau \ll 1$, and samples large enough to neglect size effects are necessary for the type of Abeles and Meiboom analysis. These conditions have been met in preliminary galvanomagnetic data by Friedman and Koenig[4] where fields of $1 \cdot 4$ gauss are used, but no detailed analysis has yet been made.

The galvanomagnetic effects which have been studied at low temperatures and high fields[46-50] such that $\omega_c \tau \gg 1$ are typified by being orders of magnitudes larger than found in other materials. As an example, a plot of transverse magnetoresistance at $4 \cdot 2°$ K is shown in Figure 4. It is seen that the resistance of sample 6, which has a resistivity ratio of

$$R_{4 \cdot 2° K} / R_{0° C} = 2 \cdot 2 \times 10^{-3}$$

increases by a factor of $2 \cdot 4 \times 10^7$ at 100 kgauss. There is also a strong dependence on purity and crystal perfection. The various curves in Figure 4 are for samples having different purities. Merely cycling the temperature has in some cases[49] been enough to make significant changes in a measured quantity.

A classical treatment[51] of high field ($\omega_c \tau \gg 1$) galvanomagnetic effects shows that the transverse magnetoresistance saturates for metals with a closed Fermi surface and a single group of carriers, whereas it increases as H^2 when both electrons and holes are present, as in bismuth. Physically, this large magnetoresistance effect stems from the inability of a semi-metal to maintain a Hall field to oppose the Lorentz force. Both electrons and holes are diverted to the same side of the sample and recombine instead of building up a charge layer. As a result, the electron and hole currents are tilted and, at high Hall angles, have a vanishingly small component of current along the axis of the rod.

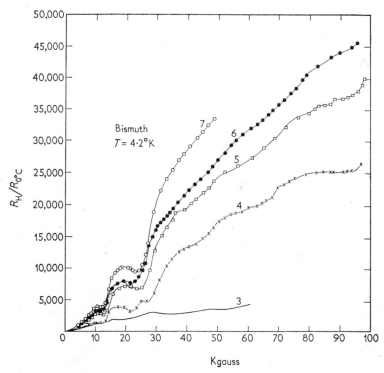

Figure 4. *The resistance along the trigonal axis R_H as a function of magnetic field H normalized to the room temperature resistance $R_{0°C}$. The resistivity ratio between room temperature and $4·2°K$ for sample 6 is $R_{4.2°K}/R_{0°C} = 2·2 \times 10^{-3}$. The various curves are for samples of different purity*

The expressions[51] for the resistivity and Hall constant for the case of equal numbers n of isotropic electrons and holes in a transverse field are

$$\rho = \frac{\sigma_e + \sigma_h}{\sigma_e \sigma_h}\left(1 + \frac{H^2}{H_0^2}\right) \qquad \dots (10)$$

and

$$R = \frac{1}{nec}\frac{1-k}{1+k} \qquad \dots (11)$$

where $k = \sigma_h/\sigma_e$, and $H_0 = cne(\sigma_e\sigma_h)^{-1/2}$. The constant H_0 is the field where $\omega_c\tau = 1$ if both carriers had the same mobilities. This analysis has been extended to the case of three groups of anisotropic carriers and the result is qualitatively similar.[52] The inclusion of quantum effects[53, 54] accounts for the observed de Haas–van Alphen oscillations, but has an insignificant influence on the monotonic portion of the resistivity tensor.

16

4.5. Thermal Conductivity

The thermal conductivity of single crystal bismuth between $25°$ C and $150°$ C has been measured by Kaye,[55] and at room temperature it was found to be

$$K_{\parallel} = 0 \cdot 054 \ \mathrm{W\,cm^{-1}\,deg.\,K^{-1}}$$

parallel to the trigonal axis, and

$$K_{\perp} = 0 \cdot 093 \ \mathrm{W\,cm^{-1}\,deg.\,K^{-1}}$$

perpendicular to the trigonal axis. In conjunction with resistivity and measurements in a magnetic field, it was deduced that the electronic contribution to the thermal conductivity dominates the lattice component. Measurements on polycrystalline material in the range 2–$150°$ K by White and Woods[56] and by Shalyt[57] show that the lattice contribution dominates the electronic below $150°$ K. The thermal conductivity has a $1/T$ temperature dependence to about $5°$ K as is expected from phonon–phonon scattering. Boundary and impurity scattering then dominates and K falls off as T^3. A value of the phonon mean free path l was calculated from K and found to rise exponentially with $1/T$ to a low temperature saturation value of $l = 1$ mm for the purest samples (resistivity ratio $= 50$).

5. EQUILIBRIUM PROPERTIES

5.1. Specific Heat

At liquid helium temperatures, the specific heat C of bismuth can be represented by

$$C = \gamma T + 1944 \left(\frac{T}{\theta}\right)^3 \ \mathrm{J\,mole^{-1}\,deg.^{-1}} \qquad \ldots (12)$$

where the first term is the electronic contribution, and the second is the lattice contribution. The Debye temperature θ has been measured by several workers and found to be $\theta = 120°$ K below $2°$ K. Above $2°$ K the Debye temperature decreases to $\theta = 95°$ K at $T = 10°$ K, and then rises to $\theta = 150°$ K at room temperature.[58, 59]

The electronic contribution to the specific heat γT is small, being about 15 per cent of the total heat capacity at $0 \cdot 3°$ K. Values of γ have been obtained from data above $1 \cdot 0°$ K,[60, 61] and to obtain more accuracy, measurements were extended to $0 \cdot 3°$ K by Kalinkina and Strekov,[33] and to $0 \cdot 1°$ K by Phillips.[62] They obtain $\gamma = 6 \cdot 7 \times 10^{-5}$ J mole^{-1} deg.^{2} and $\gamma = 2 \cdot 1 \times 10^{-5}$ J mole^{-1} deg.^{2}, respectively. The high temperature values fall between these two. However, as pointed out in sub-section 4.2, even the smallest temperature value is too large to be consistent with values of electron and hole parameters derived from other experiments.

The electronic contribution to the specific heat γ is given by

$$\gamma = \frac{\pi^2 k^2}{3} (n'_e + n'_h) \qquad \ldots (13)$$

where n_e' and n_h' are the densities of states of electrons and holes at the Fermi surface. The electron contribution can be calculated from known parameters and subtracted from γ to give the hole contribution, about which less is known. Using a single ellipsoid model for the hole band, Phillips calculates a density of states effective mass of $m_h = 0 \cdot 9 \, m$, and Kalinkina and Strekov obtain $m_h = 2 \cdot 5 \, m$, both of which are in disagreement with the cyclotron resonance value of $m_h = 0 \cdot 16 \, m$.[14] This disparity is reduced if one chooses a six ellipsoid model of the hole band.[34]

Phillips found that below $0 \cdot 3°$ K there is a large contribution to the specific heat due to the nuclear quadrupole moment of bismuth-209 (the sole isotope in naturally occurring bismuth) in the crystal field gradient. This contribution was found to be given by $C_Q = 2 \cdot 8 \times 10^{-7} T^{-2}$ J deg.mole^{-1} and becomes an appreciable addition to equation (12) at temperatures below $1°$ K.

5.2. THERMAL EXPANSION

The thermal expansion of single crystal bismuth was first measured by Fizeau,[63] who found that at room temperature, $\alpha_\parallel = 16 \cdot 5 \times 10^{-6}$ °C^{-1}, and $\alpha_\perp = 12 \cdot 4 \times 10^{-6}$ °C^{-1}. (The notation $\alpha_\parallel$ and $\alpha_\perp$ refers to expansion parallel and perpendicular to the trigonal axis.) Roberts[64] measured α from room temperature to the melting point and found that α was constant to within $25°$ of the melting point and then dropped off. Bridgman[65] made room temperature measurements which were about 15 per cent smaller than the values of Fizeau and Roberts. Measurements of the lattice constant **a** by X-ray techniques[66] showed a linear increase in **a** with temperature with no drop before the melting point. This discrepancy with bulk dimension measurements was explained[64] by the creation of interstitials which take up less room in the lattice. The volume of bismuth contracts $3 \cdot 5$ per cent upon melting and the drop in α was looked upon as a 'premelting' effect. Measurements of α by Erfling[67] from room temperature to $-250°$ C showed that α dropped with temperature proportionally to the specific heat as is predicted by Gruneisen's theory.

5.3. ELASTIC CONSTANTS

The rhombohedral structure of bismuth requires six independent elastic constants. Bridgman[68] measured the isothermal elastic constants by the usual static stress–strain measurements. More recently,[8] the adiabatic elastic constants were measured from velocity of sound measurements. The two sets can be compared, and the discrepancy between individual constants is considerably beyond experimental error, but the linear compressibilities calculated from each set of data agree. The values are

$$K_\parallel = 17 \times 10^{-13} \text{ cm}^2 \text{dyne}^{-1}$$

and
$$K_\perp = 6 \cdot 5 \times 10^{-13} \text{ cm}^2 \text{dyne}^{-1}$$

at room temperature. Measurements[8] made at 80° K and 4·2° K showed only a small percentage change in elastic constants from the room temperature values.

Betts, Bhatia, and Horton[69] calculated the Debye temperature from Bridgman's elastic constants to be $\theta = 128°$ K, which compares favourably with the measured value of $\theta = 120°$ K.

5.4. SUSCEPTIBILITY

We are concerned here only with the constant part of the magnetic susceptibility, i.e. the field-dependent oscillatory effects discussed in Section 7 are excluded.

Early measurements[70-72] on the susceptibility χ of single crystal bismuth showed a large anisotropy between magnetization along the trigonal axis $(\chi_{\parallel})$ and perpendicular to the trigonal axis $(\chi_{\perp})$, and an increase in χ at lower temperatures, as shown in Figure 5. Landau's[73] theory of the diamagnetism

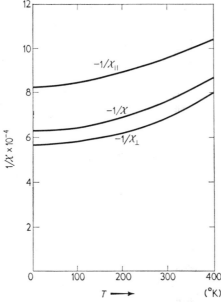

Figure 5. *The reciprocal of the volume susceptibility $1/\chi$ for directions parallel and perpendicular to the trigonal axis. The centre curve is the susceptibility for a polycrystalline sample*[95]

of free electrons as modified by Peierls[74] for the case of conduction electrons in a metal accounted only qualitatively for the temperature dependence and anisotropy.

Measurements by Goetz and Focke[75] on pure and doped bismuth were analysed in detail by Jones[10] using the Landau–Peierls theory. Jones attributed the entire susceptibility to an electron conduction band and, using his model (described previously), deduced a Fermi energy and effective masses from the data. The dependence of χ on doping was explained qualitatively using this model. An analysis of Shoenberg's [12, 13, 76] de Haas–van Alphen data produced more reliable parameters for the electrons. These differed from Jones' parameters by nearly an order of magnitude, showing that the diamagnetism could not be accounted for entirely by conduction electrons.

In the Landau–Peierls theory, a filled valence band has identically zero susceptibility. Adams,[77] however, showed that the presence of unfilled states separated by a small energy gap above a filled band will cause the filled band to exhibit a diamagnetism. The susceptibility χ of the filled band is given approximately by $\chi = \chi_0(m/m^*)$, where χ_0 is the free electron susceptibility calculated from the Landau formula, and m^* is the effective mass associated with the small energy gap. This model does not fit bismuth exactly, since the small overlap fills some of the unfilled states across the gap and leaves holes in the filled valence band. The presence of electrons and holes reduces the value of the susceptibility for the valence band below that calculated for a filled band, but a quantitative calculation for this situation has not been made. Heine[78] used this concept to explain qualitatively the changes in χ as a function of doping obtained in the experiments of Shoenberg and Uddin.[13] Brandt and Razameenko[79] used the same concept to fit their data on lead-doped bismuth.

In all of the above attempts to account for the diamagnetism of bismuth, it has been assumed that the paramagnetic contribution due to the spins of the conduction electrons is small. This is seen from the low temperature expression for the diamagnetic susceptibility of conduction electrons given by

$$\chi_{\text{dia.}} = -\tfrac{1}{3}\beta^2 n'(\epsilon_F)\left(\frac{m}{m^*}\right)^2 \qquad \ldots (14)$$

and the paramagnetic susceptibility given by

$$\chi_{\text{spin}} = \beta^2 n'(\epsilon_F)\left(\frac{g'}{2}\right)^2 \qquad \ldots (15)$$

where $n'(\epsilon_F)$ is the density of states at the Fermi level ϵ_F. For free electrons ($m^* = m$ and $g' = 2$) there is a net paramagnetism, but in a metal with a small m^*, if $g = 2$, it is seen that the conduction electrons can have a net diamagnetism as in the case of bismuth where $m^*/m = 0 \cdot 05$. However, as pointed out in Section 3, the g factor in bismuth is not $g' = 2$, but is given by $g' = 2m/m^*$, making the net susceptibility of the conduction electrons paramagnetic.

As a result, our understanding of the susceptibility is not yet complete. In addition to taking the large g factors into account, it is desirable to have a more quantitative understanding of the diamagnetic contribution of the valence electrons. Heine has suggested that measurements of χ on bismuth–antimony alloys would provide the needed information. In the semiconducting range of these alloys at low temperatures there is a completely filled valence band, and the interpretation of the data would be unhindered by the presence of conduction electrons.

5.5. MAGNETOSTRICTION

Kapitza[82] has measured the magnetostriction of bismuth from $87°$ K to $288°$ K in fields up to 250 kgauss and found the effect to be larger than in other diamagnetic substances studied. With a field of 250 kgauss along the trigonal axis, he found that the length *increased* by a factor of 2×10^{-5}, and that with the field perpendicular to the trigonal axis, the length *decreased* by a factor of 2×10^{-5}. In both cases the change in length was measured along the direction of the field. At low fields the change of length was proportional to H^2 for both orientations.

If the magnetic properties of a substance can be completely described by a bulk susceptibility, one would expect a sample with a net diamagnetic moment to contract in a magnetic field. The fact that bismuth expands with a field along the trigonal axis was left unexplained.

5.6. PRESSURE–TEMPERATURE PHASE DIAGRAM

The pressure–temperature phase diagram of bismuth is shown in Figure 6. The transitions I–II and II–III are accompanied by volume changes and

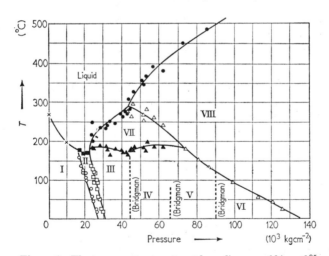

Figure 6. *The pressure–temperature phase diagram of bismuth*[85]

sharp resistance changes.[83, 84] The transitions III–IV, IV–V, and V–VI were seen by Bridgman as volume changes at room temperature without perceptible resistance changes. Bundy[85] investigated the region above

$270°$ C and 30,000 kgausscm^{-2} by observing resistance changes and discovered phases VII and VIII. The structure of all phases except I is not known. In the I–II transition, the resistance drops sharply by a factor of 6 and can be used as a pressure calibration point. The existence of high pressure phases have also been seen in shock wave measurements.[86, 87]

6. OPTICAL PROPERTIES

The infra-red and far infra-red region of the spectrum is appropriate for studies of the first interband transitions and the electronic transitions near the Fermi surface in bismuth. Higher frequency measurements explore the gross features of the band structure where all the valence electrons can participate and will be unrelated to the small pockets of carriers of interest to us in this paper. The work of Walker, Rustgi, and Weissler[88] carried out in the ultra-violet for example, shows singularities in reflection and transmission in the region of 600–800 Å. This falls near the plasma frequency calculated for the participation of all five-valence electrons. If, on the other hand, only intraband transitions are considered, then the free carrier plasma frequency falls near 50 microns.

There have been several magneto-optic studies, and this has proved to be a fruitful field of investigation. The large magnetoresistance for direct current was a motivation for an early search for magneto-optic effects by MacLennan[89] in the near infra-red. Partly because of the imperfect crystals and the small ratio of magnetic field to frequency that was employed, no effects were observed. The first results of significance were obtained by Keyes et al.,[90] who studied the reflection coefficient in the region of 15 microns and in fields up to 300 kgauss. In these experiments they were able to observe sharp discontinuities in the reflected power which occurred near the field expected for cyclotron resonance. These observations now appear to be more readily interpreted in terms of interband transitions.[24]

We will first discuss the information available at zero field and then return to the magneto-optic data.

In order to relate the optical data to other experiments through the effective mass parameter, we require expressions for the propagation constant η in terms of the conductivity. The necessary relationships are obtained by inserting plane wave solutions for the radiation fields into Maxwell's equations and eliminating the H field to obtain

$$(\eta^2 - \epsilon_0) E_i = -\frac{4\pi i}{\omega} \sigma_{ij} E_j \qquad \ldots (16)$$

Choosing a propagation direction and an appropriate set of orthogonal E vectors we obtain a secular equation from which the corresponding propagation constants are given by

$$\eta^2 = \epsilon_0 - \frac{2\pi i}{\omega} \{\text{trace } \sigma \pm [(\text{trace } \sigma)^2 - 4\|\sigma\|]^{1/2}\} \qquad \ldots (17)$$

This equation can be used in conjunction with the boundary conditions at the sample surface to determine the transmission or reflection coefficient. In general this leads to a complex set of equations, and the reader is referred to the original work for the full details. [14, 91, 113]

If we confine our attention to the case of long relaxation times so that $\omega\tau > 1$, then the second term on the right side of equation (17) is always real and η will be pure real or pure imaginary. If η is real, the reflection coefficient is given by $(\eta - 1/\eta + 1)^2$ for the particular polarization mode selected, and η is one of the roots of equation (17). If η is pure imaginary, there is no propagation into the sample and, within our approximation of infinite relaxation time, the reflection coefficient is unity.

Singularities in the optical properties therefore occur at critical values of the frequency or magnetic field which lead to a zero crossing of the propagation constant. These singularities will be of the form of a sharp minimum in the reflection coefficient followed immediately by complete reflection.

Consider first the simplest situation of propagation along an isotropic trigonal axis of the crystal at zero field, and also assume that the part of the dielectric constant ϵ_0 arising from interband transitions is constant and that the contribution from the holes can be neglected. Equation (17) then reduces to

$$\eta^2 = \epsilon_0 - \frac{4\pi n e^2}{m\omega^2} \cdot \frac{\alpha_2 + \alpha_1}{2} \qquad \ldots (18)$$

As frequency decreases, the reflection coefficient R decreases steadily from a value

$$R = \left| \frac{\sqrt{\epsilon_0} - 1}{\sqrt{\epsilon_0} + 1} \right|^2$$

at high frequencies to a minimum at a frequency

$$\omega = \left[\frac{4\pi n e^2}{m(\epsilon_0 - 1)} \cdot \left(\frac{\alpha_1 + \alpha_2}{2} \right) \right]^{1/2} \qquad \ldots (19)$$

We note that this occurs near the plasma frequency

$$\omega_p = \left[\frac{4\pi n e^2}{m\epsilon_0} \cdot \left(\frac{\alpha_1 + \alpha_2}{2} \right) \right]^{1/2}$$

However, the longitudinal plasma oscillations whose frequency is given by ω_p are not excited by a transverse electromagnetic wave. The optical singularity at the frequency given by equation (19) has been called a dielectric anomaly.

For propagation along a binary axis there are two independent plane polarized modes. One propagation constant is given by equation (19) and the other by

$$\eta_2^2 = \epsilon_0 - \frac{4\pi n e^2}{m\omega^2} \cdot \alpha_3 \qquad \ldots (20)$$

23

The resulting two dielectric anomalies in reflection experiments are shown in Figure 7. From this and other data a reliable value of the ratio $(\alpha_2 + \alpha_1)/2\alpha_3$ can be obtained and is found to be $1:37$.

With crystals sufficiently strain free and of the order of $0\cdot1$ mm thick, it is possible to carry out transmission measurements. For propagation along a binary axis there are again two low frequency cut-off points for the two degrees of polarization which yield the same ratio for $(\alpha_2 + \alpha_1)/2\alpha_3$ as obtained in reflection. At higher frequencies in the region of 20 microns, a strong absorption sets in with increasing frequency. This has been attributed to the onset of interband transitions. A precise value of the energy gap for a

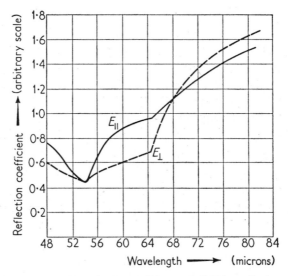

Figure 7. *The reflection coefficient at $4\cdot2°K$ for radiation incident on a binary face. $E_\perp$ and $E_\parallel$ refer to plane polarized radiation perpendicular and parallel to the trigonal axis*

vertical transition can be determined from interband magneto-optic experiments to be discussed later.

Figure 8 shows the transmission spectrum along a trigonal axis. The pass-band lies between the interband transitions and the low frequency dielectric anomaly. As expected, the low frequency cut-off occurs at the same frequency as one of the low frequency singularities along the binary axis. Well defined interference fringes are also apparent and from this the real part of the propagation constant given by equation (18) can be derived. The lower curve in Figure 9 gives this value of η as a function of frequency. The upper curve is the derived value of ϵ_0 by fitting two points on the curve and solving for the two parameters ϵ_0 and $4\pi n e^2(\alpha_1 + \alpha_2)/2m$. If we use the fact that $\alpha_1 \gg \alpha_2$ and choose $\alpha_1 = 120$ we obtain $n = 4\cdot8 \times 10^{17}$ electrons cm^{-3} and $\epsilon_0 = 99\cdot8$.

 The application of a magnetic field increases the complexity of the conductivity tensor so that in general no simple expressions such as equation (18) occur. However, singularities in the optical properties still originate in the dielectric anomalies which are now both field and frequency dependent.

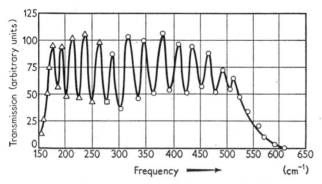

Figure 8. *Transmission spectrum with interference fringes for propagation along a three-fold axis at $T = 4\cdot2°K$ (Boyle and Brailsford[113])*

Some physical insight can be obtained by considering a single group of carriers which will dominate the conductivity near their cyclotron resonant frequency. The propagation constant for circularly polarized light is then given by

$$\eta = \left[\epsilon_0 - \frac{4\pi ne^2}{m^*(\omega - \omega_c)\omega}\right]^{1/2} \qquad \ldots (21)$$

For frequencies such that $\omega^2 > 4\pi ne^2/m^* \epsilon_0$, there will be two singularities

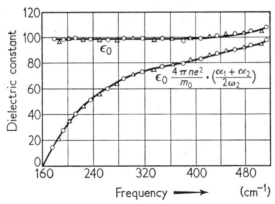

Figure 9. *The lower curve is the value of the dielectric constant derived from Figure 8 and fitted by the expression given below the curve. A two-point fit was made at 175 and 240 cm^{-1} and then the remainder of the curve used to derive the value of ϵ_0 plotted in the upper part of the Figure (See Figure 8)*

25

as the field is monotonically increased, one occurring at the first zero crossing of η^2, and the second at $\omega = \omega_c$. At frequencies such that $\omega^2 < 4\pi ne^2/m\epsilon_0$ only one singularity will occur at $\omega = \omega_c$.

The experimental data relevant to the latter case are shown in Figure 10,

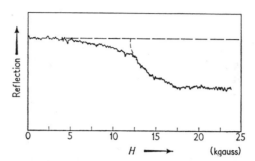

Figure 10. *Reflection from a binary face as a function of field strength; H parallel to binary axis; $T = 4 \cdot 2°K$ (See Figure 8)*

where the reflection coefficient is shown as a function of field strength for the case when both the direction of propagation and the magnetic field are along a binary axis of the crystal. The singularity which occurs at $12 \cdot 8$ kgauss is attributed to cyclotron resonance, which at the signal wavelength of 87 microns yields a cyclotron mass of $1 \cdot 04 \times 10^{-2}m$.

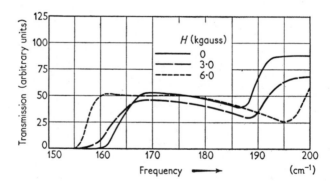

Figure 11. *Transmission spectrum with the direction of propagation and magnetic field along the binary axis. This shows the motion of the dielectric anomaly with magnetic field; $T = 4 \cdot 2°K$*

The anisotropy leads to two dielectric anomalies at zero field as described earlier but, contrary to what one would expect from the simple analysis of a single isotropic group of carriers, one of these dielectric anomalies moves to longer wavelengths with increasing field. The experimental results which illustrate this are shown in Figure 11. We will not pursue the analysis including anisotropy which is required to treat this situation. It has been shown,[113] however, that this splitting is to be expected and can be used to determine the product $\alpha_1\alpha_3$. Although this particular product can be more accurately determined from cyclotron resonance data, the numerical agreement is within experimental error and lends support to the model being used to interpret the infra-red data.

Magnetoreflection experiments have been performed at sufficiently high frequencies such that interband transitions could be excited.[26] In addition to determining the direct energy gap, they provide a means of exploring the shape of the bands beyond the immediate vicinity of the Fermi surface. In these experiments, radiation was incident on a trigonal plane of the crystal and a magnetic field was applied parallel to the surface, either along a binary

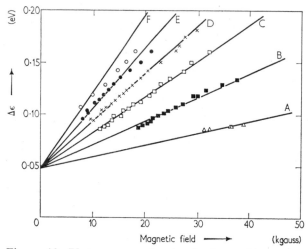

Figure 12. *Photon energy for interband transition versus magnetic field determined by magnetoreflection experiments from a trigonal face. The field is along a binary axis and $T = 4\cdot2°K$ (Brown, Mavroides, Dresselhaus, and Lax[26])*

or bisectrix axis. At liquid air temperatures and below, the reflected signal was oscillatory as a function of the applied magnetic field. Although the amplitude was not large (rising to 3 per cent at the maximum field of 40 kgauss) the sensitivity of the apparatus was such that five or more well resolved transitions could be identified over the range from 6 to 14 microns. A plot of the experimental data is shown in Figure 12, where the energy of the observed transition $\Delta\epsilon$ is plotted against the magnetic field. For vertical transitions from the valence to the conduction band (see Figure 3)

$$\Delta\epsilon = (n^C+\tfrac{1}{2})\hbar\omega_c^C \pm \tfrac{1}{2}g'\beta H + (n^V+\tfrac{1}{2})\hbar\omega_c^V \pm \tfrac{1}{2}g'\beta H + E_g \quad \ldots(22)$$

where the superscripts V and C refer to the valence and conduction bands.

Since the data can be fitted quite well by a series of straight lines corresponding to different values of n^C and n^V the following information can be obtained.

3

(1) Extrapolation to $H = 0$ gives the value of E_g which is found to be $0 \cdot 047 \pm 0 \cdot 003$ eV.
(2) The cyclotron masses and effective values g' for the conduction and valence bands. It is found that in all cases $g' = 2m/m^*$ and $m^{*V} = m^{*C}$ within an experimental error of 10 per cent.
(3) There is no apparent change in effective mass over a range of energies of $0 \cdot 07$ eV which throws considerable doubt on the validity of the two-band model (i.e. equation (6)).

7. THE SHUBNIKOV–DE HAAS EFFECT

In this section we will discuss a group of phenomena which are associated with the quantized motion of the charge carriers in a magnetic field. The common factor which correlates all these effects is that some physical parameter shows a variation with magnetic field which is periodic in the reciprocal of the field strength. These oscillations were first observed in the magnetoresistance of bismuth by Shubnikov and de Haas[93] in 1930. Soon after this, de Haas and van Alphen[70] saw a similar effect in the magnetic susceptibility. Oscillatory effects of this type are often referred to de Haas–van Alphen oscillations. The list of properties which have shown this effect includes resistivity, thermoelectric power, electronic heat capacity, infra-red transmission, thermal conductivity, and undoubtedly any other quantity in which the charge carriers play any role.

A simple qualitative explanation of the oscillations follows from a consideration of the motion of a charge carrier in a magnetic field. It is readily shown that with a magnetic field H applied in the z direction, the possible eigenvalues of the energy are

$$E_{(n,k_z)} = (n+\tfrac{1}{2})\hbar\omega_c + \frac{\hbar^2 k_z^2}{2m} \qquad \dots (23)$$

The energy is quantized into a series of bands each with k_z as a continuous variable for any particular value of the n quantum number. If we are dealing with the motion of the charge carriers in a solid and use an effective mass approximation, then the energy levels which correspond to different values of n are referred to as 'Landau bands'.

One of the simplest ways of representing this is shown in Figure 13 which shows how for a spherical Fermi surface the volume of momentum space inside the surface is divided into a series of concentric cylinders.

It can be seen from equation (23) that the density of states per unit energy dN/dE in each one of the Landau bands increases monotonically with decreasing k_z and becomes infinite at the bottom of each band as $k_z \to 0$.

This follows from the fact that the density of states in one dimensional momentum space dN/dk_z is a constant, and hence

$$dN/dE = (dN/dk_z) \cdot (dk_z/dE) \propto 1/k_z$$

i.e. $$dN/dE \to \infty \text{ as } k_z \to 0$$

28

The condition for the density of states to be infinite at the Fermi surface is therefore simply $(n+\frac{1}{2})\hbar\omega_c = \epsilon_f$ and so

$$(n+\tfrac{1}{2}) = \epsilon_f m^* c / eH\hbar \qquad \dots (24)$$

This shows the origin of the $1/H$ periodicity and also that from a measurement of the period, one obtains the product $\epsilon_f m^*$.

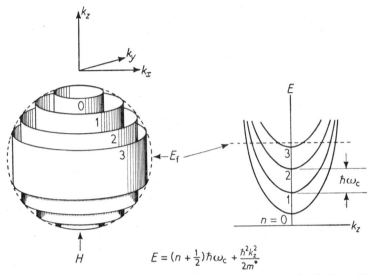

$$E = (n + \tfrac{1}{2})\hbar\omega_c + \frac{\hbar^2 k_z^2}{2m^*}$$

Figure 13. *Quantization of electron orbits in momentum space (neglecting spin) with the field along the z direction. The right side of the Figure shows the energy dependence on the quantum number n and the momentum k_z (By courtesy of J. E. Kunzler)*

It can also be shown[94] that the number of states per unit volume below some energy E, $Z(E)$ is given by

$$Z(E) = \frac{2(2m)^{1/2} eH}{\hbar^2 c} \sum_{n} [E - (n+\tfrac{1}{2})\hbar\omega_c]^{1/2} \qquad \dots (25)$$

where the summation is taken over all positive values of n up to the point where the term in brackets becomes negative. The first part of the expression allows for the degeneracy of each Landau band and the summation includes all contributing bands. Spin has not been included. If the g factor is normal, i.e. $\simeq 2$, then for small m^* all Landau bands are essentially two-fold degenerate. On the other hand, if the g factor is equal to $2m/m^*$, then the summation in equation (25) can be modified to take this into account by replacing E by $E \pm \frac{1}{2}\hbar\omega_c$. If large values of n are involved in the summation, the expression can be evaluated by approximate methods.[95] For small values of n it is instructive to evaluate the sum directly by numerical methods. We note in passing, that for certain orientations in bismuth where the product $m^* E_f$ is small, that n is equal to 1 at a magnetic field strength of about 15 kgauss. The results of such a calculation are shown in Figure 14.

For simplicity, the ratio F of $Z(E)$ at a certain field H to the corresponding number at zero field is plotted against $E/\hbar\omega_c$. For a fixed number of carriers in a band, this shows the fractional change in the Fermi energy that must occur as the field forces various Landau bands through the Fermi surface. It should be noted that for large values of $E/\hbar\omega_c$ (i.e. small fields), the Fermi level fluctuates with a changing magnetic field, but the average value remains constant. It is only when $E/\beta H$ approaches a value near 1 that the average Fermi energy increases appreciably. In bismuth, where there are several other pockets of electrons and holes, the fluctuations in the Fermi level are damped out by approximately the ratio of the density of states in the other electron and hole pockets.

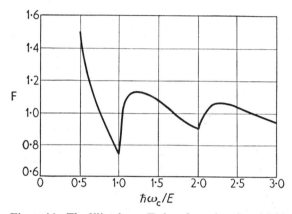

Figure 14. *The filling factor F plotted as a function of field strength in the dimensionless units of $\hbar\omega_c/E$. The filling factor is the ratio of the number of states up to some energy E, taken at a field $\hbar\omega_c/E$ compared to the value at zero field*

Although closely related, there are two distinct causes for oscillatory phenomenon: the periodic changes in the density of states at the Fermi surface and the co-existing changes in the Fermi energy. In some physical processes one will predominate over the other, and it is useful in formulating a qualitative model to distinguish between the two. It is also apparent that for small quantum numbers, the curve in Figure 14 is asymmetrical about the line $F = 1$. This leads to a difference in the period and phase factor depending on whether the upper or lower turning points are taken.[49]

The most detailed studies of oscillatory properties have been made on the magnetic susceptibility. An excellent review article on this subject has been written by Shoenberg,[32] who has himself studied a large number of metals, including bismuth. We shall therefore only outline briefly the most important features, paying specific attention to the information relating to the band structure.

A detailed consideration of the theory of the magnetic susceptibility shows that when dealing with carriers in a parabolic band,

(a) the period of the oscillatory component of the susceptibility is given by equation (24), i.e. $\Delta(1/H) = \hbar e/m^* \epsilon_f c$;

(b) the amplitude of the oscillations decreases with temperature as $\exp(-2\pi kT/\hbar\omega)c$, but the period is unaltered;

(c) the effect of broadening of the levels through finite relaxation time τ of carriers may be represented by an increase of the temperature[96]

$$\Delta T = h/2\pi^2 k\tau.$$

It is not possible to deduce the individual components of the effective mass tensor from a measurement of the periods alone, since all data involves the Fermi energy as a parameter. The extra piece of information that is required can be deduced from a measurement of the amplitude as a function of temperature. In dealing with the electrons there is the additional difficulty that one component, m_1, enters in such a way in all of the expressions for the periods that only the products $m_1 m_2$, etc., can be found. Shoenberg resorted to another independent piece of information available from a measurement of the amplitude of the oscillations. Unfortunately, the theoretical agreement with experiment for the amplitude in other metals where this problem of the linear independence of the masses does not arise is not good. It is therefore desirable to resort to experiments other than de Haas–van Alphen oscillations to deduce the individual components of the effective masses.

Because of their larger mass, it is only recently that experimental evidence has been obtained for the oscillatory contribution to the susceptibility from holes. The larger mass of the holes gives a much smaller amplitude and period compared to the electrons. By carrying out experiments at very low temperatures, i.e. $0.07°$ K, Brandt[97] has obtained excellent data on holes. This data together with the data on electrons is summarized at the end of this section in Table 2.

A phenomenon closely related to the oscillations in the magnetic susceptibility are the magneto-thermal oscillations.[81] It has been found that the temperature changes periodically in a suitably thermally isolated bismuth crystal as either the magnitude or direction of a uniform magnetic field in the crystal is varied. The temperature changes in the crystal are reversible and are a measure of the changing entropy of the electrons. Since the experiments are performed under adiabatic conditions, this results in a corresponding change in the entropy or temperature of the crystal lattice. These temperature excursions are a direct consequence of the varying density of states at the Fermi surface, and should have a shape given by the derivative of the curve in Figure 14.

The experimental procedure is quite straightforward, the only difficulty being the choice of a suitable calorimeter to give the proper sample-to-bath thermal relaxation time. It is desirable to have this relaxation time long compared to the time for the sample to go through one period, and yet sufficiently short so that the sample can be brought down to nearly the bath temperature in a convenient time. The change in magnetic field must be slow enough to avoid eddy-current heating of the sample. The experiments reported here were performed over a range of temperature from $1\cdot3°$ K to $4\cdot3°$ K; the magnitude of the temperature changes are of the order of a few thousandths of a degree and are readily detected by using a carbon resistance thermometer. Figure 15 shows the temperature oscillations that occur with a monotonically increasing magnetic field. The expected sawtooth character is clearly visible. The shape of the curve allows an unambiguous assignment of the phase of the oscillations, since the sharp singularity must occur as a Landau level passes through the Fermi surface.

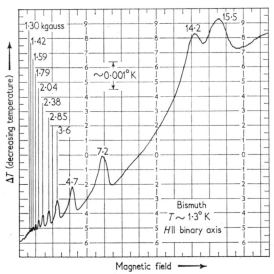

Figure 15. *The temperature variation ΔT observed as a function of magnetic field*[81]

From equation (24) a plot of the successive peaks versus $1/H$ should lead to a straight line with an intercept at $1/H \to 0$ of $1/2$. However, these magneto-thermal experiments rather unambiguously gave an intercept which was clearly not $1/2$ and indeed was almost identically zero, as shown in Figure 16. This discrepancy in the phase factor had also been observed in the susceptibility oscillations. The work of Blount and Cohen mentioned earlier on the anomalously large g factor in bismuth showed that phase shifts of this order of magnitude could be expected from the spin splitting of the Landau bands. Their theory indicates that the effective g factor is large and leads to a spin splitting approximately equal to the orbital splitting and phase factor of zero. If the spin splitting were not exactly equal to the orbital splitting, each of the individual oscillations in a magneto-thermal experiment would show fine structure.

This fine structure is actually observed in the first oscillation shown in Figure 15. At lower fields the resolution decreases rapidly and is not observable in this type of experiment. From these measurements good evidence was obtained for the anomalously large g factor with an indication that $g_{\text{eff}} = 1 \cdot 8 \; m/m^*$ for this orientation. These measurements agree with the spin resonance measurement reported in another section.

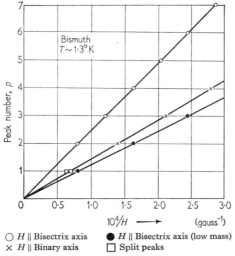

○ $H \parallel$ Bisectrix axis ● $H \parallel$ Bisectrix axis (low mass)
× $H \parallel$ Binary axis ☐ Split peaks

Figure 16. *Successive cooling peaks as a function of reciprocal field strength obtained in a magneto-thermal experiment*

The oscillatory transport properties have been reviewed recently with particular reference to bismuth.[98] We will therefore omit any discussion of this information apart from an inclusion of the periods in Table 2.

TABLE 2. PERIODS OF OSCILLATIONS

Axis (∥ to H)	Period in $1/H$ (unit 10^{-5} gauss)				
	(a)	(b)	(c)	(d)	(e)
Electrons					
Trigonal	1·2	1·18	1·57	1·6	
Binary		7·4	7·1	7·5	7·1
			0·25	0·30	
Bisectrix	4·3	4·3	4·1	4·2	4·1
	8·2	8·5	8·2	8·8	8·2
Holes					
Trigonal	1·6				
Binary	0·41				

(a) Brandt, N. B. *J. exp. theor. Phys.* **38**, 1355 (1960); Brandt, N. B., and Razumeenko, M. V. *J. exp. theor. Phys.* **39**, 276 (1960)
(b) Shoenberg, D. *Phil. Trans.* **A245**, 1 (1952)
(c) Steele, M. C., and Babiskin, J. *Phys. Rev.* **98**, 359 (1955); Babiskin, J. *Phys. Rev.* **107**, 981 (1957)
(d) Connell, R. A., and Marcus, S. A. *Phys. Rev.* **107**, 940 (1957)
(e) Kunzler, J. E., and Boyle, W. S. In press

8. RESONANCE EXPERIMENTS

The long relaxation times and small effective masses in bismuth have made possible a variety of resonance experiments from which detailed knowledge of the band structure has been obtained. Under this category we include cyclotron resonance with the magnetic field parallel to the surface of the sample, cyclotron resonance with the magnetic field perpendicular to the surface of the sample, spin resonance, and magneto-acoustic resonance.

8.1. PARALLEL FIELD CYCLOTRON RESONANCE

Classical skin effect theory predicts that for a single group of carriers a cyclotron resonance effect should not be present when the field is parallel to the surface of the metal,[99] but it has been shown by Azbel' and Kaner[100]

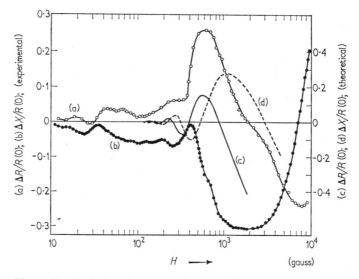

Figure 17. *Variation of surface resistance and surface reactance as a result of cyclotron resonance with the d.c. magnetic field in the plane of the sample. Theoretical curves plotted from equation (26) assuming* $Z(0) = \exp(i\pi/3)$, $\omega\tau = 3$, *and* $m^*/m_0 = 0\cdot11$ *(Aubrey and Chambers[101])*

that an effect will be seen when anomalous skin effect conditions prevail. They predicted a periodic variation of the surface impedance Z given by

$$Z = Z(0)\left[1 - \exp\left(-2\pi i \frac{\omega}{\omega_c}\right)\exp\left(-\frac{2\pi}{\omega_c\tau}\right)\right]^{1/3} \quad \ldots (26)$$

where $Z(0)$ is the zero field impedance, τ is the relaxation time, and ω the r.f. frequency. It is seen that the condition $\omega_c\tau > 1$ is needed for observation of the effect and experimentally this requires pure material, liquid helium temperatures, and microwave frequencies. From this periodic variation, one can deduce a value for the cyclotron effective mass m^*. The expressions for this cyclotron mass for bismuth in terms of the effective mass parameters are given in the Appendix.

This type of resonance was first observed in bismuth by Aubrey and Chambers,[101] and a typical plot of their data is shown in Figure 17. To sort out the effective mass parameters for electrons, they combined their data with Shoenberg's[32] de Haas–van Alphen data to arrive at the values presented in Table 1. No evidence of hole resonances was found but oscillations observed in later work by Aubrey[102] were attributed to holes and agreed with the parameters deduced from de Haas–van Alphen measurements[97] and cyclotron resonance.[14]

8.2. PERPENDICULAR FIELD CYCLOTRON RESONANCE

Cyclotron resonance in bismuth with the magnetic field perpendicular to the surface has been studied by several workers.[14, 91, 103, 104] The use of

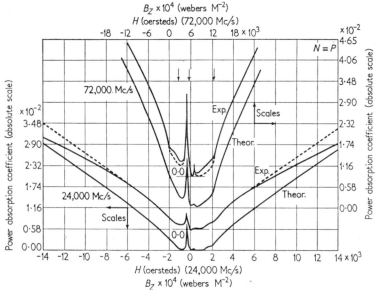

Figure 18. *Plots of power absorption coefficients versus magnetic field from both theory and experiment with magnetic field normal to the sample surface and along a two-fold axis. The vertical arrows indicate the cyclotron resonance fields*[14]

circular polarization in this geometry has the advantageous feature of distinguishing electron from hole resonances, depending on the sense of circularity with respect to the direction of the field.

In this geometry, cyclotron resonance in a metal differs from that observed in semiconductors in that the skin depth of a typical semiconductor is large compared to the sample size and the specimen is placed within a microwave cavity. For a metal, the skin depth is small compared to the sample size and the specimen is made part of the cavity wall. As a result, the absorption for the case of a metal is determined by the discontinuity in electrical properties at the surface rather than the intrinsic absorption.

The dielectric constant ϵ for the simple case of a single isotropic carrier in a lattice with dielectric constant ϵ_L is given by

$$\epsilon = \epsilon_L - \frac{ine^2\tau}{m^* \epsilon_0 \omega[1+i(\omega-\omega_c)\tau]} \qquad \ldots (27)$$

where n is the number of carriers, ϵ_0 is the permittivity of free space, and the other quantities have been defined in sub-section 8.1. For the semiconductor case, the absorption is given by the imaginary part of ϵ, and for the case of a metal, the absorption coefficient A is given by

$$A = 4Re\,(1/\sqrt{\epsilon}) \qquad \ldots (28)$$

Galt[14] has made an extensive study of cyclotron resonance in bismuth for this geometry and a plot of his data for the magnetic field along the two-fold axis is shown in Figure 18 together with theoretical curves. The resonance fields are marked by arrows and the spikes between them are singularities caused by the presence of more than one group of carriers. Such a singularity between two resonance fields occurs when the contribution of each carrier to the real part of the dielectric constant cancels to give zero and has been called a 'dielectric anomaly'. The resulting mass parameters for electrons and holes are presented in Table 1. An extension of this work to higher fields[105] has shown that no other resonances occur up to fields corresponding to an effective mass of $9m$.

8.3. SPIN RESONANCE

The existence of large g factors discussed previously ($g \simeq 200$ in some directions) has been confirmed experimentally by the observation of direct spin resonance absorption.[80] Identification of the resonances was made by placing the static magnetic field in the plane of the sample and using linearly polarized microwaves with the r.f. magnetic field both parallel and perpendicular to the static magnetic field. The appearance of a resonance when the fields are perpendicular and not when they are parallel indicates a magnetic dipole transition (see Figure 19). Transitions involving both a cyclotron resonance and a spin transition were also observed. In such a double transition, the spin energy is either added to or subtracted from the energy between Landau levels. In the notation of Figure 3, this corresponds to transitions $n=0$, $m=+\frac{1}{2}$ to $n=1$, $m=-\frac{1}{2}$ and $n=0$, $m=-\frac{1}{2}$ to $n=1$, $m=+\frac{1}{2}$, respectively.

8.4. MAGNETO-ACOUSTIC RESONANCE

Two types of resonant behaviour are possible between conduction electrons in a magnetic field and a sound wave; geometric resonance[106, 107] and cyclotron resonance. Geometric resonance has been observed by Reneker[108] in bismuth and is seen as an oscillation in the sound attenuation as a function of magnetic field. The maxima and minima in the oscillations occur when the cyclotron orbit diameter d is an integral or half integral number of sound wavelengths λ, respectively. The condition for the observation of this effect is that $l/\lambda \gg 1$, where l is the mean free path. When the magnetic field is increased so that d becomes less than λ, an increase in attenuation large compared to the resonant oscillations occurs. Harrison[109] has attributed this increase to the presence of density waves in the electron–hole carrier gas.

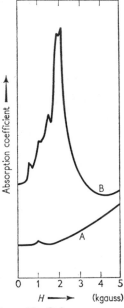

Figure 19. *Spin resonance absorption using 72 kMc plane polarized radiation. Curve A has the microwave field parallel to the static H field, and curve B has them perpendicular to one another. The static field is along the trigonal axis, and $T = 4·2°K$ (Smith, Galt, and Merritt[80])*

Cyclotron resonance is possible in principle, but it requires ultrasonic frequencies which lie in the microwave region.

Another, rather novel, effect called the 'tilt' effect was also observed by Reneker. This occurs when the magnetic field is tilted an angle ν from the direction transverse to the direction of sound propagation. If v_s is the sound velocity and v_F the Fermi velocity of the fastest group of carriers in the direction of the magnetic field, then at a critical angle given by $\sin\nu_c = v_s/v_F$, the electron will 'surf ride' along the sound wave and experience a constant acceleration. This effect appears as a peak in the ultrasonic absorption as a function of magnetic field orientation relative to the propagation direction. A detailed theoretical treatment of the effect has been given by Spector.[110, 111]

The quantity which determines the period of oscillation in the geometric resonances is a suitably chosen Fermi momentum. The quantity which determines de Haas–van Alphen periods, which were also observed in high field measurements by Reneker, are suitably chosen areas in momentum space. The tilt effect measured a Fermi velocity which has the dimensions of a Fermi momentum divided by an effective mass. Combining these measurements, a set of electron effective mass parameters given in Table 1 and a Fermi energy of $\epsilon_c = 0 \cdot 020$ eV was deduced. No effects were seen which could be attributed to holes.

9. ALLOYS OF BISMUTH

Bismuth is a Group V element and if it is doped with a Group IV element such as lead or tin, the Fermi level is lowered, resulting in an increased

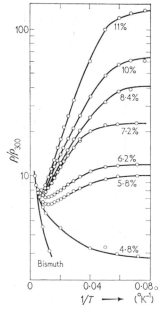

Figure 20. *The resistivity normalized to that at 300° K versus the reciprocal of the absolute temperature for samples containing 0–11 per cent antimony in bismuth*[19]

number of holes and a decreased number of electrons. In the same manner, the addition of a Group VI element increases the number of electrons and decreases the number of holes. Most of the effects discussed in previous sections have been carried out on doped samples and qualitatively confirm

BISMUTH

this model.[11, 13, 14, 75, 79] One of the main difficulties in interpretation has been ascertaining the exact doping level since the solid solubilities of lead, tin, and tellurium in bismuth are of the order of 1 per cent and this results in high segregation coefficients. Another difficulty is that the effective mass varies as the Fermi level is raised or lowered by doping,[14] and in some experiments it is difficult to distinguish quantitative changes in effective mass from changes in relaxation time.

Antimony, which is the next lightest Group V element, forms a complete solid solution with bismuth. These alloys would be expected to have a continuously changing band structure with concentration without changing the equality of electrons and holes. The electrical properties of this system were studied by Jain[112] and he found that the overlapping bands in bismuth uncrossed as the antimony content increased and the alloys became semiconductors. The uncrossing point occurred at 5 per cent antimony in bismuth and he calculates a maximum energy gap of $E_g = 0 \cdot 014$ eV occurring at 12 per cent antimony in bismuth. At higher concentrations the effective band gap becomes smaller, and band crossing occurs against 40 per cent antimony in bismuth. In Figure 20, a plot of resistivity versus temperature for several of these alloys shows the exponential rise in resistivity characteristic of the semiconducting range. The effective energy gap E_g was obtained directly from the slope of the resistivity curve. If allowance is made for the change in mobility with temperature, the 'effective' energy gap is increased and would bring it into better agreement with the infra-red data.

10. SUMMARY

We shall now briefly summarize the progress which has been made in understanding the band structure as it relates to the free carriers. To do this we utilize some of the more consistent quantities obtained from the various experiments discussed above. This will determine effective mass parameters, Fermi energies, and ellipsoid multiplicities for electrons and holes. The parabolic model of the Fermi surface presented in the Appendix will be used.

The most accurately determined periods in de Haas–van Alphen experiments (see Table 2, columns (c) and (e)) are along the binary and bisectrix axes. From these periods, the products of Fermi energy times effective mass along the bisectrix axis are $\epsilon_e m^* = 2 \cdot 84 \times 10^{-4}$ eV and $\epsilon_e m^* = 1 \cdot 42 \times 10^{-4}$ eV, and along the binary axis, $\epsilon_e m^* = 1 \cdot 64 \times 10^{-4}$ eV. The corresponding cyclotron masses[14] are $0 \cdot 0180$, $0 \cdot 0091$, and $0 \cdot 0105$. From these three sets of data, a consistent Fermi energy of $\epsilon_e = 15 \cdot 6 \times 10^{-3}$ eV is obtained. In cyclotron resonance experiments, the parameters that are determined are combinations of $\alpha_1\alpha_2$, $\alpha_1\alpha_3$, and $\alpha_1\alpha_4$. However, an independent determination of $\alpha_3/\alpha_1 = 0 \cdot 69$ by far infra-red studies allows a good set of the individual α to be determined,[113] and they are presented in Table 1 under far

39

infra-red studies. Using these α, $\epsilon_e = 15 \cdot 6$ and a six-ellipsoid model, the number of electrons is calculated from

$$N = 6 \frac{8\pi}{3h^3} \frac{(2m\epsilon_e)^{3/2}}{[\alpha_1(\alpha_2 \alpha_3 - \alpha_4)^2]^{1/2}}$$

to be
$$N_e = 5 \cdot 8 \times 10^{17} \text{ cm}^{-3}.$$

This is to be compared with the value

$$N_e = 4 \cdot 4 \times 10^{17} \text{ cm}^{-3}$$

obtained directly in infra-red measurements, and

$$N_e = 5 \cdot 5 \times 10^{17} \text{ cm}^{-3}$$

obtained from anomalous skin effect measurements.

In the same manner, we can obtain parameters for the holes using Brandt's[97] de Haas–van Alphen data and the cyclotron resonance data of Galt et al.[14] With the magnetic field tilted 60 degrees away from the trigonal axis, Brandt measures $(\beta_1^2/4) + (3\beta_1\beta_3/4) = \epsilon_h^2 \times 0 \cdot 22 \times 10^{-16}$ eV^{-2}. Using cyclotron resonance values of $\beta_1 = 14 \cdot 7$ and $\beta_3 = 1 \cdot 07$ yields a hole Fermi energy of $\epsilon_h = 17$ MeV which agrees with the value of $\epsilon_h = 16$ MeV obtained from the temperature variation of de Haas–van Alphen amplitudes. The number of holes per ellipsoid is calculated to be $N = 6 \cdot 9 \times 10^{17}$ cm^{-3} so that the condition that the number of holes equals the number of electrons indicates that there is a one-hole ellipsoid.

APPENDIX

In this Appendix the analytical expression for the Fermi surface and the relationships between the components of the effective masses and the inverse effective masses are presented. Generalized expressions for the cyclotron masses and the specific masses along principal crystal directions are given.

ELECTRONS

Assuming that the parabolic model holds and choosing x, y, z to be the binary, bisectrix, and trigonal axes, then one of the electron ellipsoids is given by

$$E_{(k)} = \frac{\hbar^2}{2m}(\alpha_{xx} k_x^2 + \alpha_{yy} k_y^2 + \alpha_{zz} k_z^2 + 2\alpha_{yz} k_y k_z) \qquad \ldots (A1)$$

Two others are obtained by rotations of ± 120 degrees about the trigonal axis and a total of six may be obtained by applying inversion. Another notation which is often used is $\alpha_1 = \alpha_{xx}$, $\alpha_2 = \alpha_{yy}$, $\alpha_3 = \alpha_{zz}$, and $\alpha_4 = \alpha_{yz}$. Equation (A1) is the most general ellipsoidal form allowed by the symmetry of the crystal.

The cross-terms arise because the principal axes of the ellipsoidal energy surface do not lie along the crystal axes but are rotated by an angle θ around the binary axis. If $1'$, $2'$, $3'$ are the principal axes of the co-ordinate system in which α is diagonal then

$$\alpha_1' = \alpha_{xx}$$

$$\alpha_2' = \frac{\alpha_{yy}+\alpha_{zz}+[(\alpha_{yy}-\alpha_{zz})^2-4\alpha_{yz}^2]^{1/2}}{2}$$

$$\alpha_3' = \frac{\alpha_{yy}+\alpha_{zz}-[(\alpha_{yy}-\alpha_{zz})^2-4\alpha_{yz}^2]^{1/2}}{2}$$

and
$$\theta = \tan^{-1} 2\alpha_{yz}/\alpha_{yy}-\alpha_{zz} \qquad \ldots (A2)$$

Some data are presented in terms of the effective mass tensor where $m = \alpha^{-1}$. In terms of the α, the effective mass tensor is

$$\begin{bmatrix} 1/\alpha_{xx} & 0 & 0 \\ 0 & \dfrac{\alpha_{zz}}{\alpha_{zz}\alpha_{yy}-\alpha_{yz}^2} & -\dfrac{\alpha_{yz}}{\alpha_{zz}\alpha_{yy}-\alpha_{yz}^2} \\ 0 & -\dfrac{\alpha_{yz}}{\alpha_{zz}\alpha_{yy}-\alpha_{yz}^2} & \dfrac{\alpha_{yy}}{\alpha_{zz}\alpha_{yy}-\alpha_{yz}^2} \end{bmatrix} \qquad \ldots (A3)$$

With a magnetic field applied along some direction z' in the crystal then the kinetic energy of the charge carriers is given by

$$E(n, k_{z'}) = (n+\tfrac{1}{2})\hbar\omega_{cz'}+\frac{\hbar^2 k_{z'}^2}{2m_{z'}} \qquad \ldots (A4)$$

where $\omega_{cz'}$ is the angular cyclotron frequency $= eH/cm_{cz'}$, and

$$m_{cz'} = m(\mu_1^2\alpha_2'\alpha_3'+\mu_2^2\alpha_3'\alpha_1'+\mu_3^2\alpha_1'\alpha_2')^{-1/2} \qquad \ldots (A5)$$

Here μ_1, μ_2, μ_3 are the direction cosines of H with respect to the principal axes $1'$, $2'$, $3'$. The second term in equation (A4) which gives the contribution to the energy from the unquantized motion along the field direction

$$m_z' = m\left(\frac{\mu_1^2}{\alpha_1'}+\frac{\mu_2^2}{\alpha_2'}+\frac{\mu_3^2}{\alpha_3'}\right) \qquad \ldots (A6)$$

The cyclotron masses for the magnetic field along the principal crystal directions are:

$H\|z$ (trigonal axis)
$$m^* = m\,[(m_{yy}\,m_{zz}-m_{yz}^2)\,m_{xx}/m_{zz}]^{1/2}$$
$$= m\,(\alpha_{xx}\,\alpha_{yy})^{-1/2}$$

$H\|x$ (binary axis)
$$m_1^* = m\,(m_{yy}\,m_{zz}-m_{yz}^2)^{1/2}$$
$$= m\,(\alpha_{yy}\,\alpha_{zz}-\alpha_{yz}^2)^{-1/2}$$
$$m_2^* = \left[\frac{2mm_{xx}(m_{yy}\,m_{zz}-m_{yz}^2)}{m_{xx}+3m_{yy}}\right]^{1/2}$$
$$= 2m\,(3\alpha_{xx}\,\alpha_{yy}+\alpha_{yy}\,\alpha_{zz}-\alpha_{yz}^2)^{-1/2}$$

$H\|y$ (bisectrix)

$$m_1^* = m\left[(m_{yy}m_{zz}-m_{yz}^2)\,m_{xx}/m_{yy}\right]^{1/2}$$
$$= m\,(\alpha_{xx}\alpha_{zz})^{-1/2}$$
$$m_2^* = 2m\left[\frac{m_{xx}(m_{yy}m_{zz}-m_{yz}^2)}{3m_{xx}-m_{yy}}\right]^{-1/2}$$
$$= 2m\left[\alpha_{zz}\alpha_{xx}+3(\alpha_{yy}\alpha_{zz}-\alpha_{yz}^2)\right]^{-1/2}$$

HOLES

Most experimental evidence points to a more symmetrical Fermi surface for holes which consists of ellipsoids of revolutions about the trigonal axis.

Hence
$$E_{(k)} = \frac{h^2}{2m}[\beta_1(k_x^2+k_y^2)+\beta_3 k_z^2] \qquad \ldots(A7)$$

and $\beta_1 = 1/m_{xx}$, $\beta_3 = 1/m_{zz}$.

The cyclotron mass m^* is given by

$$m^* = m\,(\beta_1\beta_3\sin^2\theta+\beta_1^2\cos^2\theta)^{-1/2} \qquad \ldots(A8)$$

where θ is the angle between the direction of the magnetic field and the trigonal axis.

ACKNOWLEDGEMENT

The authors are grateful to J. K. Galt and E. I. Blount for valuable discussion concerning parts of this paper.

REFERENCES

1. BARRETT, C. S. *Austr. J. Phys.* **13**, 209 (1960)
2. PORBANSKY, E. M. *J. appl. Phys.* **30**, 1455 (1959)
3. WERNICK, J. H., BENSON, K. E., and DORSI, D. *Trans. Amer. Inst. min. (metall.) Engrs* **209**, 996 (1957)
4. FRIEDMAN, A. N., and KOENIG, S. H. *I.B.M.J. Res. Developm.* **4**, 158 (1960)
5. LOVELL, L. C., and WERNICK, J. H. *J. appl. Phys.* **30**, 234 (1959)
6. SMITH, G. E. *Phys. Rev.* **115**, 1561 (1959)
7. BARRETT, C. S. *Structure of Metals*, 2nd Edn (McGraw-Hill, New York, 1953)
8. ECKSTEIN, Y., LAWSON, A. W., and RENECKER, D. H. *J. appl. Phys.* **31**, 1534 (1960); **32**, 752 (1961)
9. SALKOVITZ, E. I. *J. Metals, N.Y.* **8**, 176 (1956)
10. JONES, H. *Proc. roy. Soc.* **A147**, 396 (1934); **A155**, 653 (1936)
11. UFFORD, C. W. *Phys. Rev.* **32**, 505 (1928)
12. BLACKMAN, M. *Proc. roy. Soc.* **A166**, 1 (1938)
13. SHOENBERG, D., and ZAKI UDDIN, M. *Proc. Camb. phil. Soc.* **32**, 499 (1936); *Proc. roy. Soc.* **A156**, 687 (1936)
14. GALT, J. K., YAGER, W. A., MERRITT, F. R., CETLIN, B. B., and BRAILSFORD, A. D. *Phys. Rev.* **114**, 1396 (1959)
15. BRANDT, N. B. *J. exp. theor. Phys.* **11**, 975 (1960); **10**, 405 (1960)
16. COHEN, M. H. *Phys. Rev.* **121**, 387 (1961)
17. MASE, S. *J. phys. Soc. Japan* **13**, 434 (1958); **14**, 584 (1959)
18. CONDON, E. U., and SHORTLEY, G. H. *The Theory of Atomic Spectra* (Cambridge University Press, London, 1951)
19. JAIN, A. L. *Phys. Rev.* **114**, 1518 (1959)
20. BOYLE, W. S., and RODGERS, K. F. *Phys. Rev. Lett.* **2**, 338 (1959)
21. LAX, B. *Rev. mod. Phys.* **30**, 122 (1958)

22. COHEN, M. H., and BLOUNT, E. I. *Phil. Mag.* **5**, 115 (1960)
23. LAX, B. *Bull. Amer. phys. Soc.* Ser. II, **5**, No. 3, 167 (1960)
24. LAX, B., MAVROIDES, J. G., ZEIGER, H. J., and KEYES, R. J. *Phys. Rev. Lett.* **5**, 241 (1960)
25. WOLFF, P. A. Private communication
26. BROWN, R. N., MAVROIDES, J. G., DRESSELHAUS, M. S., and LAX, B. *Phys. Rev. Lett.* **5**, 243 (1960)
27. ABELES, B., and MEIBOOM, S. *Phys. Rev.* **101**, 544 (1956)
28. PRICE, P. J. *I.B.M. J. Res. Developm.* **4**, 152 (1960)
29. CHESTER, M. *Phys. Rev. Lett.* **5**, 91 (1960)
30. PIPPARD, A. B., and CHAMBERS, R. G. *Proc. phys. Soc. Lond.* **A65**, 955 (1952)
31. PIPPARD, A. B. *Proc. roy. Soc.* **A224**, 273 (1954)
32. SHOENBERG, D. *Progress in Low Temperature Physics*, Vol. II, p. 255 (North-Holland, Amsterdam, 1957)
33. KALINKINA, I. N., and STRELKOV, P. G. *J. exp. theor. Phys.* **34**, 616 (1958;) *Soviet Phys. JETP* **7**, 426 (1958)
34. SMITH, G. E. *J. Phys. Chem. Solids* **20**, 168 (1961)
35. CHANDRASEKHAR, B. S. *J. Phys. Chem. Solids* **11**, 268 (1959)
36. SATO, T. *J. phys. Soc. Japan* **6**, 125 (1951)
37. SAVORNIN, J., and POGGI, A. *C. R. Acad. Sci. Paris* **238**, 656 (1956)
38. STEELE, M. C., and BABISKIN, J. *Phys. Rev.* **98**, 359 (1955)
39. KAPITZA, P. *Proc. roy. Soc.* **A119**, 358 (1928)
40. STIERSTADT, O. *Z. Phys.* **95**, 355 (1935)
41. DE HAAS, W. J., BLOM, J. W., and SCHUBNIKOW, L. *Physica* **2**, 907 (1935)
42. GERRITSEN, A. N., and DE HAAS, W. J. *Physica* **8**, 802 (1940)
43. GERRITSEN, A. N., DE HAAS, W. J., and VAN DER STAR, P. *Physica* **9**, 241 (1942)
44. TANABE, Y. *Sci. Rep. Res. Insts Tôhoku Univ.* **A2**, 341 (1950)
45. JONES, H. *Proc. roy. Soc.* **A155**, 653 (1936)
46. BRODIE, L. C. *Phys. Rev.* **93**, 935 (1954)
47. REYNOLDS, J. M., HEMSTREET, H. W., LEINHARDT, T. E., and TRIANTOS, D. D. *Phys. Rev.* **96**, 1203 (1954)
48. CONNELL, R. A., and MARCUS, J. A. *Phys. Rev.* **107**, 940 (1957)
49. BABISKIN, J. *Phys. Rev.* **107**, 981 (1957)
50. ALERS, P. B., and WEBBER, R. T. *Phys. Rev.* **91**, 1060 (1953)
51. LIFSHITZ, I. M., AZBEL', M. YA., and KAGANOV, M. I. *J. exp. theor. Phys.* **31**, 63 (1956); *Soviet Phys. JETP* **4**, 41 (1957)
52. BASS, F. G., KAGANOV, M. I., and SLEZOV, V. V. *Phys. Metals Metallogr.* **5**, No. 3, 24 (1957)
53. ARGYRES, P. N. *Phys. Rev.* **109**, 1115 (1958)
54. LIFSHITZ, I. M. *J. exp. theor. Phys.* **32**, 1509 (1957); *Soviet Phys. JETP* **5**, 1227 (1957)
55. KAYE, G. W. C. *Proc. roy. Soc.* **A170**, 561 (1939)
56. WHITE, G. K., and WOODS, S. B. *Phil. Mag.* **3**, 342 (1958)
57. SHALYT, S. *J. Phys., Moscow* **8**, 315 (1944)
58. KEESOM, W. H., and VAN DEN ENDE, J. H. *Proc. Acad. Sci. Amst.* **33**, 243 (1930); **34**, 210 (1931); ANDERSON, C. T. *J. Amer. chem. Soc.* **52**, 2720 (1930)
59. ARMSTRONG, L. D., and GRAYSON-SMITH, H. *Canad. J. Res.* **A27**, 9 (1949)
60. RAMANTHAN, K. G., and SRINIVASAN, T. M. *Phys. Rev.* **99**, 442 (1955)
61. KEESOM, P. H., and PEARLMAN, N. *Phys. Rev.* **96**, 897 (1954)
62. PHILLIPS, N. E. *Phys. Rev.* **118**, 644 (1960)
63. FIZEAU, H. *C. R. Acad. Sci., Paris*, **68**, 1125 (1869)
64. ROBERTS, J. K. *Proc. roy. Soc.* **A106**, 385 (1924)
65. BRIDGMAN, P. W. *Proc. nat. Acad. Sci., Wash.* **10**, 411 (1924)
66. GOETZ, A., and HERGENROTHER, R. C. *Phys. Rev.* **38**, 2075 (1931); **39**, 548 (1932); **40**, 137 (1932); **40**, 643 (1932)
67. ERFLING, H. D. *Ann. Phys. Lpz.* **34**, 136 (1939)
68. BRIDGMAN, P. W. *Proc. Amer. Acad. Arts Sci.* **60**, 305 (1925)
69. BETTS, D. D., BHATIA, A. B., and HORTON, G. K. *Phys. Rev.* **104**, 43 (1956)
70. DE HAAS, W. J., and VAN ALPHEN, P. M. *Proc. Acad. Sci. Amst.* **33**, 1106 (1930)

71. FOCKE, A. B. *Phys. Rev.* **36**, 319 (1930)
72. KAPITZA, P. *Proc. roy. Soc.* **A131**, 243 (1931)
73. LANDAU, L. *Z. Phys.* **64**, 629 (1930)
74. PEIERLS, R. *Z. Phys.* **80**, 763 (1933); **81**, 186 (1933)
75. GOETZ, A., and FOCKE, A. B. *Phys. Rev.* **45**, 170 (1934)
76. SHOENBERG, D. *Proc. roy. Soc.* **A170**, 341 (1939)
77. ADAMS, E. N. *Phys. Rev.* **89**, 633 (1953)
78. HEINE, V. *Proc. phys. Soc. Lond.* **A69**, 513 (1956)
79. BRANDT, N. B., and RAZUMEENKO, M. V. *J. exp. theor. Phys.* **39**, 276 (1960); *Soviet Phys. JETP* **12**, 198 (1961)
80. SMITH, G. E., GALT, J. K., and MERRITT, F. R. *Phys. Rev. Lett.* **4**, 276 (1960)
81. BOYLE, W. S., HSU, F. S. L., and KUNZLER, J. E. *Phys. Rev. Lett.* **4**, 278 (1960)
82. KAPITZA, P. *Proc. roy. Soc.* **A135**, 537 (1932); *Nature, Lond.* **124**, 53 (1929)
83. BRIDGMAN, P. W. *American Institute of Physics Handbook*, Section 4d, p. 4 (McGraw-Hill, New York, 1957); *Proc. Amer. Acad. Arts Sci.* **81**, 228 (1952); *Phys. Rev.* **48**, 896 (1935)
84. BUTUZOV, V. P., GONIKBERG, M. G., and SMIRNOV, S. P. *C. R. Acad. Sci. U.R.S.S.* **89**, 651 (1953) Translation: *National Science Foundation tr-76*
85. BUNDY, F. P. *Phys. Rev.* **110**, 314 (1958)
86. DUFF, R. E., and MINSHALL, F. S. *Phys. Rev.* **108**, 1207 (1957)
87. HUGHES, D. S., GOURLEY, L. E., and GOURLEY, M. F. *J. appl. Phys.* **32**, 624 (1961)
88. WALKER, W. C., RUSTGI, O. P., and WEISSLER, G. L. *J. opt. Soc. Amer.* **49**, 471 (1959)
89. McLENNAN, J. C., ALLIN, E. J., and BURTON, A. C. *Phil. Mag.* **14**, 508 (1932)
90. KEYES, R. J., ZWERDLING, S., FONER, S., KOLM, H. H., and LAX, B. *Phys. Rev.* **104**, 1804 (1956)
91. LAX, B., BUTTON, J., ZEIGER, H. J., and ROTH, L. M. *Phys. Rev.* **102**, 715 (1956)
92. BOYLE, W. S., BRAILSFORD, A. D., and GALT, J. K. *Phys. Rev.* **109**, 1396 (1958)
93. SCHUBNIKOW, L., and DE HAAS, W. J. *Commun. phys. Lab. Univ. Leiden* 207a, 207c, 207d, 210a (1930)
94. PEIERLS, R. E. *Quantum Theory of Solids* (Clarendon, Oxford, 1955)
95. WILSON, A. H. *Theory of Metals*, 2nd Edn (Cambridge University Press, London, 1953)
96. DINGLE, R. B. *Proc. roy. Soc.* **A211**, 517 (1952)
97. BRANDT, N. B. *J. exp. theor. Phys.* **38**, 1355 (1960), *Soviet Phys. JETP* **11**, 975 (1960); BRANDT, N. B., DUBROVSKAYA, A. E., and KYTIN, G. A. *J. exp. theor. Phys.* **37**, 572 (1959), *Soviet Phys. JETP* **10**, 405 (1960)
98. KAHN, A. H., and FREDERIKSE, H. P. R. *Solid State Physics*, Vol. 9, p. 257 (Academic, New York, 1959)
99. ANDERSON, P. W. *Phys. Rev.* **100**, 749 (1955)
100. AZBEL', M. YA., and KANER, E. A. *J. exp. theor. Phys.* **30**, 811 (1956); *Soviet Phys. JETP* **3**, 772 (1956)
101. AUBREY, J. E., and CHAMBERS, R. G. *J. Phys. Chem. Solids* **3**, 128 (1957)
102. AUBREY, J. E. *J. Phys. Chem. Solids* **19**, 321 (1961)
103. GALT, J. K., YAGER, W. A., MERRITT, F. R., CETLIN, B. B., and DAIL, H. W. *Phys. Rev.* **100**, 748 (1955)
104. DEXTER, R. N., and LAX, B. *Phys. Rev.* **100**, 1216 (1955)
105. GALT, J. K. private communication
106. PIPPARD, A. B. *Phil. Mag.* **2**, 1147 (1957)
107. COHEN, M. H., HARRISON, M. J., and HARRISON, W. A. *Phys. Rev.* **117**, 937 (1960)
108. RENEKER, D. H. *Phys. Rev.* **115**, 303 (1959)
109. HARRISON, M. J. *Phys. Rev.* **119**, 1260 (1960)
110. SPECTOR, H. N. *Phys. Rev.* **120**, 1261 (1960)
111. SPECTOR, H. N. *Phys. Rev. Lett.* **6**, 407 (1961)
112. JAIN, A. L. *Phys. Rev.* **114**, 1518 (1959)
113. BOYLE, W. S., and BRAILSFORD, A. D. *Phys. Rev.* **120**, 1943 (1960)
114. COOKSON, J. W. *Phys. Rev.* **47**, 194 (1935)
115. ALLEN, M. *Phys. Rev.* **42**, 848 (1932); **49**, 248 (1936)
116. KEYES, R. W. *Phys. Rev.* **104**, 665 (1956); *J. Electron.* **2**, 279 (1956)

THE PHYSICAL PROPERTIES OF SINGLE CRYSTAL BISMUTH TELLURIDE

J. R. DRABBLE, Ph.D., F.Inst.P.

Physics Department,
University of Exeter, Devon, U.K.

MS. *received August 1961*

THE PHYSICAL PROPERTIES OF SINGLE CRYSTAL BISMUTH TELLURIDE

1. INTRODUCTION

As a result of the interest in thermoelectric devices, bismuth telluride and its alloys have been the subject of a large number of investigations. Naturally, many of these have been concerned with the improvement of the thermo-electric figure of merit and have not included any systematic study of the fundamental physical properties. Such work will not be considered in this paper, which is concerned with the basic properties of single crystal bismuth telluride and the interpretation of these according to modern solid state theory. The restriction to single crystal material is made because, in the author's view, the anisotropy of the physical properties is of basic importance in the interpretation and provides information which cannot be obtained on materials possessing cubic symmetry.

The review relies heavily on the work of the Solid Physics Group of the Research Laboratories of the General Electric Company, in which, for some five years, a programme of basic research on bismuth telluride was carried out under the direction of D. A. Wright. A short review of the work of this group has been given previously by Wright.[1] The author, who was for some years a member of this group, is grateful to the other members for their assistance, either direct or indirect, in forming the views expressed in this review.

2. PREPARATION OF SINGLE CRYSTALS

One of the first accounts of the preparation of single crystals of bismuth telluride was that given by Ainsworth.[2] He tried various methods of preparation in order to get single crystals of uniform properties. Of the methods tried, the Stockbarger technique (lowering of charge through a sharp temperature gradient) and a horizontal freezing method were found to be unsatisfactory because of segregation of tellurium towards the last end to freeze. Good quality single crystals of uniform composition were grown by pulling from the melt (Czochralski method) in an atmosphere of hydrogen. These were all P-type crystals with a Seebeck coefficient of 200–215 μV deg. C^{-1}, even when appreciable departures from the stoichiometric composition, Bi_2Te_3, were made in the parent charge.

Satterthwaite and Ure[3] investigated the effect of departures from stoichiometry in more detail using the Stockbarger method. They partly overcame the difficulties of segregation encountered by Ainsworth by using a much larger volume of melt so that changes in composition of the liquid over a small part of the grown crystal were small. However, it appeared that their resulting crystals were somewhat inhomogeneous, although not sufficiently so to prevent some systematic results from being obtained. By taking samples from the first part to freeze and assuming that the properties of these corresponded to the composition of the parent charge, they investigated the effect of variations of tellurium concentration in the range 59 to 66 atomic per cent tellurium (stoichiometric composition 60 atomic per cent tellurium). A phase diagram was constructed for this region and it was concluded that the maximum melting point of 585° C was not at the stoichiometric composition but slightly displaced on the tellurium rich side. From their results it was concluded that stoichiometric composition gave rise to P-type material and that only when the tellurium content was raised was N-type material obtained. An intrinsic composition was obtained at about 62·7 atomic per cent tellurium.

A horizontal zone melting technique has been found to be most suitable for the preparation of good quality single crystals of reasonably uniform composition.[1] With initial seeding, large single crystals can be produced, but even without seeding, the resultant polycrystalline ingot usually contains single crystal regions of appreciable size. The preferred direction of growth is normal to the three-fold axis and the single crystal regions are orientated with the three-fold axis vertical. This tends to limit the length of specimens cut parallel to the three-fold axis.

All workers have found that, when grown from a stoichiometric composition, crystals are P-type although estimates of the carrier concentration present under such conditions vary. The reasons for this are not fully understood. Harman et al.[4] suggested that it was due to a 'wrong atom' type of defect caused by the interchange of similarly bonded bismuth and tellurium atoms in the lattice.

The electrical properties of crystals can be altered either by altering the composition of the parent melt or by the deliberate addition of impurities. Excess bismuth gives more highly doped P-type material while excess tellurium, as already mentioned, tends to make the material more N-type. The most common doping materials for producing P-type material are lead and cadmium. Donor type centres are produced by Group I elements (copper) and group 7 elements (halogens).

3. STRUCTURAL ASPECTS

3.1. SPACE GROUP, SYMMETRY, AND UNIT CELL

The space group and atomic positions for bismuth telluride were first published by Lange[5] and to the author's knowledge this work has never been confirmed directly by any other workers. Lange gave the space group as D_{3d}^5 (Schoenflies) which corresponds to $R\bar{3}m$ in the Hermann–Mauguin notation.

The symmetry elements associated with the point group $\bar{3}m$ are (a) one three-fold rotation axis, (b) three reflection planes containing the three-fold axis, (c) three two-fold axes normal to the three-fold axis and bisecting the angles between the reflection planes, and (d) a centre of symmetry. According to the accepted convention[6] the z-axis of a Cartesian co-ordinate system is taken along the direction of the three-fold axis and the x-axis is taken along the direction of a two-fold axis. This convention will be used throughout this paper to discuss the physical properties, except where stated otherwise.

The basic unit cell is rhombohedral but for structural work a hexagonal unit cell is frequently used instead. The relation between the basis vectors $\mathbf{a}_i^H$ of the hexagonal unit cell and the basis vectors $\mathbf{a}_i^R$ of the rhombohedral cell are[7]

$$\left.\begin{aligned} \mathbf{a}_1^H &= -\mathbf{a}_2^R + \mathbf{a}_3^R \\ \mathbf{a}_2^H &= \mathbf{a}_1^R - \mathbf{a}_3^R \\ \mathbf{a}_3^H &= \mathbf{a}_1^R + \mathbf{a}_2^R + \mathbf{a}_3^R \end{aligned}\right\} \qquad \ldots (1)$$

The magnitudes of $\mathbf{a}_1^H$ and $\mathbf{a}_2^H$ correspond to the 'a' dimension of the hexagonal lattice and the magnitude of $\mathbf{a}_3^H$ corresponds to the 'c' dimension.

Thus, since $\mathbf{a}_1^R$, $\mathbf{a}_2^R$, and $\mathbf{a}_3^R$ are all of equal magnitude a^R and are all inclined to each other at the same angle α, then

$$a = 2a^R \sin(\alpha/2), \quad c = \sqrt{(3)} \cdot a^R (1 + 2\cos\alpha)^{1/2} \qquad \ldots (2)$$

where a and c refer to the hexagonal unit cell.

With reference to a right-handed set of Cartesian axes taken as defined above, if $\mathbf{i}$, $\mathbf{j}$, and $\mathbf{k}$ are unit vectors taken along the x, y, and z directions, respectively, then

$$\left.\begin{aligned} \mathbf{a}_1^R &= \frac{a}{2}\mathbf{i} + \frac{a}{2\sqrt{3}}\mathbf{j} + \frac{c}{3}\mathbf{k} \\[2mm] \mathbf{a}_2^R &= -\frac{a}{2}\mathbf{i} + \frac{a}{2\sqrt{3}}\mathbf{j} + \frac{c}{3}\mathbf{k} \\[2mm] \mathbf{a}_3^R &= -\frac{a}{\sqrt{3}}\mathbf{j} + \frac{c}{3}\mathbf{k} \end{aligned}\right\} \qquad \ldots (3)$$

The rhombohedral parameters were originally given by Lange as

$$a^R = 10\cdot45 \text{ Å}, \quad \alpha = 24 \text{ degrees 8 minutes} \qquad \ldots (4)$$

Vasenin and Konovalov[8] measured the intensities of diffraction lines from sintered specimens and concluded that bismuth telluride could exist in two forms, a rhombohedral form and a hexagonal polymorphic form. However, a careful study by Francombe[9] on effectively single crystal material did not support this conclusion.

The lattice parameters were determined with considerable accuracy by Francombe[9]. He found that there were slight, but systematic, variations in the hexagonal unit cell dimensions with departures from stoichiometric composition. For stoichiometric composition, he obtained, at room temperature

$$a = 4\cdot3835 \pm 0\cdot0005 \,\text{Å}; \; c = 30\cdot487 \pm 0\cdot001 \,\text{Å} \qquad \ldots (5)$$

These correspond to rhombohedral unit cell parameters of

$$a^R = 10\cdot473 \,\text{Å}, \quad \alpha = 24 \text{ degrees } 9 \text{ minutes } 32 \text{ seconds} \quad \ldots (6)$$

In this work, Francombe also determined the variation of a and c with temperature over the range -195 to $400°\text{C}$. The coefficients of expansion were defined as

$$\alpha_{T[100]} = \left(\frac{\mathrm{d}a}{\mathrm{d}T}\right)_T \Big/ a_T, \; \alpha_{T[001]} = \left(\frac{\mathrm{d}c}{\mathrm{d}T}\right)_T \Big/ c_T \qquad \ldots (7)$$

At $20°\text{C}$ the values of these were

$$\alpha_{T[100]} = 12\cdot9 \times 10^{-6} \text{deg.C}^{-1}, \quad \alpha_{T[001]} = 22\cdot2 \times 10^{-6} \text{deg.C}^{-1} \quad \ldots (8)$$

Below this temperature, the parameters did not vary very much with temperature but large variations were found at higher temperatures. The larger expansion coefficient in the c direction was attributed to the weaker interatomic binding forces in this direction (see below).

Note added in proof. A recent paper by Taylor[61] quotes values of the expansion coefficients in the temperature range from room temperature to the melting point. Anomalies in both coefficients were found in the vicinity of $100°\text{C}$. The values differ appreciably from those reported by Francombe.

3.2. THE BRILLOUIN ZONE

The form of the first Brillouin zone of bismuth telluride is of interest from several points of view, particularly in discussing the possible band structure and the lattice vibration spectrum.

The first Brillouin zone is usually defined in terms of the reciprocal lattice space multiplied by a scale factor of 2π. In this lattice space we draw the perpendicular bisecting planes of the lattice vectors drawn from one lattice point, taken as the origin, to all other lattice points. The zone cut off by such planes surrounding the origin is then the first Brillouin zone containing all the non-equivalent wave vectors for the electrons and phonons.

The primitive lattice vectors for bismuth telluride are given by equations (3) and the reciprocal lattice vectors obtained from these are

$$\mathbf{b}_1 = \frac{1}{a}\mathbf{i} + \frac{1}{\sqrt{(3)}.a}\mathbf{j} + \frac{1}{c}\mathbf{k}$$

$$\mathbf{b}_2 = -\frac{1}{a}\mathbf{i} + \frac{1}{\sqrt{(3)}.a}\mathbf{j} + \frac{1}{c}\mathbf{k}$$

$$\mathbf{b}_3 = -\frac{2}{\sqrt{(3)}.a}\mathbf{j} + \frac{1}{c}\mathbf{k}$$

The reciprocal lattice has, of course, the same symmetry as the original lattice and, in particular, the three basis vectors defined above are equal in length and equally inclined to each other and to the z-axis.

We shall work with these vectors and ignore the scale factor of 2π. The problem of finding the first Brillouin zone for bismuth telluride is the same as the problem of determining the symmetrical (Wigner–Seitz) unit cell for the above set of primitive vectors. This problem has been considered by Koster.[10]

A perspective drawing of a scale model of the shape of the zone is shown in Figure 1. The two boundary planes normal to the z-axis are the perpendicular bisectors of the vectors $\pm(\mathbf{b}_1+\mathbf{b}_2+\mathbf{b}_3) = \pm 3\mathbf{k}/c$. These planes cut off regular hexagons from the zone. There are twelve other faces, six of which have six sides and six have four sides. The six-sided faces are determined as the plane perpendicular bisectors of the vectors $\pm\mathbf{b}_1$, $\pm\mathbf{b}_2$,

Three fold axis

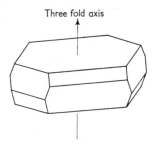

Figure 1. *The first Brillouin zone of bismuth telluride*

and $\pm\mathbf{b}_3$ while the four-sided faces are the bisectors of $\pm(\mathbf{b}_1+\mathbf{b}_2)$, etc. The whole zone has, of course, three-fold symmetry about $0z$, two-fold symmetry about the x-axis, reflection symmetry in the y-plane, and inversion symmetry.

From the physical point of view, the interest of this zone lies in its very narrow extent parallel to the z-axis compared with its dimensions normal to this axis. The distance between the hexagonal faces is $0\cdot0984$ Å^{-1}, while the distance between two parallel edges of one of these faces is $0\cdot255$ Å^{-1}. Thus, the zone is highly compressed parallel to the three-fold axis. This fact implies that the usual approximations of replacing the Brillouin zone by an equivalent sphere (as occurs for example in the Debye theory of the lattice vibrations) are likely to be very poor for bismuth telluride. A more reasonable approximation would be to consider an equivalent cylindrical zone; however, this would require a minimum of two parameters to describe it.

3.3. Atomic Positions and Bonding

The positions of the atoms in the rhombohedral unit cell were given by Lange in the form:

One tellurium atom at $(0,0,0)$;
Tellurium atoms at $(x_1,x_1,x_1)(\bar{x}_1,\bar{x}_1,\bar{x}_1)$, with $x_1 = 0\cdot792$;
Bismuth atoms at $(x_2,x_2,x_2)(\bar{x}_2,\bar{x}_2,\bar{x}_2)$, with $x_2 = 0\cdot399$.

Thus, there are tellurium atoms at the vertices of the rhombohedral unit cell and the remaining atoms are on the diagonal of this cell through the origin. This diagonal is the **c** vector of the hexagonal unit cell (equation (1)) and in the Cartesian system of axes is denoted by $c\mathbf{k}$ (equation (3)). It is, of course, also the direction of the three-fold axis.

These positions imply a layer-like structure with layers of similar atoms normal to the three-fold axis. The position of the atoms in the unit cell with respect to the tellurium atom at the origin are:

Tellurium atoms at $0\cdot208\ c\mathbf{k}$ and $0\cdot792\ c\mathbf{k}$;
Bismuth atoms at $\quad0\cdot399\ c\mathbf{k}$ and $0\cdot601\ c\mathbf{k}$.

Since each of the rhombohedral basis vectors gives a translation of $c/3$ in the z-direction, the sequence of layers starting from the origin of the unit cell and going in the 'c' direction is

$$\text{Te}^{(2)} - \text{Bi} - \text{Te}^{(1)} - [\text{Te}^{(1)} - \text{Bi} - \text{Te}^{(2)} - \text{Bi} - \text{Te}^{(1)}] - \text{Te}^{(1)} -$$

For example, the second layer in this sequence is the layer obtained by a translation of the bismuth atoms at $0\cdot399\ c\mathbf{k}$ through $-c\mathbf{k}/3$ (with, of course, corresponding sideways translations).

The sequence of layers is repeated in units of five and for discussion it is convenient to consider this unit as the one enclosed in brackets. Super-scripts are used to distinguish between two types of tellurium atoms according to the way in which they are surrounded by neighbouring atoms. Thus the $\text{Te}^{(2)}$ atoms are at centres of symmetry in the lattice and have six bismuth atoms as their nearest neighbours, three coming from each of the adjoining layers. The $\text{Te}^{(1)}$ atoms, however, are not symmetrically co-ordinated. On one side they have three bismuth atoms as their nearest neighbours and, on the other, three $\text{Te}^{(1)}$ atoms. It follows that bismuth atoms have three $\text{Te}^{(1)}$ atoms on one side and three $\text{Te}^{(2)}$ atoms on the other side as their nearest neighbours.

It is a simple matter, in principle, to work out the bond lengths and angles for the nearest neighbours to any atom. Unfortunately, the results are not likely to be very accurate. Consider for example a $\text{Te}^{(2)}$ atom at $(0,0,0)$. This has three nearest neighbour bismuth atoms on one side whose positions are given by

$$\mathbf{r}_i = 0\cdot399c\mathbf{k} - \mathbf{a}_i^R \ (i = 1,2,3) \qquad \dots(9)$$

Using equations (3) we find

$$\left.\begin{aligned}
\mathbf{r}_1^2 = \mathbf{r}_2^2 = \mathbf{r}_3^2 &= \frac{a^2}{3} + c^2(0 \cdot 066)^2 \\[2mm]
\mathbf{r}_1.\mathbf{r}_2 = \mathbf{r}_2.\mathbf{r}_3 = \mathbf{r}_3.\mathbf{r}_1 &= -\frac{a^2}{6} + c^2(0 \cdot 066)^2
\end{aligned}\right\} \qquad \ldots (10)$$

Accuracy is lost through the measured factor for the position of the bismuth atoms. The best estimate gives the $Te^{(2)}$—Bi bond length as $3 \cdot 22$ Å and the angle between the bonds from $Te^{(1)}$ to the three bismuth atoms on one side as about 85 degrees 30 minutes. Thus the $Te^{(2)}$ atoms are surrounded approximately octahedrally by six bismuth atoms.

The Bi—$Te^{(1)}$ bond length is about $3 \cdot 12$ Å and the corresponding interbond angle is about 89 degrees 20 minutes. Thus the bismuth atoms are also co-ordinated approximately octahedrally in the lattice. The $Te^{(1)}$—$Te^{(1)}$ bonds have a bond length of about $3 \cdot 57$ Å and an interbond angle of about 75 degrees 42 minutes. These atoms are, of course, highly unsymmetrical in their co-ordination.

3.4. Chemical Bonding

The nature of the chemical bonding in bismuth telluride has been the subject of a certain amount of controversy. Mooser and Pearson[11] put forward a theory of a 'semiconducting bond' for elementary and compound semiconductors which, from considerations of the known crystal structure, should allow a distinction between metals and semiconductors to be made. The criterion for semiconductivity given by them was summarized in the rule

$$\frac{n_e}{n_a} + b = 8 \qquad \ldots (11)$$

in which n_e is the number of valence electrons per molecule, n_a is the number of atoms per molecule belonging to groups IV to VII (with the exception of the transition metals), and b is the number of bonds formed by one such atom with a similar atom. Such bonds must form a continuous one-, two-, or three-dimensional network running through the whole crystal.

While such a scheme co-ordinated a large number of semiconducting materials, it did not predict bismuth telluride to be a true semiconductor. From consideration of the interatomic distances, Mooser and Pearson[12] concluded that the bonding between two adjacent $Te^{(1)}$ layers involved the promotion of bonding electrons to higher orbitals, thus leaving empty orbitals in the valence shell. This, according to their theory, would give a metallic-like behaviour in which the normal energy gap between the conduction and valence bands was bridged by a low density-of-states band.

An alternative point of view was put forward by Lagrenaudie[13] who accepted that bismuth telluride was a semiconductor and attempted to use the same type of bonding model that had previously been proposed by Krebs[14] for lead sulphide.

Both these schemes were criticized by Drabble and Goodman[15] on the grounds that neither was compatible with the known structure and experimental behaviour of bismuth telluride. They put forward an alternative theory, the essential feature of which was that the bonds between adjacent $Te^{(1)}$ layers were essentially of the Van der Waals type, i.e. not involving any electron sharing. By taking into account the two different types of bismuth–tellurium bonds, it was concluded that a fully saturated bonding could be obtained if the outer ($Te^{(1)}$) tellurium atoms used only p orbitals in the bonding, the two $5s$ electrons of these atoms forming a lone pair. The bismuth and remaining tellurium ($Te^{(2)}$) atoms were assumed to use hybridized sp^3d^2 orbitals, thus accounting for the nearly octahedral coordination of these atoms. The different types of bismuth–tellurium bonds were accounted for by assuming electron transfer between the $Te^{(1)}$ and Bi atoms, thus giving a partly ionic character to these bonds and accounting for their shorter length as compared with the Bi—$Te^{(2)}$ bonds.

Suchet[16] has given an extension of the rule of Mooser and Pearson taking into account different types of crystal structure. He considers bismuth telluride to consist of partially covalent lattices of the type $[Bi—Te^{(1)}]^+$, two of these being stabilized in each five-layer set through the central $Te^{(2)}$ layer. Thus, the formula would be written as $[BiTe^{(1)}]_2^{2+}[Te^{(2)}]^{2-}$.

It does not seem to be possible to distinguish between these last two theories at the present time and it is difficult to see where the evidence is going to come from that will allow such a distinction to be made. Drabble and Goodman cited the evidence of Austin and Sheard[17] on the optical energy gap in bismuth telluride–bismuth selenide alloys as being in favour of their model. The electrical properties of alloys in the system $Sb_x Bi_{2-x} Te_{3-y} Se_y$ recently reported by Teramoto and Takayanagi[18] were also shown to be consistent with this scheme.

Haneman[19] showed that there was no measurable adsorption of oxygen, nitrogen, carbon monoxide, or ozone on fresh cleavage surfaces of bismuth telluride and that the sticking coefficient of water was very low. These results were cited as evidence that there were no 'dangling' bonds on such surfaces and that the surface bonds were saturated and directed into the interior. This was quoted as evidence in favour of the chemical bonding scheme of Drabble and Goodman but it seems probable that it is equally consistent with the more elaborate scheme given by Suchet.

A review of chemical bonding in semiconductors, by Mooser and Pearson, appeared in Volume 5 of this series.[20] Their original rule (equation (11)) for the existence of semiconducting behaviour was modified to take into account the possible existence of cation–cation bonds. They suggest that the bonding between bismuth atoms and the surrounding tellurium atoms is associated with $p^3 d^3$ hybrid orbitals but do not discuss the general structure in detail.

4. ELASTIC CONSTANTS

To the author's knowledge there has been no determination of the complete set of elastic constants of bismuth telluride. However, in view of the importance of these parameters in the general theory of solids and particularly in the interpretation of the specific heat and the thermal conductivity, it has been thought worthwhile to include a brief phenomenological account of these in this paper. In particular the propagation of long wavelength elastic waves is discussed since this is one of the standard methods leading to the determination of the elastic constants.

In bismuth telluride, the number of independent elastic moduli is reduced by the symmetry from the value of 21, present in a crystal without symmetry, to six. The non-vanishing elastic moduli and the relations between them are given in the usual notation by

$$c_{11}, c_{22} = c_{11}, c_{33}, c_{12}, c_{13}, c_{23} = c_{13}, c_{44}, c_{55} = c_{44}, c_{66}$$
$$= \tfrac{1}{2}(c_{11}-c_{12}), c_{14}, c_{56} = c_{14}, c_{24} = -c_{14} \qquad \ldots (12)$$

The propagation of plane elastic waves in a general direction $\mathbf{s}$ in a solid is governed by the set of differential equations[6]

$$\rho \frac{\partial^2 u_i}{\partial t^2} = \sum_j \Gamma_{ij} \frac{\partial^2 u_j}{\partial s^2} (i,j = 1, 2, 3) \qquad \ldots (13)$$

where ρ is the density of the solid, u_1, u_2, and u_3 are the components of elastic displacement along the three co-ordinate axes, and the coefficients Γ_{ij} are the so-called Christoffel moduli. If $\mathbf{s}$ has direction cosines α_1, α_2, and α_3 with respect to the co-ordinate axes, the general forms for the Christoffel moduli are

$$\left.\begin{aligned}
\Gamma_{11} &= \alpha_1^2 c_{11} + \alpha_2^2 c_{66} + \alpha_3^2 c_{55} + 2\alpha_2 \alpha_3 c_{65} + 2\alpha_3 \alpha_1 c_{51} + \\
&\quad + 2\alpha_1 \alpha_2 c_{16} \\
\Gamma_{22} &= \alpha_1^2 c_{66} + \alpha_2^2 c_{22} + \alpha_3^2 c_{44} + 2\alpha_2 \alpha_3 c_{24} + 2\alpha_3 \alpha_1 c_{46} + \\
&\quad + 2\alpha_1 \alpha_2 c_{62} \\
\Gamma_{33} &= \alpha_1^2 c_{55} + \alpha_2^2 c_{44} + \alpha_3^2 c_{33} + 2\alpha_2 \alpha_3 c_{43} + 2\alpha_3 \alpha_1 c_{35} + \\
&\quad + 2\alpha_1 \alpha_2 c_{54} \\
\Gamma_{23} &= \alpha_1^2 c_{65} + \alpha_2^2 c_{24} + \alpha_3^2 c_{43} + \alpha_2 \alpha_3 (c_{23} + c_{44}) + \\
&\quad + \alpha_3 \alpha_1 (c_{45} + c_{63}) + \alpha_1 \alpha_2 (c_{64} + c_{25}) \\
\Gamma_{31} &= \alpha_1^2 c_{51} + \alpha_2^2 c_{46} + \alpha_3^2 c_{35} + \alpha_2 \alpha_3 (c_{45} + c_{36}) + \\
&\quad + \alpha_3 \alpha_1 (c_{31} + c_{55}) + \alpha_1 \alpha_2 (c_{56} + c_{41}) \\
\Gamma_{12} &= \alpha_1^2 c_{16} + \alpha_2^2 c_{62} + \alpha_3^2 c_{54} + \alpha_2 \alpha_3 (c_{64} + c_{52}) + \\
&\quad + \alpha_3 \alpha_1 (c_{56} + c_{14}) + \alpha_1 \alpha_2 (c_{12} + c_{66})
\end{aligned}\right\} \qquad \ldots (14)$$

In general, $\Gamma_{ij} = \Gamma_{ji}$.

Plane wave solutions of equations (13) can be obtained by putting

$$u_1 = p\zeta, \quad u_2 = q\zeta, \quad u_3 = r\zeta$$

so that the u_i are the components of the vector displacement ζ which has direction cosines p, q, and r with respect to the co-ordinate axes. This vector displacement has the form

$$\zeta = A\zeta \exp[i(ks - \omega t)] \qquad \ldots (15)$$

where A is a unit vector with the direction cosines p, q, r. Putting this into the equation, we obtain

$$\left. \begin{array}{l} p\Gamma_{11} + q\Gamma_{12} + r\Gamma_{13} = pc \\ p\Gamma_{12} + q\Gamma_{22} + r\Gamma_{23} = qc \\ p\Gamma_{13} + q\Gamma_{23} + r\Gamma_{33} = rc \end{array} \right\} \qquad \ldots (16)$$

where $c = \rho\omega^2/k^2 = \rho v^2$, where v is the velocity of propagation.

This set of equations has generally three roots c_i $(i = 1, 2, 3)$ (which can be shown to be positive). Each root leads to a possible plane wave propagating in the direction s with a velocity $v_i = (c_i/\rho)^{1/2}$

The roots are obtained by solving the determinant

$$\begin{vmatrix} \Gamma_{11} - c, & \Gamma_{12}, & \Gamma_{13} \\ \Gamma_{12}, & \Gamma_{22} - c, & \Gamma_{23} \\ \Gamma_{13}, & \Gamma_{23}, & \Gamma_{33} - c \end{vmatrix} = 0 \qquad \ldots (17)$$

Each root c_i leads to a set of direction cosines (p_i, q_i, r_i) for the elastic displacement. These are given by

$$\left. \begin{array}{l} p_i = [(\Gamma_{22} - c_i)(\Gamma_{33} - c_i) - \Gamma_{23}^2]/W_i \\ q_i = [\Gamma_{13}\Gamma_{23} - \Gamma_{12}(\Gamma_{33} - c_i)]/W_i \\ r_i = [\Gamma_{12}\Gamma_{23} - \Gamma_{13}(\Gamma_{22} - c_i)]/W_i \end{array} \right\} \qquad \ldots (18)$$

where W_i is such that $p_i^2 + q_i^2 + r_i^2 = 1$.

From these equations the angle ψ_i between the direction of propagation and the direction of elastic displacement for the ith root can be obtained. This is given by

$$\cos\psi_i = p_i\alpha_1 + q_i\alpha_2 + r_i\alpha_3 \qquad \ldots (19)$$

A value of $\psi_i = 0$ corresponds to a pure longitudinal wave and $\psi_i = \frac{1}{2}\pi$ corresponds to a pure transverse wave. In general the waves are neither purely longitudinal nor purely transverse.

Applying these general results to bismuth telluride, we first consider propagation in the z direction, i.e. parallel to the three-fold axis. For this direction $\alpha_1 = \alpha_2 = 0$ and $\alpha_3 = 1$ and hence, using equations (12) and (14)

$$\Gamma_{11} = c_{44}, \ \Gamma_{22} = c_{44}, \ \Gamma_{33} = c_{33}, \text{ all other } \Gamma_{ij} = 0 \qquad \ldots (20)$$

The secular equation (equation (17)) reduces to

$$(c_{44}-c)(c_{44}-c)(c_{33}-c) = 0 \qquad \ldots (21)$$

with two coincident roots and one separate root. It is a simple matter to show that the root c_{33} is associated with a purely longitudinal wave which can thus propagate parallel to the three-fold axis with a velocity $v = (c_{33}/\rho)^{1/2}$. The other two coincident roots are associated with pure transverse vibrations propagating with velocity $v = (c_{44}/\rho)^{1/2}$. These waves can be polarized in any direction normal to the three-fold axis. Such results are quite general for any n-fold rotation axis with $n > 2$.

Next, consider propagation parallel to a diad axis (x direction) so that $\alpha_1 = 1$, $\alpha_2 = \alpha_3 = 0$. Using the above procedure we find that a true longitudinal mode of propagation parallel to this axis occurs with a velocity of propagation $v = (c_{11}/\rho)^{1/2}$. Since it may be shown that the three possible modes of propagation are all mutually orthogonal to each other, there are also two purely transverse modes for propagation in this direction. However, in contrast to the previous case, these transverse modes have specific polarizations and, since these are not known in advance, they cannot be used directly to obtain the appropriate combination of elastic constants. In general an external transverse excitation will excite both possible modes and these will travel with different velocities.

The third symmetry direction is normal to the three-fold axis and parallel to a reflection plane (y direction). For this case, we find that a purely transverse wave can be propagated with a specific polarization for which the displacement is parallel to the x direction. The corresponding velocity of propagation is $v = (c_{66}/\rho)^{1/2}$. The other two modes of propagation in this direction are not 'pure'.

Measurements on the velocity of sound in single crystal bismuth telluride have been reported by Blitz et al.[21] and Blitz.[22] It was found that polarization modes, in which the direction of displacement was normal to the three-fold axis, were difficult to set up and detect and no measurements on such modes were reported. The only two measurements reported which allow a direct estimate of any elastic moduli were the velocity of longitudinally excited waves parallel to the three-fold axis and (nearly) parallel to a diad axis. For the former case, the velocity of longitudinal waves was found to be 2,500 $m\,sec^{-1}$ and, rather surprisingly, the same value was found in the latter case also. Taking the density of bismuth telluride[1] as $7 \cdot 86\ g\,cm^{-3}$ these results lead to values of c_{33} and c_{11} of $4 \cdot 9 \times 10^{11}\ dyn\,cm^{-2}$.

Of the remaining results reported, the velocity of waves propagating nearly parallel to the y axis were measured with both longitudinal external excitation and with an external transverse polarization parallel to the z axis. The velocity in the former case was 2,900 $m\,sec^{-1}$ and in the latter 2,500 $m\,sec^{-1}$. However, a unique interpretation of these results is not possible since the external excitation used does not lead to a propagation of a 'pure' mode. Similar remarks apply to the other reported measurement, viz., propagation nearly parallel to the x axis using an external transverse excitation polarized parallel to the z direction. For this case a velocity of 1,400 m sec^{-1} was reported.

The fact that the two elastic constants governing the propagation of longitudinal waves parallel and normal to the three-fold axis have the same magnitude is rather surprising in view of the well known mechanical weakness of bismuth telluride in a direction parallel to the three-fold axis. This fact, however, is consistent with a closely related property, viz., that the anisotropy of the lattice thermal conductivity is not as pronounced as one might expect at first sight, being only of the order of two (see Section 9). Both properties are probably associated with the fact that the Te$^{(1)}$—Te$^{(1)}$ bonds in the lattice, which have the weakest force constants, are inclined at an angle to the three-fold axis of very nearly 45 degrees (actually 44 degrees 50 minutes). The properties of this type of bond would be expected to dominate the expressions for the elastic constants and for the acoustical part of the vibration spectrum.

5. THE SPECIFIC HEAT

Measurements of the specific heat of bismuth telluride at low temperatures were made at the Clarendon Laboratory in 1958, by C. A. Bailey. These results have so far not been published and the author is particularly grateful to Dr. Bailey for permission to include them in this review.

Table 1 gives the smoothed out results obtained together with values of the Debye temperature θ_D derived from them.

The accuracy of the experimental results was estimated to be

± 1 per cent at 20° K decreasing to ± 3 per cent at 4·2° K

± 2 per cent at 4° K decreasing to ± 3 per cent at 2° K

The four lowest experimental specific heat points, when plotted on a graph of C/T versus T^2, lay on a line passing through the origin, indicating the absence of any electronic specific heat contribution. The corresponding limiting value of the Debye temperature was 145°.

The variation of θ_D with T is of course fairly normal and is in accordance with the ideas first put forward by Blackman[23] and since substantiated experimentally in a large number of materials. It arises essentially from the fact that any discrete lattice has a much more complicated frequency–wave number relationship than is assumed in the simple Debye theory, which is based on the spectrum for a continuous medium. In the case of bismuth telluride with its highly compressed form of the first Brillouin zone and its anisotropic structure it is perhaps surprising that the departures are not more marked than they appear to be from the specific heat data. In the simple Debye theory, the normal modes are specified by a set of wave vector values which are assumed to be distributed throughout a sphere in wave vector space of such a size that the total number of modes is equal to the number of degrees of freedom. The shape of the Brillouin zone for bismuth telluride suggests that a better approximation for this material would be to take the normal modes as lying within a cylinder (see Figure 1). Such a theory would require two parameters to specify the appropriate physical quantities such as the specific heat.

TABLE 1. Low Temperature Specific Heat Data
for Bismuth Telluride

T (°K)	C_p (joules per mole)	θ_D (per gram atom)
1·0	0·00316	145·2
1·5	0·0107	145·2
2·0	0·0255	145·2
2·5	0·0522	142·6
3·0	0·0978	139·2
3·5	0·166	135·8
4·0	0·268	133·0
5·0	0·581	127·7
6·0	1·12	123·1
7·0	1·89	119·1
8·0	3·18	116·2
9·0	4·56	115·8
10·0	6·10	116·8
11·0	7·82	118·3
12·0	9·61	120·4
13·0	11·5	122·7
14·0	13·6	125·2
15·0	15·8	127·6
16·0	18·0	130·3
17·0	20·2	133·1
18·0	22·5	136·0
19·0	24·9	138·8
20·0	27·2	141·7

If the simple Debye theory is used, the average velocity of sound calculated in the usual way is found to be

$$\bar{v} = 1·58 \times 10^5 \, \text{cm sec}^{-1}$$

This is surprisingly close to the measured values discussed in the last section.

6. PHENOMENOLOGICAL DISCUSSION OF THE TRANSPORT PROPERTIES

As an introduction to the next four sections, it will be useful to discuss the phenomenological aspects of the transport properties of bismuth telluride and in particular to consider the relations imposed on the transport co-efficients by thermodynamic considerations and by the crystal symmetry.

For any solid, the basic equations governing the flow of electric current and of total energy can be put in the form

$$\mathbf{j} = \frac{1}{q}\boldsymbol{\sigma}.\mathbf{grad}\,\tilde{\mu} - \boldsymbol{\sigma}.\mathbf{Q}.\mathbf{grad}\,T \qquad \ldots (22a)$$

$$\mathbf{w} = \left(\boldsymbol{\pi} - \frac{\tilde{\mu}}{q}\right).\mathbf{j} - \boldsymbol{\varkappa}.\mathbf{grad}\,T \qquad \ldots (22b)$$

in which $\mathbf{j}$ and $\mathbf{w}$ are the electric current and energy fluxes, T is the temperature, and $\tilde{\mu}$ is the electrochemical potential of the system of free charge carriers in the solid. If the solid is of uniform composition, then $\mathbf{grad}\,\tilde{\mu}$ can be replaced by $q\mathbf{E}$, where q is the electronic charge and $\mathbf{E}$ is the electric field. It will be assumed in the further discussion that this substitution can be made. The above equations are derived from the equations giving the flow of particles and energy obtained on the basis of irreversible thermodynamics.[24] The various transport properties as normally defined are all included in the four second order tensors $\boldsymbol{\sigma}$, $\mathbf{Q}$, $\boldsymbol{\pi}$, and $\boldsymbol{\varkappa}$.

The components of these tensors in general depend on the composition of the solid and on the temperature. In addition they also depend on the value of any magnetic induction $\mathbf{B}$ which may be acting on the solid. The dependence on $\mathbf{B}$ is governed by the Onsager reciprocal relations which take the form

$$\left.\begin{aligned} \sigma_{ij}(\mathbf{B}) &= \sigma_{ji}(-\mathbf{B}) \\ \varkappa_{ij}(\mathbf{B}) &= \varkappa_{ji}(-\mathbf{B}) \\ \pi_{ij}(\mathbf{B}) &= T\mathbf{Q}_{ji}(-\mathbf{B}) \end{aligned}\right\} \qquad \ldots (23)$$

The physical significance of the various tensors may be obtained by reference to two standard situations. In the first of these the temperature is constant and the equations take the form

$$\mathbf{j} = \boldsymbol{\sigma}.\mathbf{E} \qquad \ldots (24a)$$

$$\mathbf{w} = \left(\boldsymbol{\pi} - \frac{\tilde{\mu}}{q}\right)\mathbf{j} \qquad \ldots (24b)$$

The first of these equations establishes the relation between the current density and the electric field and thus $\boldsymbol{\sigma}$ is a generalized conductivity tensor. The components of $\boldsymbol{\sigma}$ in the absence of a magnetic field define the electrical conductivity in the normal sense. In the presence of a magnetic field, the components change from the zero field values and these changes are associated with the so-called galvanomagnetic effects, including the Hall effect and the magnetoresistance. This point is discussed in more detail later in this Section.

Equation (24b) relates the total flow of energy to the electric current density under isothermal conditions. The associated physical effects are most pronounced at a junction between two dissimilar materials. If there is no divergence of **j** across the junction there is in general a divergence of the energy flow and this corresponds to an absorption or liberation of energy at the junction at a rate

$$(\pi_2 - \pi_1) . \mathbf{j} - \frac{1}{q}(\tilde{\mu}_2 - \tilde{\mu}_1)\mathbf{j}$$

in which subscripts 1 and 2 distinguish between the two materials. The second term vanishes if the electrical contact between the two materials is a perfect one, otherwise giving rise to liberation of energy at the junction caused by Joule heating. The first term corresponds to a source (or sink) of energy at the junction associated with the passage of current which defines the Peltier effect. This effect is normally defined in the absence of a magnetic field but we may call π the generalized Peltier tensor for the solid, taking into account that the effect does depend on any magnetic field that may be present.

The second standard situation which leads to the interpretation of the other two tensors **Q** and $\varkappa$ in equation (22) is the open circuit condition $\mathbf{j} = 0$. The equations are then of the form

$$\sigma . \mathbf{E} - \sigma . \mathbf{Q} . \operatorname{grad} T = 0 \quad \text{or} \quad \mathbf{E} = \mathbf{Q} . \operatorname{grad} T$$

$$\mathbf{w} = -\varkappa . \operatorname{grad} T \qquad \qquad \dots (25)$$

The first of these establishes a relation between the electric field and the temperature gradient under open circuit conditions. In the absence of a magnetic field, this relation is defined by the Seebeck coefficient (thermoelectric power). In the presence of a magnetic field the changes in the components of **Q** from the zero field values are associated in particular with such properties as the Nernst effect and other magneto-thermoelectric effects.

The second equation gives the total energy flow in terms of the temperature gradient in the absence of any electrical current and $\varkappa$ thus corresponds to a generalized thermal conductivity tensor allowing for possible effects associated with a magnetic field.

In the absence of a magnetic field, all the tensors σ, **Q**, π, and $\varkappa$, in addition to the restrictions imposed by equations (23) (with **B** = 0) also possess the full symmetry of the point group of the particular crystal considered. They are then normal second order tensors and the number of independent components that they possess is determined by the particular crystal class of the solid. This problem is discussed in full in many references (e.g. reference 25).

For bismuth telluride the number of independent components, in the absence of a magnetic field, of each of the tensors is two (as far as the crystal symmetry is concerned). These two components in each case characterize situations parallel and perpendicular to the three-fold axis, respectively, there being full isotropy for all directions normal to the axis. Taking, as is usual, the z-axis to coincide with the three-fold axis, all the tensors are diagonal with the 11 and 22 components equal to each other and a separate 33 component.

In the presence of a magnetic field **B** of arbitrary orientation the components of all tensors change from their zero field value and are functions of **B**. We shall discuss these changes in detail only for the case of the conductivity tensor since, as will be seen later, the resultant coefficients are of particular importance in investigating the band structure of the solid. Some remarks, however, will be made about the other tensors.

Equation (24a) written out explicitly in terms of the components is

$$j_k = \sigma_{kl}(\mathbf{B})E_l \qquad \ldots (26)$$

where the tensor summation convention of summation over repeated symbols is used. Instead of working with this equation, it is of more convenience to work with the inverse relation

$$E_k = \rho_{kl}(\mathbf{B})j_l \qquad \ldots (27)$$

in which the ρ_{kl} are the components of the generalized resistivity tensor ρ reciprocal to σ. The reason for working with this equation is that in most experiments, the components of the current density are controlled independently and measurements are made of the resultant electric field components.

If the magnetic field is not too large, the components of ρ can be expanded in powers of the magnetic field components

$$\rho_{kl}(\mathbf{B}) = \rho_{kl}(0) - \rho_{klm}B_m + \rho_{klmn}B_m B_n + \ldots \qquad \ldots (28)$$

and for most purposes it is necessary to consider only terms up to and including the second order effects in the field. Insertion of this relation into the previous one gives

$$E_k = \rho_{kl}j_l - \rho_{klm}j_l B_m + \rho_{klmn}j_l B_m B_n \qquad \ldots (29)$$

in which the various coefficients are independent of the current density and of the magnetic field. (The negative sign in the second term is introduced only for convenience in discussion.) Each set of coefficients is subject to the general thermodynamic restrictions and also to the restrictions imposed by the symmetry of the solid.

For bismuth telluride, the only non-zero components of the zero field resistivity tensor ρ_{kl} referred to the axis system introduced in Section 4 (z-axis parallel to the three-fold axis, x-axis parallel to a diad axis) are[26]

$$\rho_{11}, \rho_{22} = \rho_{11}, \rho_{33} \qquad \ldots (30)$$

For the tensor ρ_{klm} the thermodynamic restrictions impose the conditions that $\rho_{klm} = -\rho_{lkm}$ and that ρ_{klm} is zero unless k, l, and m are all different from each other. In addition, the symmetry of the crystal leads to $\rho_{312} = \rho_{231}$. Thus, the non-vanishing components of ρ_{klm} can all be expressed in terms of two independent components. The complete list of these is[26]

$$\rho_{123}, \rho_{213} = -\rho_{123}, \rho_{231}, \rho_{321} = -\rho_{231}, \rho_{312} = \rho_{231}, \rho_{132} = -\rho_{231} \cdots (31)$$

The physical significance of, for example, ρ_{123} is that it gives the electric field in the 1 direction when current is flowing in the 2 direction with the magnetic field in the 3 direction. It thus corresponds to a Hall coefficient. A similar interpretation holds for the other components and there are thus two independent Hall coefficients for bismuth telluride.

The tensor ρ_{klmn} may be called the magnetoresistance tensor since some of its components correspond to the longitudinal and transverse magneto-resistivities as normally defined. For this tensor, the thermodynamic restrictions lead to

$$\rho_{klmn} = \rho_{lkmn} \qquad \cdots (32)$$

Also, use of the tensor summation convention in equation (29) implies that

$$\rho_{klmn} = \rho_{klnm} \qquad \cdots (33)$$

The further restrictions imposed by crystal symmetry have been discussed in reference 26 in which, however, the y-axis was taken as being parallel to a diad axis. With the system of axes adopted here some of these terms are modified. The non-vanishing components and their relations to each other in this system are

$$\left.
\begin{aligned}
&\rho_{1111}, \rho_{2222} = \rho_{1111} \\
&\rho_{3333} \\
&\rho_{1122}, \rho_{2211} = \rho_{1122}, \rho_{1212} = \tfrac{1}{2}(\rho_{1111} - \rho_{1122}) \\
&\rho_{1133}, \rho_{2233} = \rho_{1133} \\
&\rho_{3311}, \rho_{3322} = \rho_{3311} \\
&\rho_{1123}, \rho_{2223} = -\rho_{1123}, \rho_{1231} = \rho_{1123} \\
&\rho_{3131}, \rho_{2323} = \rho_{3131} \\
&\rho_{2311}, \rho_{2322} = -\rho_{2311}, \rho_{3112} = \rho_{2311}
\end{aligned}
\right\} \quad \cdots (34)$$

Other terms are obtained using equations (32) and (33).

There are thus eight independent components of the magnetoresistance tensor. The first five of these as given above correspond to longitudinal and transverse magnetoresistivities, as normally defined, with various orientations of the magnetic field and current. The remaining three are cross terms and in general do not have such a simple interpretation.

A similar analysis to the above holds for the thermal conductivity tensor for which the same thermodynamic and symmetry restrictions apply. In this case the terms linear in the magnetic field are associated with the Righi–Leduc effect (transverse temperature gradient arising from the action of a transverse magnetic field in the presence of a primary temperature gradient). The five principal quadratic terms correspond to longitudinal and transverse magnetothermal resistivities. Most of these terms are difficult to measure, but are of interest because they afford a means of distinguishing between the electronic and lattice contributions to the thermal conduction process.

The analysis for the remaining tensors, the Seebeck tensor and the Peltier tensor, is more elaborate since there are no thermodynamic restrictions on the components of either of the two separately but only relations between the components of one and those of the other. For example, if the components of the Seebeck tensor are expanded in powers of the magnetic field, there are terms which are odd in the field, which correspond to an extension of the Ettingshausen–Nernst effect (electric field set up as a result of the action of a magnetic field in the presence of a temperature gradient, all being mutually perpendicular). These correspond to the Hall effect terms in the electrical conductivity tensor. However, owing to the absence of the thermodynamic restrictions, there are also terms which are odd in the magnetic field which give rise to electric fields which are not perpendicular to both the primary temperature gradient and the magnetic field. Such terms have not, to the author's knowledge, been studied in bismuth telluride. There are also extra terms, as compared with equations (34), in the set of coefficients which are quadratic in the magnetic field.

7. MEASUREMENT OF THE GALVANOMAGNETIC COEFFICIENTS AND THEIR INTERPRETATION IN TERMS OF THE BAND STRUCTURE

7.1. GENERAL

On the usual type of interpretation, the numerous transport coefficients discussed in the last section depend upon the band structure of the solid, the number of free charge carriers, and the scattering processes to which these charge carriers are subjected. These last two factors are, of course, affected by the composition and temperature. (The contribution of the lattice vibrations to the thermal conductivity is being neglected for the present—see Section 9.)

In the simplest model that can be used to describe the main features of the transport coefficients of a semiconductor when it is in the so-called extrinsic range (i.e. when only one band is effectively contributing to the properties), the three features mentioned above are described in terms of three parameters. The first of these is the effective mass for the particular band concerned, assuming that the surfaces of constant energy in wave vector space are spherical and are centred on the mid-point of the first Brillouin zone. The second is the position of the Fermi energy with respect to the band states, this usually being defined by a dimensionless parameter η which gives the position of the Fermi energy with respect to the extreme energy of the band in units of kT. This parameter is determined by the composition and temperature. The third parameter λ describes the way in which the scattering processes vary over the band states. The scattering processes are assumed to be described in terms of a relaxation time τ which varies only with the kinetic energy ϵ of the quantum state according to the relation $\tau = \tau_0 \epsilon^\lambda$, where τ_0 may depend on the composition and temperature but is independent of the quantum state.

These parameters are sufficient in principle to obtain expressions for such transport properties as the electrical conductivity, the Seebeck coefficient, the electronic thermal conductivity, the Hall effect, the longitudinal and transverse magnetoresistance, and other magnetic field effects. Usually what one tries to do in practice is to make measurements of as many of the above properties as possible and, from these, deduce the variation with composition and temperature of the parameters. These variations are then compared with those to be expected on the basis of further physical considerations. For example, the density of free charge carriers is a function of the effective mass m^* and the position of the reduced Fermi level η. In a semiconductor the mechanism of the production of free charge carriers leads to the expectation that, over an appreciable temperature range, this density should remain constant.

If measurements are extended to the intrinsic region, where both the conduction and valence bands contribute to the transport properties, then parameters for both bands enter into the resultant expressions for these properties, together with the width of the forbidden energy gap.

The point to be made here is that this simple model has a band structure which is described in terms of a single parameter. From its very nature it would only be applicable, if at all, to the case of a solid possessing cubic symmetry in which the extreme energy of the band occurs at the centre of the Brillouin zone. For such a system all the simple transport properties such as the electrical conductivity, Hall coefficient, Seebeck coefficient, etc., would be isotropic, each tensor possessing a single independent component. Such a model is therefore not sufficient for a discussion of the transport properties of bismuth telluride.

It is well known that the model is also inadequate for some materials possessing cubic symmetry. The most thoroughly studied examples are N-type germanium and N-type silicon in which it has been established that the conduction band structure is of the so-called many-valley type. For this type of band structure, the conduction band has a number of equivalent minima in the Brillouin zone, which are related to each other by symmetry operations of the crystal. Around each minimum energy point the energy of the quantum states can be expanded as a quadratic function of the wave vector, but in the above examples this relation involves two effective mass parameters instead of the single parameter of the simple model. The reason why there are two parameters is that the energy minima lie on symmetry axes. If this was not the case, more parameters would be involved. The properties of such many-valley semiconductors with cubic symmetry have been investigated in detail by Herring[27] and Herring and Vogt.[28] The combinations of the contributions of the various valleys to the overall transport properties must conform to the overall symmetry of the crystal and, if this is cubic, all second order tensors reduce to scalars possessing a single independent component. Apart from the problem of summation over valleys the theory is very similar to that of the more simple model. In particular, if the scattering processes for each valley are described in terms of a relaxation time $\tau = \tau_0 \epsilon^\lambda$, the only difference is that, in the final expressions for the transport properties, the single effective mass parameter m^* of the simple model is replaced by various combinations of the band structure parameters of the more complex model. The combinations are in general different for the different transport properties. Various refinements of the description of the scattering processes have been discussed in reference 28 and shown to lead to a very satisfactory agreement with observations on N-type germanium.

A similar, though slightly more general, situation holds if a many-valley type of band structure is assumed to hold for a material which does not possess overall cubic symmetry. Whatever the arrangement of the valleys in the Brillouin zone, it must conform to the crystal symmetry and this overall symmetry is retained in the expressions for the components of the transport tensors obtained by summing the contributions from individual valleys. Thus, the overall transport tensors automatically possess the number of independent components required by the crystal symmetry. If a simple form of relaxation time is used to describe the scattering within each valley, then each component of a transport tensor is of the same form as for the corresponding property for the simple model, with the difference that the single effective mass parameter of this model is replaced by combinations of the parameters describing the many-valley band structure. These combinations are different for the different independent components of the tensor, and, of course, are different in form for different transport tensors. For a general type of model, the number of parameters describing the many-valley type of band structure is quite large. There are six parameters describing the shape and orientation of the valleys and a further parameter giving the number of valleys.

The theory in the general case gets quite complicated but is considerably simplified when, as in the case of bismuth telluride, the crystal possesses a principal axis of three-, four-, or six-fold rotational symmetry. The expressions for the galvanomagnetic coefficient in this case have been given in general form by Keyes.[29]

This type of model is the simplest one which can account in principle for all the independent components of the transport tensors in the case of materials with non-cubic symmetry. It was used by the author and co-workers[26,30] in an attempt to account for the observed components of the galvanomagnetic tensors in N- and P-type bismuth telluride and hence to deduce the relevant band structure parameters. The galvanomagnetic coefficients are the simplest of the transport properties to measure which allow an adequate comparison between experiment and theory.

An important feature in deciding the choice of this type of model was the observation, made earlier by Goldsmid,[31] that in both P- and N-type bismuth telluride the Seebeck coefficient is very nearly isotropic. In P-type material the values of the Seebeck coefficients measured parallel and per-pendicular to the three-fold axis were found to be equal to each other within experimental accuracy over the temperature range 150° K to 300° K. In N-type material there was a small systematic difference in the two coefficients but the two were still closely equal and had a similar temperature depen-dence over the range.

The type of model proposed above predicts complete isotropy of the Seebeck coefficient in materials of non-cubic symmetry.[32] The basic feature which leads to this prediction is not the form of the band structure but the assumption that the scattering process within a single valley can be described in terms of a scalar relaxation time which is a function only of the energy of the charge carriers. Actually, a more general model used by Herring and Vogt[28] in their analysis on N-type germanium, in which the valley relaxation time is taken to be a second order tensor, leads to the same result, provided that the components of the tensor all vary with energy in the same way. In the work on bismuth telluride, however, the simpler form of relaxation time was used.

Within the framework of the many-valley model, there are a number of possible choices. The model used in analysing the bismuth telluride results was one in which the energy minima of the valleys lay on reflection planes in the Brillouin zone. This is not the most general type but was chosen for investigation because it contains less parameters than a more general model and also because there are reasons for supposing that in a many-valley type of band structure the energy extrema tend to lie on symmetry elements. Basically this is because at the energy extremes the gradient of the energy–wave number relationship is zero and with valleys lying on symmetry elements one or more of the components of this gradient vector are automatically zero by symmetry. For the above model there would be in general six valleys occurring in two sets of three. The valleys in one set are related by the three-fold rotational symmetry and the two sets by the inversion symmetry. However, if it should happen that the energy minima of each valley lie at the edge of the Brillouin zone, then the two sets coincide, being related to each other by a reciprocal lattice translation across the zone.

Such a situation may well occur since, in general, the normal component of the gradient of the energy–wave vector relation vanishes across the zone boundary.

The galvanomagnetic coefficients for this type of structure were given in reference 26 and in a somewhat different corrected form in reference 30. The description of the band structure involves basically four parameters. These may be thought of in two ways, which are of course related to each other. If we consider one of the valleys and consider the energy–wave vector relation for this valley referred to the principal axes of this valley, this relation has the form

$$\epsilon(\mathbf{k}) = \epsilon_0 + \frac{\hbar^2}{2m}(\alpha_1 k_1^2 + \alpha_2 k_2^2 + \alpha_3 k_3^2) \qquad \dots (35)$$

where $\mathbf{k}$ is the departure of the wave vector from the extreme energy position (with energy ϵ_0) and has components $k_i (i = 1, 2, 3)$ referred to principal axes. The quantities α_i are dimensionless and m/α_i gives the effective mass along the ith axis, where m is the free electron mass. In addition to these three parameters, the orientation of the principal valley axes with respect to the crystal axes must be specified. When the valleys are assumed to be in reflection planes, this orientation can be specified by a single parameter since both one of the crystal axes and one of the principal valley axes are normal to a reflection plane. Thus a simple rotation through an angle θ about this axis is sufficient to bring the valley axes into coincidence with the crystal axes.

An alternative description used by Keyes[29] is to express the energy–wave vector relation for a valley directly with respect to the crystal axes. This has the general form

$$\epsilon(\mathbf{k}) = \epsilon_0 + \frac{\hbar^2}{2m}[\alpha_{11} k_1^2 + \alpha_{22} k_2^2 + \alpha_{33} k_3^2 + 2\alpha_{12} k_1 k_2 + \\ + 2\alpha_{23} k_2 k_3 + 2\alpha_{31} k_3 k_1] \qquad \dots (36)$$

where $\mathbf{k}$ has the same significance as previously but its components are now referred to the crystal axes. If the valley lies on a reflection plane then symmetry requires that two of the cross coefficients are zero. In the above references the crystal x-axis was taken to be parallel to a reflection plane and the y-axis normal to it, leading to the result that $\alpha_{12} = \alpha_{23} = 0$ for the valley in the y–z plane. The four remaining parameters can all be expressed, using simple tensor transformation rules, in terms of the parameters of equation (35) and the angle θ. The relations are

$$\left.\begin{aligned} \alpha_{11} &= c^2 \alpha_1 + s^2 \alpha_3 \\ \alpha_{22} &= \alpha_2 \\ \alpha_{33} &= s^2 \alpha_1 + c^2 \alpha_3 \\ \alpha_{31} &= cs(\alpha_1 - \alpha_3) \end{aligned}\right\} \qquad \dots (37)$$

in which $c = \cos\theta$, $s = \sin\theta$.

The galvanomagnetic coefficients can all be expressed in terms of the four band structure parameters together with other parameters such as τ_0 and λ in the assumed form of the relaxation time and the position of the reduced Fermi level with respect to the band edge. The analysis is complicated by the fact that the theory leads to estimates of the components of the generalized conductivity tensor and it is necessary to transform these into the components of the resistivity tensor. When all this is carried out it is found[30] that certain combinations of the galvanomagnetic coefficients can be formed which contain at most four parameters. Three of these involve the ratios of the α_{ij} in equation (36) and thus describe the shape and orientation of the valleys without reference to their actual size. The fourth parameter involves the ratio of Fermi–Dirac integrals and is a function of both η and λ.

It is worth noting here that three possible combinations are simpler still in that they involve only the first three parameters and are thus dependent only on the shape and orientation of the constant energy surfaces. These ratios are

$$\left.\begin{aligned}
\rho_{33}/\rho_{11} &= (1+u)/2v \\
\rho_{231}/\rho_{123} &= (w+uv)(1+u)/4uv \\
\rho_{1111}/\rho_{3333} &= v^2(w-5uw+3uv+u^2v)/2(1+u)^2(v-w)
\end{aligned}\right\} \quad \ldots (38)$$

where $\quad u = \alpha_{22}/\alpha_{11}, \quad v = \alpha_{33}/\alpha_{11}, \quad w = (\alpha_{11}\alpha_{33}-\alpha_{13}^2)/\alpha_{11}^2 \quad \ldots (39)$

Thus, experimental investigation of these ratios under different conditions of temperature and composition should lead directly to important conclusions about the validity of the proposed model.

7.2. MEASUREMENTS ON P-TYPE BISMUTH TELLURIDE

Measurements of nine out of the possible twelve galvanomagnetic coefficients of P-type bismuth telluride at 77° K were reported in reference 30 for two different compositions. For each composition three different experimental arrangements were used. In one of these, measurements were made with current flowing parallel to the three-fold axis. Cross checks between the various arrangements showed that there was no significant difference between the various specimens used for each composition.

From the measurements, seven dimensionless combinations were formed which, according to the model discussed above, should be functions of four parameters. For each composition, a numerical choice of the four parameters was found to be possible which made the theoretical expressions agree with the experimental values to within 5 per cent accuracy. The corresponding experimental and theoretical values obtained for the two compositions are given in Table 2.

Although agreement for the individual compositions was good it will be seen that it was necessary to use a different set of band structure parameters u, v, and w for the two compositions. This was due essentially to the fact that principal ratios like ρ_{33}/ρ_{11} and ρ_{231}/ρ_{123} were different in the two cases, whereas for the proposed model they should be the same. The tentative conclusion would seem to be that the model describes the main features of the band structure and scattering processes, but that on the basis of the above results, if it is to be used realistically, then it is necessary to assume that the band structure parameters vary somewhat with degree of degeneracy. Such a situation is known to exist in other semiconductors, in particular in N-type indium antimonide, and the theory of this, as given for example by Kane,[33] shows that it is likely to occur in semiconductors of small energy gap. Since the energy gap of bismuth telluride is even smaller than that of indium antimonide, it would not be too surprising to find the same effect.

TABLE 2

	Ingot 19		Ingot 23	
	Expt.	Calc.†	Expt.	Calc.‡
ρ_{33}/ρ_{11}	2·96	2·81	3·14	3·16
ρ_{231}/ρ_{123}	2·04	2·08	2·38	2·53
$\rho_{11}\,\rho_{1111}/\rho_{123}^2$	0·472	0·495	1·029	0·979
ρ_{1122}/ρ_{1111}	1·32	1·32	1·20	1·20
ρ_{1133}/ρ_{1111}	2·74	2·74	2·03	2·03
$\rho_{11}\,\rho_{3333}/\rho_{123}^2$	0·674	0·642	3·23	3·35
ρ_{3311}/ρ_{3333}	0·900	0·896	0·372	0·344

† Parameters used: $u = 6\cdot254$, $v = 1\cdot252$, $w = 1\cdot134$, $\beta = 0\cdot894$
‡ Parameters used: $u = 8\cdot416$, $v = 1\cdot492$, $w = 0\cdot962$, $\beta = 0\cdot881$

It may be noted here that Satterthwaite and Ure[3] measured the ratio of the two Hall coefficients in a P-type specimen of bismuth telluride at 77° K and found a value of $1\cdot4$. The value of the coefficient ρ_{123} for their specimen was slightly less than 2 cm^3 coulomb^{-1} compared with values of $1\cdot06$ and $0\cdot240$ for ingots 19 and 23 in the above results. It would therefore seem that there is a definite trend of this ratio in that it increases with increasing concentration of carriers.

In the simple model of the band structure discussed at the beginning of this section the single Hall coefficient R is related to the density of carriers in the solid by the relation

$$R = r/nq \qquad \qquad \dots (40)$$

where r is a dimensionless factor involving the ratio of Fermi–Dirac integrals which are functions of η and λ. The value of r is usually fairly close to unity. However, for bismuth telluride, there are two independent Hall coefficients and the interpretation of these in terms of the density of carriers is not so straightforward. Indeed, the work on the band structure was motivated by this problem. On the basis of the many-valley model given above, the Hall component ρ_{123} is related to the total density of carriers p by the relation

$$\rho_{123} = \frac{r}{pq} \times \frac{4u}{(1+u)^2} \qquad \ldots (41)$$

where u is defined by equation (39) and r is the same factor as occurs in the simple model. The multiplying factor $4u/(1+u)^2$ has the values $0 \cdot 475$ and $0 \cdot 380$ for the ingots 19 and 23 on the basis of the values given above.

All of the above measurements were made at liquid nitrogen temperature. The resistivity and Hall coefficients ($\rho_{11}, \rho_{33}, \rho_{123}, \rho_{231}$) were also measured on the same specimens over the temperature range $77°$ K to room temperature for the two compositions.

The temperature range was extended in the work of Yates[34] who made measurements of the Hall coefficient and resistivity on three P-type specimens over the temperature range $1 \cdot 3$ to $600°$ K. One of the specimens that he used (SBTC/19/F$_2$) was the same as that used by the author[30] to measure the galvanomagnetic coefficients with current flow parallel to the three-fold axis. Thus the results for this specimen extend the measurements of ρ_{33} and ρ_{231} reported by the author for the particular composition of specimens from ingot 19.

Yates also attempted to extend the measurements of ρ_{11} and ρ_{123} for the same composition but unfortunately he had to use a different specimen from that used by the author. A specimen (SBTC/19/H) from the same ingot was used but this turned out to have a somewhat different composition, presumably owing to segregation in the process of preparation.

Thus the values of resistivity and Hall coefficient reported by Yates for the specimen SBTC/19/F$_2$ agree numerically with the values of ρ_{33} and ρ_{231} given by the author in reference 30 for ingot 19 over the temperature range 77 to $300°$ K. However, his values for the resistivity and Hall coefficient of his specimen SBTC/19/H differ somewhat from the values of ρ_{11} and ρ_{123} for ingot 19 given by the author over the range $77°$ K to room temperature.

Other workers have reported measurements of the resistivity and Hall coefficient for various temperature ranges but the interpretation of these measurements in terms of individual components of the corresponding tensors is not always clear. Exceptions are the work of Satterthwaite and Ure[3] who measured the components ρ_{11} and ρ_{123} from liquid nitrogen temperature up to about $400°$ K. Values of the same components for P-type material have been reported by Shigetomi and Mori,[35] Black et al.,[36] and Mansfield and Williams.[37]

Of these various measurements, those of Yates are the only ones which extend below $77°$ K. The significant feature of his results at low temperatures is that the Hall coefficients of the three specimens investigated all remained virtually constant with temperature below $50°$ K or so. Thus in no case was there any tendency for the carriers to freeze out even at liquid helium temperatures.

A possible explanation of this is that, at the level of purity observed, the impurity levels responsible for the carriers are effectively merged with the valence band continuum of states. Such a process is to be expected for such relatively high carrier concentrations for which the wave functions on different impurity levels merge together to form an impurity band which may merge with the valence band. In view of the very high value of the dielectric constant of bismuth telluride (see Section 10) this process would be expected to take place at carrier concentrations even lower than those achieved so far in practice.

The behaviour of the Hall coefficient at very low temperatures was paralleled by the behaviour of the resistivity. This saturated in a metallic-like way below about 20° K, the residual resistivity being lowest for the specimen which had the lowest Hall coefficient.

It is possible that the merging of the impurity levels with the band continuum is one of the reasons for the previously discussed discrepancies in the proposed band model. Such a merging must have an influence on the density of states near the extreme energy and must modify the energy-wave number relation in this region.

At higher temperatures, the resistivity ρ_{11} of P-type material starts to rise with increasing temperature. As already mentioned, both resistivity components and both Hall components were investigated by the author over the range 77° K to room temperature. The ratio of the two resistivity components ρ_{33}/ρ_{11} was found to decrease very slightly over the first part of the range, being $2\cdot97$ at 77° K and $2\cdot85$ at 224° K for ingot 19. For the other ingot the ratio varied from $3\cdot10$ at 77° K through $2\cdot88$ at 222° K to $2\cdot85$ at 292° K. No significant variation of the ratio ρ_{231}/ρ_{123} of the two Hall coefficients was found over the temperature range investigated for either ingot.

These results are significant when interpreted in terms of the proposed many-valley model since it has been shown that these ratios should be independent of temperature for this model. It will be useful at this stage to discuss the resistivity ratio in a slightly different way. For the many-valley model, the essential features contributing to the overall conductivity are the conductivity tensors for the individual valleys. If these tensors have principal components σ_1, σ_2, and σ_3, then the anisotropy of the overall conductivity tensor is a function of the ratios of these three principal components. For the case where the valleys are centred on reflection planes one finds, for example, that the ratio of the two conductivities for the crystal as a whole is given by

$$\sigma_{11}/\sigma_{33} = (c^2\sigma_1+\sigma_2+s^2\sigma_3)/(s^2\sigma_1+c^2\sigma_3) \qquad \ldots(42)$$

where c and s are defined following equation (37). Thus any variation in the ratio reflects a variation in the ratio of the principal components of the valley conductivity tensors (omitting the possibility that the orientation of these might vary). The latter type of variation involves the anisotropy of the scattering within a single valley and thus involves the basic physical scattering mechanisms. The lack of any significant variation in the variation of the ratio σ_{11}/σ_{33} with temperature implies that all three principal components vary in the same way with temperature as each other and as either of the overall components. Over an appreciable temperature range this variation was found to follow a law of the form $\rho_{11} = \text{const.} \times T^{-1 \cdot 98}$. In a non-degenerate semiconductor this could be interpreted directly as a mobility variation, since the corresponding Hall coefficients showed only slight variations over the same range of temperature indicating that the density of carriers stayed constant. However, for the P-type specimens studied, other evidence, particularly from measurements of the Seebeck coefficient, showed that there was appreciable degeneracy present and this would modify somewhat the temperature dependence of the mobility.

In the extrinsic region, the individual Hall components ρ_{123} and ρ_{231} showed a slight temperature dependence which could not be explained on the usual basis of a change in the degree of degeneracy. The variations seemed to be systematically related to the impurity concentration and were explained by Yates on the basis of an impurity band model.

At higher temperatures, the resistivity components and Hall coefficients of the P-type specimens measured by Yates showed behaviour characteristic of a semiconductor in the intrinsic region in that they both commenced to decrease rapidly with increasing temperature. For the specimen SBTC/19/H the Hall coefficient ρ_{123} changed sign from positive to negative at a temperature of 439° K. This confirmed a similar observation reported earlier by Shigetomi and Mori[35] indicating that the high temperature mobility of electrons was greater than that of holes. A similar result was obtained by Black et al.[36] who found a reversal in sign of the Hall coefficient at a similar temperature in two P-type specimens. Mansfield and Williams[37] obtained the same type of behaviour. On the other hand, no such behaviour was observed for one of the P-type specimens (D.7) used by Satterthwaite and Ure[3], and this would have been expected on the basis of the above results.

Note added in proof. In a publication which has just come to the author's notice,[62] Efimova et al. report an extensive series of measurements of the galvanomagnetic properties of P-type bismuth telluride. Measurements of the nine principal galvanomagnetic coefficients were made over the temperature range 4° K to room temperature and were analysed using the six-valley model of the band structure. The major difference between the analysis and that used in reference 30 was that they allowed for a possible anisotropy of the relaxation time. The relaxation time within a valley was taken to be a second order tensor whose components, however, all varied in the same way with energy. In this way they were able to account for the temperature dependence of the galvanomagnetic coefficients in terms of the change in the anisotropy of the relaxation time with the change in the relative importance of impurity scattering. It is stated in their paper that the discrepancies between specimens 19 and 23 of reference 30, discussed in the text, can be accounted for in this way. Their findings seem to confirm the six-valley model of the band structure and lead to values of the effective mass anisotropies close to those given in the text.

7.3. Measurements on N-type Bismuth Telluride

The pattern of measurements and their discussion for N-type material is very similar to that of P-type material. Measurements of the galvano-magnetic coefficients at 77° K were undertaken by the author and co-workers[26] and interpreted in terms of the many-valley model. Unfortun-ately, these measurements were less complete than for P-type material. For some reason, not fully understood, it was found that the mechanical strength of N-type specimens cut parallel to the three-fold axis was so small that no suitable specimens could be obtained for making measurements with current flow parallel to this axis. This meant that the important coefficients ρ_{33}, ρ_{3333}, and ρ_{3311} could not be measured.

In the absence of any measurements of these components the test of the validity of the proposed many-valley model was severely restricted. Only six of the twelve galvanomagnetic coefficients could be measured with reasonable accuracy and the theoretical expressions for these involve six parameters. One of these parameters involves the combination of certain Fermi–Dirac integrals and in general is a function of the reduced Fermi level and the exponent in the scattering law. For highly degenerate material, however, the parameter reduces to a constant value independent of these. In the analysis, it was assumed that the material was sufficiently degenerate at 77° K for this approximation to apply and the number of parameters was therefore reduced to five. A choice of these was found to be possible such that the six theoretical expressions fitted the experimental results to better than 2 per cent, which was within experimental error.

A further indirect check was made by computing the theoretical value of the ratio of the two resistivity components ρ_{33}/ρ_{11} which turned out to be $4\cdot1$. An experimental value of this ratio was estimated from measurements made earlier by Goldsmid[31] who had measured the components over a restricted temperature range on similar N-type specimens. These results, when extrapolated to 77° K (the temperature of the galvanomagnetic measurements), gave a value of $3\cdot9$ for the ratio.

On the basis of these results it was concluded that the best fit to the pro-posed model was given by

$$\alpha_2/\alpha_1 = 1\cdot21, \quad \alpha_2/\alpha_3 = 0\cdot093, \quad \cos^2\theta = 0\cdot0546 \qquad \ldots (43)$$

in the notation of, and following equation (35). The first principal valley axis is thus inclined at nearly 90 degrees to the crystal axis which lies in the reflection plane and is normal to the three-fold axis. The second principal valley axis is parallel to the crystal diad axis. The constant energy surfaces are thus almost spherical about the third valley axis and are highly compressed parallel to this axis.

However, it is clear that the validity of the proposed model for the conduction band in bismuth telluride has not been subjected to a very stringent degree of testing. Even if it describes the main features of the band structure, it is highly probable that the same criticisms which were made of the results for P-type material apply with even more force to N-type material. That this is so is shown by some recent results of Goldsmid[38] who has carried out similar measurements on more highly doped N-type specimens. The parameters which Goldsmid used in fitting his results to the model were

$$\alpha_2/\alpha_1 = 1\cdot0, \quad \alpha_2/\alpha_3 = 0\cdot05, \quad \cos^2\theta = 0\cdot06 \qquad \ldots (44)$$

While showing the same general features as the previous set, these differ appreciably in magnitude.

As in the discussion for P-type material following equation (40) the Hall coefficients for N-type bismuth telluride, expressed in terms of the density of carriers, contain anisotropy coefficients involving the band structure parameters. On the basis of the parameters of equation (43) it is found that, at 77° K

$$\rho_{123} = -\frac{r}{nq}\times0\cdot326, \quad \rho_{231} = -\frac{r}{nq}\times0\cdot670 \qquad \ldots (45)$$

where n is the density of electrons.

Measurements on N-type material at temperatures other than 77° K nearly all refer to the resistivity and Hall coefficient components which can be measured with current flow normal to the three-fold axis, i.e. to the components ρ_{11}, ρ_{123}, and ρ_{231}. The one exception seems to be the recent results of Goldsmid[38] who has reported measurements of the resistivity ratio ρ_{33}/ρ_{11} at room temperature for a number of N-type specimens of varying composition. These were obtained by the use of a four-probe resistivity apparatus which avoided the necessity of cutting specimens in the direction of the three-fold axis. As shown in Figure 2 the ratio appears to increase systematically with increasing carrier concentration, as measured by the conductivity normal to the three-fold axes. This again supports the conclusion that either there are defects in the proposed model or that an actual change in the band structure parameters occurs with change in degree of degeneracy. Both the above results and the difference between the sets of parameters of equations (43) and (44) are consistent with the assumption that the parameter α_3 increases with increasing degree of degeneracy.

Other reported measurements in the extrinsic region do not throw much light on the basic mechanisms involved and show considerable variation between each other. One of the most comprehensive sets of measurements, covering the temperature range from liquid helium to 600° K, was made by Yates[34] on four N-type specimens. The author and co-workers[26] measured the coefficients ρ_{11}, ρ_{123}, and ρ_{231} from liquid nitrogen to room temperature for one of the N-type specimens used in the galvanomagnetic measurements. Satterthwaite and Ure[3] reported measurements of ρ_{11} and ρ_{123} on two N-type specimens from 77 to 375° K.

As in the case of P-type material, the resistivity and Hall coefficients measured by Yates saturated at very low temperatures. At higher temperatures, there were minor variations in the Hall coefficients before these started to decrease rapidly with increasing temperature as the intrinsic

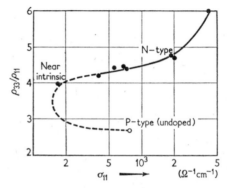

Figure 2. *Variation of resistivity ratio with composition. After Goldsmid[38]*

range was reached. Even at the highest temperatures, there was no evidence of a change of sign of the Hall coefficient in N-type material. In contrast, in the work of Satterthwaite and Ure, a change of sign from negative to positive was reported for two N-type specimens at temperatures of 270 and 320° K, respectively.

This discrepancy is puzzling in view of the fact that one of the specimens used by Yates (SBTC/27/D) had a Hall coefficient ρ_{123} at 77° K of approximately 10 cm^3 coulomb^{-1} which was practically the same as the corresponding coefficient of one of the specimens (D.5) used by Satterthwaite and Ure. There was, however, a considerable difference in the corresponding conductivities of the two specimens. Thus at 100° K the Hall mobilities ($\rho_{123}\sigma_{11}$) for the two specimens were 2,200 and 500 cm^{2}sec^{-1}V^{-1}, respectively, and for the latter specimen, the conductivity fell off much more rapidly with temperature than for the former. It would thus appear that for some reason the electron mobility in the specimens measured by Satterthwaite and Ure was abnormally low. It should be remembered in this connection that these latter authors did not find the change in sign of the Hall coefficient in P-type material reported by a number of other workers. They concluded from their measurements that the hole mobility was larger than the electron mobility over the range 270 to 320° K.

8. THERMOELECTRIC PROPERTIES

Although many workers have reported measurements of the Seebeck coefficient of bismuth telluride in view of its applications in thermoelectric devices, very few of these have been made on a basis appropriate to the objects of the present article and only a few of the results will be discussed in detail.

The measurements by Goldsmid[31] of the two principal components of the Seebeck tensor in both N- and P-type material have already been mentioned in the preceding section. The Seebeck coefficient in P-type material was found to be isotropic in the range from 150° K to room temperature. In N-type material, a slight anisotropy was observed over the same range.

The importance of the Seebeck coefficient lies in the fact that, in conjunction with measurements of the electrical conductivity and Hall coefficient, it leads to a determination of a density-of-states effective mass. For the many-valley model discussed in the last Section, this allows the individual band structure parameters, instead of just their ratio, to be obtained.

One of the most comprehensive studies of the Seebeck coefficient in bismuth telluride was made by Goldsmid,[39] who measured the component of the Seebeck tensor normal to the three-fold axis in a large number of N- and P-type specimens over the temperature range 150 to 300° K. These were correlated with measurements of the corresponding conductivity component over the same temperature range.

Goldsmid found that, provided the Seebeck coefficient was high enough in absolute value (greater than 190 μV deg^{-1} for N-type material and greater than 170 μV deg^{-1} for P-type material), the graphs of the Seebeck coefficient against $\ln T$ were linear over an appreciable temperature range, until in fact the specimens were clearly becoming intrinsic. The N-type specimens had a common slope of 167 μV deg^{-1} and the P-type specimens a slope of 150 μV deg^{-1} in this range.

The results were interpreted by Goldsmid in terms of a simple model of the band structure described by a single effective mass parameter m^* and a relaxation time τ for the scattering processes of the form $\tau = \tau_0 \epsilon^\lambda$. The parameter τ_0 was assumed to vary as $1/T$ (which would be the case for scattering by the acoustic lattice vibrations) and λ was treated as an adjustable parameter.

For such a theoretical model, the density of carriers n is given by

$$n = \frac{1}{2\pi^2}\left(\frac{2m^* kT}{\hbar^2}\right)^{3/2} F_{1/2}(\eta) \qquad \ldots (46)$$

where η is the position of the Fermi energy measured in units of kT from the appropriate band edge and $F_{1/2}(\eta)$ is a Fermi–Dirac integral of the general class

$$F_r(\eta) = \int_0^\infty \frac{x^r}{1+\exp{(x-\eta)}}\, dx \qquad \ldots (47)$$

In the non-degenerate limit when η is sufficiently negative, $F_r(\eta)$ can be approximated by

$$F_r(\eta) = \exp{(\eta)}\,\Gamma(r+1) \qquad \ldots (48)$$

where $\Gamma(r+1)$ is the gamma function. Such an approximation is usually accurate if $\eta < -2$.

The Seebeck coefficient is given by

$$Q = \frac{k}{q}\left[\eta - \frac{(2\lambda+5)\,F_{\lambda+3/2}}{(2\lambda+3)\,F_{\lambda+1/2}}\right] \qquad \ldots (49)$$

It is to be expected on physical grounds that the density of carriers remains constant with temperature over an appreciable temperature range. For this region, assuming that the non-degenerate approximation (48) is valid, the Seebeck coefficient Q should vary with temperature according to the equation

$$|Q| = \frac{k}{q}\left(\frac{3}{2}\ln T + \text{const.}\right) \qquad \ldots (50)$$

Thus the slope of the graph of Q vs $\ln T$ should be $3k/2q$ or $129\ \mu\mathrm{V\,deg^{-1}}$. The discrepancies between this theoretical value and the observed slopes were discussed by Goldsmid but no satisfactory explanation was found in terms of his model.

However, the linear variation of Q with $\ln T$ was interpreted as showing that the density of carriers remained constant with temperature over this range and hence that the variation of electrical conductivity was determined by the variation in mobility. This mobility variation is dominated by the value of the exponent λ and thus the observed variations were used to obtain values of λ for N- and P-type material. Values of λ of $-0\cdot72$ and $-0\cdot94$ were found. These values were then used in conjunction with equation (49) to determine the value of η for the different specimens at different temperatures. From these values of η Goldsmid was able to calculate the value of a function, which we shall call here x, defined by

$$x = \frac{1}{2\pi^2}\left(\frac{2mkT}{\hbar^2}\right)^{3/2} F_{1/2}(\eta) \qquad \ldots (51)$$

From equation (46) it is seen that x is related to the carrier concentration n by the equation

$$x = n(m/m^*)^{3/2} \qquad \ldots (52)$$

78

As a final step, the numerical values of x were used in conjunction with the observed values of the conductivity to determine the numerical values of the quantity σ/qx in the different specimens at different temperatures. A mobility μ was defined by the equation $\sigma = nq\mu$ and from the last two equations

$$\sigma/qx = \mu(m^*/m)^{3/2} \qquad \ldots (53)$$

On the theoretical model, the value of μ as defined above should be given by

$$\mu = \frac{2q}{3m^*}\tau_0(\lambda+\tfrac{1}{2})(kT)^\lambda F_{\lambda+1/2}(\eta)/F_{1/2}(\eta) \qquad \ldots (54)$$

Thus, in the various specimens of one type at a particular temperature, μ should vary in a predictable way owing to differences in the value of η for the specimens. The theoretically predicted variation of $\mu(m^*/m)^{3/2}$ at a particular temperature, taking m^* to be constant, was compared with the experimental variation deduced as given above for N- and P-type specimens at 150 and 300° K.

The analysis has been discussed in the above way in order to bring out some of the points involved when the more complex many-valley model is used. Before discussing these, however, the results which Goldsmid found should be mentioned. The theoretical variation of $\mu(m^*/m)^{3/2}$ with position of the reduced Fermi energy η was found always to lie below the variation of σ/qx with η. It was therefore stated by Goldsmid that in practice the effective mass m^* increases with increasing degree of degeneracy. However, it appears to the present author that this statement requires further consideration. The difficulty is that, according to the deformation potential theory of lattice scattering, the parameter τ_0 in equation (54) should vary with the effective mass parameter according to an inverse three-halves power law, as well as varying inversely with temperature. Thus on this basis the product $\mu(m^*/m)^{3/2}$ contains the factor $(m^*)^{-1}$. The fact that the experimentally deduced variation with η is always larger than the theoretically deduced variation, assuming that m^* is constant, implies that, in the latter derivation, a value of m^* should be used in such a way that m^* *decreases* with increasing degree of degeneracy.

A similar conclusion holds if the results are analysed in terms of the many-valley model. The only difference in the analysis is that in the various equations involving m^*, this parameter is replaced by combinations of the band structure parameters. Thus, the total density of carriers is given by

$$n = (3s)\frac{1}{2\pi^2}\left(\frac{2m}{\hbar^2\alpha^*}\right)^{3/2}(kT)^{3/2}F_{1/2}(\eta) \qquad \ldots (55)$$

where $3s$ is the total number of valleys (which must be an integral multiple of 3 because of the three-fold rotational symmetry). The value of s is either

1 or 2 depending on whether the energy extremes fall at the edge of, or inside, the first Brillouin zone. The value of α^* is given in terms of the parameters of equation (35) by

$$\alpha^* = (\alpha_1 \alpha_2 \alpha_3)^{1/3} \qquad \ldots (56)$$

Alternatively, in terms of the parameters of equation (36)

$$(\alpha^*)^3 = \det(\alpha_{ij}) \qquad \ldots (57)$$

The (isotropic) Seebeck coefficient is given by the same expression (49) as applies for the simple model. The analysis then follows similar lines except that the conductivity discussed by Goldsmid is taken as the component of the conductivity normal to the three-fold axis. If we define the mobility component μ_{11} by the equation

$$\sigma_{11} = nq\mu_{11} \qquad \ldots (58)$$

then the theoretical expression for μ_{11} may be obtained from reference 30 as

$$\mu_{11} = \tfrac{1}{2}(\alpha_{11}+\alpha_{22})\frac{2q}{3m}\tau_0(kT)^\lambda F_{\lambda+1/2}(\eta)/F_{1/2}(\eta) \qquad \ldots (59)$$

Following the analysis through on the same lines as previously, with obvious modifications, it is found that the numerical values of x determined by Goldsmid are to be interpreted on the more general model as

$$x = n(\alpha^*)^{3/2}/3s \qquad \ldots (60)$$

The values of σ/qx are to be interpreted as σ_{11}/qx and should be given by

$$\sigma_{11}/qx = \mu_{11}(3s)/(\alpha^*)^{3/2} \qquad \ldots (61)$$

with the theoretical value of μ_{11} given by equation (59).

On this interpretation, the fact that the experimentally deduced values of the left-hand side of equation (61) vary with η in such a way that they lie above the theoretically deduced variation of the right-hand side, using the expression (59) to determine μ_{11}, has similar implications to those obtained for the more simple model. However, the problem is more complicated in that although the parameter τ_0 certainly depends on the parameters α_1, α_2, and α_3 there is no simple argument which can be used to derive this dependence. The dependence, however, should be such that in order to account for the above observations, one or more of these parameters increases with increasing degree of degeneracy. This observation is consistent, at least for N-type material, with the galvanomagnetic observations, for which it has already been noted that, within the framework of the many-valley model, the parameter α_3 increases with increasing degree of degeneracy.

The values of σ/qx given by Goldsmid ($\mu(m^*/m)^{3/2}$ in his notation) can be used in conjunction with measurements of the Hall coefficient to obtain a density-of-states effective mass and hence to individual values of the band structure parameters, instead of just the ratios given by the galvanomagnetic measurements. Using equation (41) for the Hall coefficient ρ_{123} in conjunction with equation (58) it is found that

$$\mu_{11} = (\sigma_{11}\rho_{123}) \times \frac{1}{r}\frac{(1+u)^2}{4u} \qquad \ldots (62)$$

Thus, equation (61) can be rewritten in the form

$$\frac{3s}{(\alpha^*)^{3/2}} = \left(\frac{\sigma_{11}}{qx}\right)\frac{1}{(\sigma_{11}\rho_{123})} \times r \times \frac{4u}{(1+u)^2} \qquad \ldots (63)$$

The term (σ_{11}/qx) is obtained from Goldsmid's results and the term $(\sigma_{11}\rho_{123})$, which corresponds to a Hall mobility, can be obtained from measurements. Thus the value of the left-hand side may be obtained in principle.

In practice, however, the experimental results so far reported do not allow this procedure to be carried out completely. For N-type material, the value of u was obtained at $77°$ K from the galvanomagnetic measurements of reference 26 for one specimen designated as F. The factor $(4u)/(1+u)^2$ was obtained as $0 \cdot 326$. The Hall coefficient ρ_{123} and resistivity ρ_{11} were not measured as functions of temperature on this specimen but were measured on a specimen G of closely similar composition. At $150°$ K (the temperature at which Goldsmid obtained values of σ/qx), the product $\rho_{123}\sigma_{11}$ was found to be $1 \cdot 15 \times 10^3$ cm^{2}V^{-1}sec^{-1}. Values in this range were also obtained by Yates.[34] Goldsmid's value of σ/qx at this temperature was $1 \cdot 07 \times 10^3$ cm^{2}V^{-1}sec^{-1} for $\eta < +2$. Using these values leads to the result

$$(3s)^{2/3}/\alpha^* = 0 \cdot 45 \times r^{2/3} \qquad \ldots (64)$$

The result is put in this form because the left-hand side is the ratio of the density of states effective mass to the free electron mass (cf. equations (46) and (55)).

The value of $r^{2/3}$ is unlikely to be very much different from unity and in view of the approximate nature of the argument and the fact that the effective mass parameters appear to vary with degree of degeneracy, there seems little point in a more refined calculation of r.

Taking the value of α^* given by equation (64), assuming a value of s of either 1 or 2, and using the parameters u, v, and w determined by the galvanomagnetic measurements, it is possible in principle to obtain the individual parameters α_1, α_2, and α_3 for N-type material. This is a simple calculation which, however, will not be attempted here in view of the various uncertainties involved.

A similar calculation can be applied to P-type material. The anisotropy factor $4u/(1+u)^2$ for the specimens from ingot 19 used by the author[30] had a value of $0 \cdot 476$. The product $\rho_{123}\sigma_{11}$ for these specimens had a value of $1 \cdot 04 \times 10^3$ cm^{2}V^{-1}sec^{-1} at $150°$ K. Goldsmid's value of σ/qx for P-type material at $150°$ K was $1 \cdot 26 \times 10^3$. These values lead to

$$(3s)^{2/3}/\alpha^* = 0 \cdot 69 \times r^{2/3} \qquad \ldots (65)$$

In reference 30 a value of $0\cdot51$ for this parameter was quoted. This was based on an estimation of the Seebeck coefficient for specimens from ingot 19 at $77°$ K provided by measurements of Walker.[40] The value of the Seebeck coefficient used in the analysis was $120\ \mu V\,\mathrm{deg}^{-1}$ (Walker's specimen SBTC/19). It seems, however, that this value may have been appreciably in error. Measurements of the Hall coefficients σ_{123} and the conductivity σ_{11} were made by Yates[34] on the same specimen as that used by Walker for the measurements of the Seebeck coefficient (Yates' specimen SBTC/19/H). It has already been mentioned that the values of conductivity and Hall coefficient obtained by Yates for this specimen differed significantly from the corresponding values for the specimens of ingot 19 reported by the author. At $77°$ K, the values of σ_{11} and ρ_{123} reported by Yates were $3\cdot16\times10^{-4}\ \Omega\mathrm{cm}$ and $0\cdot69\ \mathrm{cm}^3\mathrm{coulomb}^{-1}$ as contrasted with values of $4\cdot23\times10^{-4}$ and $1\cdot06$, respectively, given in reference 30. Thus there appears to be a significant change in the density of carriers and, therefore, the value of the Seebeck coefficient at $77°$ K for the specimens of ingot 19 used by the author may be appreciably in error.

Turning now to other measurements of the Seebeck coefficients, the results of Walker[40] covering the temperature range 6 to $200°$ K should be mentioned. Here again, these provided evidence that when interpreted on the basis of the standard model, it was necessary to assume that the parameters used varied with the degree of degeneracy.

The behaviour of the Seebeck coefficient in the intrinsic range of temperature has been reported by Goldsmid[39] and by Mansfield and Williams.[37] In this region the Seebeck coefficient is negative and rather insensitive to temperature variations. Such a behaviour is to be anticipated if the electron mobility exceeds the hole mobility in this range. The Seebeck coefficient Q when both bands are contributing to the transport processes is given by

$$\sigma Q = \sigma_n Q_n + \sigma_p Q_p \qquad \ldots(66)$$

where Q_n and Q_p are Seebeck coefficients for the two bands separately (with their appropriate algebraic signs). If the densities of states effective masses for electrons and holes are equal in magnitude, then in the intrinsic range $Q_p = - Q_n$ and since the total conductivity $\sigma = \sigma_n+\sigma_p = n_i q(\mu_n+\mu_p)$ we obtain

$$Q = Q_n(b-1)/(b+1)$$

where b is the ratio of electron to hole mobility. The value of Q_n is approximately

$$Q_n = \frac{k}{q}\left(\frac{-\epsilon_G}{2kT}-2\right)$$

where ϵ_G is the thermal energy gap. Thus, the overall Seebeck coefficient will be negative if $b>1$, and will vary only slowly with temperature over a limited range. The complications introduced when the densities of states effective masses for electrons and holes are different are relatively minor in the case of bismuth telluride. From results on one of his specimens Goldsmid obtained values of $b \simeq 1 \cdot 2$, $m_n^*/m_p^* \simeq 0 \cdot 9$.

To conclude this Section, mention should be made of two magneto-thermoelectric investigations. The first of these was the measurement of the Nernst effect by Mansfield and Williams[37] on P- and N-type specimens. At low temperatures, the Nernst coefficient was found to be negative in all specimens. This is to be expected on a simple model only if the exponent λ in the assumed form of the relaxation time is negative for both electrons and holes.[41] On such a model, the sign of the Nernst coefficient is expected to change at sufficiently high temperatures and this was found to be the case. Also of interest in this work was the anisotropy of the Nernst coefficient. On one specimen, the ratio of the effect measured with the magnetic field parallel to the cleavage planes to that measured with the field normal to the cleavage planes was found to be $2 \cdot 4$, this being independent of temperature in the extrinsic region.

The change of the Seebeck coefficient in a magnetic field (magnetothermo-electric effect) was investigated by Bowley et al.[42] in conjunction with magnetoresistance measurements. The change in the Seebeck coefficient ΔQ should be of the same sign as Q if the exponent in the relaxation time is negative and of opposite sign if it is positive. Measurements were made at liquid nitrogen temperatures on two P-type specimens and three N-type specimens of varying compositions. In all cases, even in very highly doped material, λ was found to be negative.

Both these investigations confirm that even in very highly doped bismuth telluride, any scattering of the charge carriers due to ionized impurities must be very small compared with the lattice scattering effects in both P- and N-type material, since λ would be expected to be positive if ionized impurity scattering was dominant. The absence of any appreciable scattering of this type is probably closely related with the abnormally high value of the dielectric constant of bismuth telluride (Section 10).

9. THERMAL CONDUCTIVITY

Like the other transport properties entering into the thermoelectric figure of merit, the thermal conductivity of bismuth telluride has been investigated by a large number of workers. Here, we shall concentrate on those measurements which have been made on effectively single crystal material.

In the usual type of analysis, the thermal conductivity of a solid is regarded as being due to two contributions κ_L and κ_e from the lattice and the free charge carriers, respectively. For semiconductors of high purity the latter can usually be neglected in comparison with the former especially when κ_L is large. For bismuth telluride, however, it is necessary to take the electronic contribution into account in the analysis of the measurements

83

of thermal conductivity. There are two reasons for this, first that it has not so far been possible to obtain specimens with a low carrier concentration and second that the value of the lattice thermal conductivity turns out to be much lower than for most semiconductors.

As discussed in Section 6, the thermal conductivity tensor in the absence of a magnetic field has two principal components and in a first analysis each of these is written in the form

$$\kappa = \kappa_L + \kappa_e \qquad \qquad \ldots (67)$$

where the first term is the lattice contribution and the second the electronic contribution.

The value of κ_e is related to the electrical conductivity by the Lorenz extension of the Wiedemann–Franz law. For a semiconductor of cubic symmetry, the relation is

$$\kappa_e = L\sigma T \qquad \qquad \ldots (68)$$

where L is the Lorenz number, T the absolute temperature, and σ is the (scalar) electrical conductivity. The Lorenz number is of the form

$$L = A(k/q)^2 \qquad \qquad \ldots (69)$$

where k is Boltzmann's constant, q is the electronic charge, and A is a numerical parameter which takes on different values under different conditions. For a semiconductor in the extrinsic range, the value of A depends on the degree of degeneracy and the scattering mechanism for the charge carriers. If this latter is described in terms of a relaxation time of the form $\tau = \tau_0 \epsilon^\lambda$ and a simple band structure is used for the analysis, then the value of A is given by

$$A = [(\lambda + \tfrac{7}{2})(\lambda + \tfrac{3}{2}) F_{\lambda+5/2} F_{\lambda+1/2} - (\lambda + \tfrac{5}{2})^2 F^2_{\lambda+3/2}]/(\lambda + \tfrac{3}{2})^2 F^2_{\lambda+1/2} \quad \ldots (70)$$

The functions F_r are Fermi–Dirac functions of the position of the reduced Fermi level η. For non-degenerate statistics (η large and negative) the dependence on η disappears and A reduces to $(2\lambda+5)/2$. For completely degenerate statistics, A has the value $\pi^2/3$ independent of both η and λ.

Considerable modification of the value of the Lorenz number is to be expected when the semiconductor is in the intrinsic range of temperature when both electrons and holes are contributing to the transport process. In this case the value of L is given by[24]

$$L = \frac{L_n \sigma_n + L_p \sigma_p}{\sigma} + \frac{\sigma_n \sigma_p}{\sigma^2} \left(\frac{k}{q}\right)^2 \left(r_n + r_p + \frac{\epsilon_G}{kT}\right)^2 \qquad \ldots (71)$$

where L_n, L_p are Lorenz numbers of the type discussed above for the electrons and holes, respectively, and σ_n and σ_p are the respective contributions to the total electrical conductivity $\sigma = \sigma_n + \sigma_p$. The last term in this expression is the bipolar contribution arising from the fact that electron–hole pairs are generated at the hot end of the specimen, diffuse down the temperature gradient, and recombine at the cold end, thus transporting their energy of activation down the temperature gradient. In this term, r_n and r_p are numerical factors which enter into the expressions for the Seebeck co-efficients Q_n and Q_p of the electrons and holes, respectively. These latter are of the form

$$Q_n = \left(\frac{k}{q}\right)(\eta - r_n), \quad Q_p = \left(\frac{k}{q}\right)(-\theta + r_p) \qquad \ldots (72)$$

with
$$\eta = (\tilde{\mu} - \epsilon_c)/kT, \quad \theta = (\epsilon_v - \tilde{\mu})/kT$$

where $\tilde{\mu}$ is the position of the Fermi energy and ϵ_c and ϵ_v are the extreme energies of the conduction and valence bands, respectively. Finally, ϵ_G in equation (71) is given by

$$\epsilon_G = \epsilon_c - \epsilon_v \qquad \ldots (73)$$

The above results have been given as if for a semiconductor of cubic symmetry and, as might be expected, there are modifications arising from the anisotropy in the case of bismuth telluride. However, these modifications are very simple in form if the model of the band structure and scattering mechanisms discussed in Section 7 is used. In the extrinsic range, the Lorenz number calculated for this model is isotropic. Thus each component of κ_e is related to the corresponding component of the electrical conductivity tensor by an equation of the form of equation (68) with the same value of L for both components. This value of L is the same as for the simple model, being given by the combination of equations (69) and (70). In the intrinsic range the Lorenz number for relating each component of κ_e to the corresponding component of σ is of the same form as in equation (71) and all that is necessary is to use the appropriate component for σ_n and for σ_p in this equation.

Using arguments similar in principle to the above, Goldsmid[31] calculated both components of the electronic thermal conductivity tensor from measurements of the electrical conductivity. By subtracting these from the measured value of the components of the total thermal conductivity, he obtained the components of the lattice contribution. He found that the lattice thermal conductivity normal to the three-fold axis was greater than that parallel to the axis by a factor of $2 \cdot 1$. This calculation was insensitive to the detailed calculations of the electronic contributions which only amounted to a small part of the total.

Measurements of the thermal conductivity of a number of P- and N-type specimens of varying composition over the temperature range 150 to 300° K were reported later by Goldsmid.[43] This work was confined to the component normal to the three-fold axis. The electronic contributions were calculated using values of the reduced Fermi level η and the scattering index λ obtained from the analysis of the Seebeck coefficient and electrical conductivity given in the last section.

85

For P-type material, it was found that the variation of the total thermal conductivity with the electrical conductivity at a particular temperature (which is given by combining equations (67) and (68)) could be accounted for, at all temperatures in the extrinsic range, on the assumption that the lattice component κ_L was independent of composition. Such a result cannot, of course, be expected *a priori*, since the electrical conductivity at a particular temperature can only be varied by the addition of impurity atoms. Such atoms would be expected to give rise to scattering of phonons and hence affect the lattice thermal conductivity. However, it was concluded that such effects were negligibly small in comparison with other phonon scattering processes for various types of acceptor atoms in bismuth telluride.

For the N-type specimens in the extrinsic range, however, the situation was more complex. Some of these specimens were obtained by doping the parent ingot with chlorine or iodine. For such specimens, the calculations of the electronic component showed that the variation of the total thermal conductivity with the electrical conductivity at a particular temperature could not be accounted for, unless it was assumed that the lattice component varied with the degree of halogen doping. This result was peculiar to halogen-doped specimens. On other N-type specimens, obtained by doping with excess tellurium, lithium, or aluminium the results could be accounted for by assuming that κ_L was independent of composition at a particular temperature. The conclusion was that halogen atoms in bismuth telluride act as strong scattering centres for the phonons.

At a particular temperature, the extrapolation of the measurements of the total thermal conductivity to zero electrical conductivity on both N- and P-type specimens should give a common value of the true lattice thermal conductivity at that temperature; this was found to be the case. The values of κ_L at 150 and 300° K (normal to the three-fold axis) were found to be $0 \cdot 0268$ and $0 \cdot 0157$ W cm^{-1}deg^{-1}, respectively. Thus, over this range, there were appreciable departures from a $1/T$ law. The values of κ_L obtained by Goldsmid[43] are included in Figure 3 (portion C–D).

A similar procedure to the above for separating the electronic and lattice components was used in the work of Walker[40] who made measurements of the thermal conductivity component normal to the three-fold axis, in the temperature range 8 to 200° K. In this range, the electronic component is only a small fraction of the total so that any errors in its estimation do not affect greatly the calculated lattice contribution. Walker used a series of specimens containing increasing amounts of iodine, going from undoped material to material containing $0 \cdot 20$ per cent of added iodine.

The lattice contribution to the thermal conductivity obtained by Walker for the undoped specimen is shown as a function of temperature in Figure 3. In the region above 150° K his results coincide with those obtained by Goldsmid. From 50 to 150° K, κ_L was given by the equation

$$\kappa_L = 4 \cdot 3 \, T^{-1 \cdot 0} \, \text{W cm}^{-1} \text{deg}^{-1}$$

As the temperature was lowered below 50° K, κ_L at first increased faster with decreasing temperature than according to this law and then more slowly, tending towards a flat maximum value in the lower temperature range.

Measurements down to a lower temperature of 2° K have been reported by MacDonald et al.[44] but no details of composition were given. However, they did observe a flat maximum in the total thermal conductivity which for N-type material was $0 \cdot 56 \, \text{W cm}^{-1} \text{deg}^{-1}$ at 9° K and for P-type material was $0 \cdot 29$ at 7° K. Neither of these values agrees very well with the results of Walker.

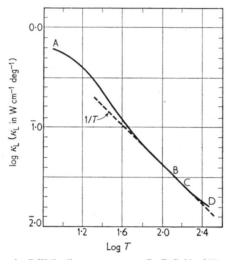

A—B Walker[40]   C—D Goldsmid[43]

Figure 3. *The lattice thermal conductivity of bismuth telluride*

The low temperature maximum of the thermal conductivity cannot be the one usually associated with the onset of boundary scattering processes, since estimates of the phonon mean free path at the maximum are several orders of magnitude smaller than the relevant specimen dimensions. Walker suggested that the maximum was associated with the presence of dislocations in the material.

Measurements of the thermal conductivity as a function of temperature have also been reported by Satterthwaite and Ure.[3] Over the temperature range 80 to 170 K° they found that κ_L was given by

$$\kappa_L = 5 \cdot 1 \, T^{-1 \cdot 0} \, \text{W cm}^{-1} \text{deg}^{-1}$$

This equation gives values of κ_L some 20 per cent higher than those estimated by Walker.

In the other specimens investigated by Walker, containing various amounts of added iodine, a systematic decrease of the estimated lattice thermal conductivity with increasing iodine concentration was observed at all temperatures. This confirmed the effect observed by Goldsmid at higher temperatures. The measured effect of iodine on the thermal conductivity was compared with the effect predicted by the formula of Berman et al.[45] Reasonable agreement was obtained on the assumption that $\frac{3}{4}$ of the iodine atoms were in substitutional sites in the lattice while the remaining $\frac{1}{4}$ were in interstitial positions. However, recent evidence on the density of iodine-doped bismuth telluride suggests that all the iodine atoms are in substitutional positions on tellurium sites (sub-section 11.4).

The extra thermal resistance caused by iodine does not vary very strongly with temperature. For one specimen which was estimated to contain $0 \cdot 124$ per cent by weight of iodine, the extra thermal resistivity compared with the undoped specimens amounted to 3 W^{-1} cm deg. K at $10°$ K and to 7 W^{-1} cm deg. K at $300°$ K. On simple reasoning, this extra thermal resistance should vary as $1/T$ at low temperatures and tend to become independent of T at higher temperatures. The measured values do not conform to this simple behaviour.

A further check on the effect of iodine was provided by the magneto-thermal measurements of Bowley et al.[42] In this work the magnetothermal resistance and magnetothermoelectric effects were measured in P- and N-type bismuth telluride at $77°$ K. Both measurements lead in principle to estimates of the reduced Fermi energy η and to the scattering index λ in the relaxation time. The first effect could not be measured on N-type specimens but gave good agreement with the second effect on P-type material. Values of η and λ were determined from the magnetothermoelectric effects on both types and used to calculate the Lorenz number (equation (69)) and hence the electronic contribution to the thermal conductivity. When this was subtracted from the total thermal conductivity, it was found that the residual lattice contribution was independent of composition for the P-type specimens but decreased with increasing iodine concentration for the N-type specimens.

To conclude this Section we briefly mention the bipolar thermodiffusion contribution in the intrinsic range of temperature, reported by Goldsmid.[46] At room temperature the graphs of the total thermal conductivity κ versus the product σT (T constant) for a number of specimens of varying composition showed a pronounced rise at low values of σ where the specimens were intrinsic. By extrapolation of the curves from higher values of σ, the extra contribution to the thermal conductivity in the intrinsic region was obtained. This contribution was shown to be consistent with that predicted by the last term in equation (71) provided that a value of the energy gap ϵ_G of $0 \cdot 15$ eV was used. This forbidden gap width is close to the value obtained from infra-red transmission measurements, which are discussed in Section 10.

10. OPTICAL PROPERTIES

The optical properties of single crystal bismuth telluride have been reported in a series of papers by Austin.[47-49] In the first of these, the shape of the absorption edge was studied for different compositions in the temperature range $-155°$ to $20°$ C. In general, measurements were made with light propagating parallel to the three-fold axis.

The variation of the absorption coefficient with wavelength in semiconductors has been thoroughly reviewed elsewhere.[50] In the region of the absorption edge the absorption is due in the main to photon-induced transitions of electrons from the valence to the conduction band. At longer wavelengths absorption by free carriers, if present, becomes predominant. The individual contribution of interband transitions can usually be separated out fairly reliably by extrapolating the free carrier contribution at longer wavelengths to the region of the absorption edge. This was the procedure adopted by Austin.

A detailed account of the various mechanisms which may contribute to the shape of the absorption edge in semiconductors has been given by McLean,[51] with special reference to germanium and silicon. Many of the effects (such as exciton contributions) would, however, only be expected to be observed with higher resolving powers and at lower temperatures than were used by Austin.

The main form of the absorption edge due to interband transitions is different according to whether such transitions are predominantly of the direct or indirect type, i.e. whether a change in the value of the electron wave vector (electron crystal momentum) takes place or not, in the transition. In the latter case, conservation of momentum requires the co-operation of phonons in the transition process.

For germanium and silicon, the maximum energy of the valence band lies at the centre of the Brillouin zone, with electron wave vector $\mathbf{k} = 0$. The lowest energy states of the conduction band form a series of groups ('valleys') with extreme values at points in the Brillouin zone which are related to each other by crystal symmetry and therefore have a common value of the magnitude of the wave vector. Indirect photon-induced transitions between the valence band states and the conduction band states can take place with either the emission or absorption of a phonon having a wave vector such that the total change in crystal momentum (sum of electron and phonon wave vectors) is zero. Thus, in germanium and silicon, only phonons with one particular magnitude of the wave vector are involved in the indirect transitions. Since energy is conserved in the overall process, the frequency at which indirect transitions begin involves the energy of such phonons as well as the difference in energy ϵ_G between the states of extreme energy of the valence and conduction bands. There are a number of contributions to the shape of the absorption edge. Indirect transitions may be associated with either emission or absorption of a phonon. The former type begin at shorter wavelengths than the latter so that the respective contributions are displaced with respect to each other (by twice the energy of the phonon). Since in general a given magnitude of the wave vector corresponds to more than one phonon energy because of the presence of different branches of the vibration spectrum, there will be contributions involving different phonon energies, and thus displaced from each other in wavelength.

Not all these contributions are equally important and, for example, in the first studies on germanium, Macfarlane and Roberts[52] were able to fit the observed shape of the absorption edge very well with an expression which took into account the indirect transitions associated with the absorption and emission of phonons of only one energy. Only when more precise measurements with higher resolutions were made[53] were other contributions isolated from these major ones.

Austin attempted to fit the shape of the absorption edge in bismuth telluride to the expression given by Macfarlane and Roberts for indirect transitions involving phonons of only one energy. However, the attempt was not very successful and the possibility of a more refined analysis was prevented by insufficient resolution. It was suggested that a possible reason for the discrepancy was that, in accordance with the proposed many-valley model for both the conduction and valence bands, there must be at least two phonons involved in the indirect transitions. These correspond to transitions between valence band states and conduction band states on the same reflection plane and on different reflection planes, respectively.

From measurements on the purest of his specimens, Austin concluded that the thermal energy gap at room temperature was close to $0 \cdot 13$ eV and that this had a temperature coefficient of $-0 \cdot 95 \times 10^{-4}$ eV deg.$^{-1}$. In other specimens investigated, with higher carrier concentrations, the absorption edge was found to be shifted to higher energy values, this being attributed to the increased occupation of states near the band edges.

An interesting observation was made on the effect of polarization on the transmission spectrum for light propagating normal to the three-fold axis. The free carrier absorption was found to be appreciably larger when the electric vector of the radiation was also normal to the axis (and, of course, normal to the direction of propagation) than when the electric vector was parallel to the axis. On the other hand, the position and shape of the absorption edge were almost unaffected by the change in polarization. These results were consistent with the hypothesis that the interband transitions were of the indirect type.

In some of the specimens used by Austin, well defined transmission fringes were observed on the long wavelength side of the absorption edge. These were used in conjunction with measurements of the specimen thickness to obtain the refractive index in this region. This was found to have a value of $9 \cdot 2$ over the wavelength interval 8 to 14 microns. Such a high value of the refractive index is presumably associated with the high electronic polarizability of the constituent atoms of bismuth telluride. It has the implication that the dielectric constant is very high, of the order of 85. Such a high value would be responsible for the observed lack of any activation energy of impurities at low temperatures (Section 7) and for the absence of any appreciable impurity scattering of charge carriers (Section 8).

Austin has also reported measurements of the infra-red Faraday rotation in N- and P-type bismuth telluride.[49] On a simple view, there are two contributions to the effect. Near the absorption edge interband transitions play some part but for longer wavelengths the principal contribution is associated with free carriers.

The theory of the rotation due to free carriers in bismuth telluride assuming a many-valley form of the band structure was given previously by Austin.[48] It was shown that for light propagating parallel to the three-fold axis, the rotation was given by

$$\theta = \frac{L}{2\mu}\left(\frac{q^3}{cm_0^2\,\epsilon_0}\right)\frac{n}{\omega^2}\alpha_3' B \qquad \ldots (74)$$

where L is the sample thickness, μ is the refractive index in the absence of a magnetic field, q and m_0 are the charge and mass of an electron, n is the total carrier concentration, ω is the angular frequency, and B the magnetic induction. The parameter α_3' is a particular combination of the band structure parameters. Using the parameters of equation (36) this last parameter is given by

$$\alpha_3' = \alpha_{11}\alpha_{22} \qquad \ldots (75)$$

Using equations (39) and (41) the Hall coefficient for the same conditions (magnetic field parallel to the three-fold axis) is given by

$$\rho_{123} = \frac{4\alpha_3'}{(\alpha_{11}+\alpha_{22})^2}\times\frac{r}{nq} \qquad \ldots (76)$$

Thus, the combined measurements of the free carrier Faraday rotation and the Hall coefficient allow the elimination of the carrier concentration n between equations (74) and (76) and therefore lead to an estimate of the parameter

$$\frac{(\alpha_3')^2}{(\alpha_{11}+\alpha_{22})^2} = \frac{\alpha_{11}^2\,\alpha_{22}^2}{(\alpha_{11}+\alpha_{22})^2} \qquad \ldots (77)$$

For other directions of propagation of the radiation, it was shown that the rotation should be very much less and, in particular, for propagation normal to the three-fold axis the rotation due to free carriers should be proportional to the square of the magnetic field.

Numerical values of the parameter in equation (77) were given by Austin. The free carrier Faraday rotation should be proportional to the square of the

7

wavelength and should be positive for N-type materials and negative for P-type materials. The observed rotation was found to obey these rules for wavelengths well beyond the absorption edge but, for shorter wavelengths, showed considerable deviations. Such deviations have been observed in other semiconductors and are usually attributed to the contributions from interband transitions. A puzzling feature in the bismuth telluride measurements was that the deviations were of different sign for N- and P-type specimens. Such a feature is not, of course, to be expected for an intrinsic property of the crystal. Some assumptions about the form of these deviations had to be made in order to obtain the true free carrier contribution and hence to obtain numerical values for the parameter of equation (77) for N- and P-type specimens.

These numerical values were checked by measurements of the free carrier absorption contribution to the normal absorption spectrum. It was shown that measurements of this, again combined with measurements of the Hall coefficient, led to an estimate of the same parameter. The two sets of measurements were shown to lead independently to very nearly the same values.

The combination of the above measurements with the value of the parameters u, v, and w (equation (39)) obtained from the galvanomagnetic measurements led to an absolute determination of the separate parameters α_{11}, α_{22}, α_{33}, and α_{13} for both N- and P-type material. Knowing these values, the value of α^* could be calculated from equation (57) and hence the value of s, the number of equivalent valleys related by crystal symmetry, could be obtained from equations (64) and (65). The values obtained by Austin are given in Table 3.

TABLE 3. EFFECTIVE MASS PARAMETERS AND NUMBER
OF VALLEYS FOR BISMUTH TELLURIDE

	α_{11}	α_{22}	α_{33}	α_{13}	s
P-type	2·15	13·1	2·73	0·66	3·1
N-type	40	3·9	5·4	0·89	5·1

Because of the three-fold symmetry, the number of valleys should be an integral multiple of 3 and, for the proposed model, should be either 3 or 6 depending on whether the extreme energy states lie at the edge of or within the first Brillouin zone. For P-type material the estimate of s is very satisfactorily close to a multiple of 3 and indicates that the valence band maxima are at the edge of the Brillouin zone. For N-type material the result is not so satisfactory, due possibly, amongst other factors, to the uncertainty in the galvanomagnetic measurements discussed in

Section 7. The indications are, however, that a six-valley model is more appropriate for N-type material.

11. MISCELLANEOUS MEASUREMENTS

A number of measurements which possess considerable interest in themselves but do not fit into the more general scheme of the previous Sections are briefly discussed in this Section.

11.1. DIFFUSION OF COPPER

A comprehensive study of the diffusion of copper into bismuth telluride was made by Carlson.[54] Radioactive copper was used to follow the penetration and measurements were made over the temperature range from room temperature to near the melting point (585° C). The anisotropy of diffusion was studied by initially depositing copper on to faces of specimens both parallel to and perpendicular to the cleavage planes. A marked difference was found for the two cases. The diffusion coefficients $D_{\parallel}$ and $D_{\perp}$ for diffusion parallel and perpendicular to the cleavage planes, respectively, were found to be given by

$$D_{\parallel} = 3 \cdot 4 \times 10^{-3} \exp - (0 \cdot 21 \, eV/kT) \, cm^2 sec^{-1}$$
$$D_{\perp} = 7 \cdot 1 \times 10^{-2} \exp - (0 \cdot 80 \, eV/kT) \, cm^2 sec^{-1}$$

Thus, $D_{\perp}$ was always considerably less than $D_{\parallel}$ and was estimated (by extrapolation of the results at higher temperatures) to be approximately 3×10^{-15} cm^{2}sec^{-1} at room temperature as compared with the value 10^{-6} cm^{2}sec^{-1} for $D_{\parallel}$.

The results were shown by Carlson to be in reasonable agreement with the theory of diffusion given by Zener.[55] A difference in the entropy associated with the diffusion processes in the two directions was found to be necessary in order to explain the results, this in turn being associated with the change in the lattice strain energy due to the diffusing particle.

11.2 SURFACE STUDIES

Haneman[19] has made studies of the low energy electron diffraction patterns from cleavage surfaces of bismuth telluride. Very little difference was observed between the patterns obtained from surfaces which were freshly cleaved in vacuo and surfaces which had undergone an ionic bombardment and annealing cleaning process. Haneman concluded that the surface atoms had the same spacing as the bulk atoms, in contrast to the situation for surfaces of other semiconductors like germanium and silicon. This was regarded as evidence that there were no 'dangling bonds' at the cleavage surface and it was concluded that the surface bonds were saturated and directed into the interior. This conclusion was supported by measurements of the adsorption of various gases. There was no measurable adsorption of

93

oxygen, nitrogen, carbon monoxide, or ozone on the cleavage surface. The sticking coefficient for water vapour was found to be very low (10^{-5}) and any water vapour adsorbed could be easily removed by heating at 50° C for 1 to 3 hr.

The secondary emission and work function of cleavage surfaces were also measured by Haneman.[56] The properties of such surfaces are summarized in Table 4.

TABLE 4. PROPERTIES OF (0001) CLEAVAGE SURFACES OF
BISMUTH TELLURIDE

Work function	$5 \cdot 30 \pm 0 \cdot 03$ eV
Structure	Same as in bulk planes—triangular atomic spacing of $4 \cdot 384$ Å
Surface bonding	Bonds saturated and directed towards interior
Sticking coefficient	For $O_2 = 0$, $CO = 0$, $N_2 = 0$, $H_2O = 10^{-5}$
Secondary emission	$0 \cdot 25$ at 20 eV increasing linearly to $0 \cdot 79$ at 250 eV

The significance of these results in terms of the chemical bonding is discussed in sub-section 3.4.

11.3. MAGNETIC SUSCEPTIBILITY

The magnetic susceptibility of bismuth telluride has been investigated by Mansfield.[57] Measurements were made of the mass susceptibilities $\chi_\perp$ and $\chi_{||}$ with the magnetic field perpendicular and parallel, respectively, to the three-fold axis. The temperature range covered was from 100 to 600° K and values of the Hall coefficient ρ_{123} were obtained for the same specimens over this range. In all, three specimens were investigated, two of these being P-type and the other N-type.

The anisotropy of the susceptibility was quite marked. Both components were diamagnetic over the whole temperature range and $\chi_{||}$ was always larger in magnitude than $\chi_\perp$. At the higher temperatures all specimens tended to have common values for $\chi_{||}$ and for $\chi_\perp$ indicating a common intrinsic behaviour. In this range both components were decreasing with increasing temperature but at different rates. At lower temperatures differences in the values of $\chi_{||}$ and of $\chi_\perp$ were obtained for different specimens. The specimens with the larger Hall coefficients and therefore presumably the smaller number of carriers had the largest diamagnetic susceptibility. It thus appeared that the free carriers gave rise to a paramagnetic contribution.

In other semiconductors, measurements of the magnetic susceptibility have been useful in obtaining the band structure parameters in those cases where it has been possible to isolate the free carrier contribution. For bismuth telluride, however, Mansfield concluded that the main diamagnetic contribution to both components was due to the core and valence electrons and that, in addition, there was a temperature dependent paramagnetic contribution from this source. The large contribution of both these terms made it very difficult to sort out the free carrier contribution in the specimens measured by him. The free carriers apparently gave rise to a paramagnetic contribution which decreased with increasing temperature but the magnitude of this contribution was not in accordance with the paramagnetic contribution which would have been expected on the basis of the Langevin–Peierls formula. Consequently, it was not possible to obtain any information on the band structure parameters from these measurements.

11.4. Effects of Impurities

Goldsmid[58] has recently reported a detailed study of the variation of the density of bismuth telluride as a function of iodine concentration. The density of undoped material was found to be $7 \cdot 8587$ gcm$^{-3} \pm 0 \cdot 0002$. The density was found to decrease linearly at the rate $0 \cdot 0035$ gcm^{-3} for an atomic concentration of iodine of one part per thousand. It was concluded, from this and other data, that iodine atoms enter the lattice substitutionally in tellurium sites, probably with a small expansion of the lattice.

In the same reference, studies on tin-doped material were reported. In contrast to the behaviour in material containing other doping agents, the electrical conductivity of a specimen containing $0 \cdot 1$ per cent tin varied only slowly with temperature over the range $77°$ K to room temperature and showed a very shallow maximum at about $150°$ K. The Hall coefficient varied by a factor of about 3 over the range 77 to $200°$ K, being largest at the lower temperature. The interpretation of these results is not clear but it seems probable that they are associated with the formation of trapping centres by the tin atoms.

11.5. Radiation Damage

The electrical resistivity and Seebeck coefficient of P- and N-type specimens of bismuth telluride were found by Frost et al.[59] to be affected by irradiation with fast neutrons (energies greater than 1 MeV). For N-type material both properties increased in magnitude as a result of irradiation. For material which was originally P-type the Seebeck coefficient eventually changed sign. In all cases practically complete recovery of the original properties was achieved by annealing at temperatures above $150°$ C.

11.6. Effects of Unidirectional Pressure on the
Seebeck Coefficient

The effect of pressure applied parallel to the three-fold axis on the Seebeck coefficient parallel to this axis have been reported by Tantraporn.[60] The effect was measured at room temperature. The fractional change approached saturation of a few per cent and was of the same sign as the original Seebeck coefficient. The magnitude of the change varied with the carrier density and could be explained qualitatively in terms of the change in carrier density by the pressure.

Note added in proof: Effects of pressure on the electrical conductivity.

Li et al.[63] have measured the effect of pressure on the energy gap. From measurements of the resistivity as a function of temperature and pressure they deduced that the energy gap decreased from a value of $0 \cdot 171$ eV at 1 atm to $0 \cdot 104$ eV at 30,000 atm.

Ilisavshii[64] has measured piezoresistance coefficients in the temperature range 78 to 300° K for three different specimens of P-type materials.

12. SUMMARY AND CONCLUSION

It will be apparent from the various Sections of this paper that the understanding of the basic properties of bismuth telluride has not reached the same level as that of germanium and silicon or even as that of the simpler compound semiconductors such as indium antimonide. This, of course, is not surprising in view of the more complex problems involved. The chief obstacles to all basic investigations are the extreme mechanical weakness of single crystal specimens and the difficulty of obtaining specimens with a sufficiently low carrier concentration. Until methods for overcoming these problems are available, it seems unlikely to the author that any major advance in our understanding of bismuth telluride will be achieved. In the meantime, it appears that the many-valley model of the band structure, which forms the basis of this paper, is the best available to account for the transport properties, provided that, wherever possible, values of the band structure parameters are used which are appropriate to the degree of degeneracy.

ACKNOWLEDGEMENTS

Thanks are due to Dr. C. A. Bailey for permission to include the hitherto unpublished measurements of the low temperature specific heat and to Dr. H. J. Goldsmid for two preprints of papers presented at recent conferences. The permission of Dr. Goldsmid and of the Institute of Physics and The Physical Society to reproduce Figure 2 from a forthcoming publication is also gratefully acknowledged.

REFERENCES

1. WRIGHT, D. A. *Research, Lond.* **12**, 300 (1959)
2. AINSWORTH, L. *Proc. phys. Soc. Lond.* **B69**, 606 (1956)
3. SATTERTHWAITE, C. B., and URE, R. W. *Phys. Rev.* **108**, 1164 (1957)
4. HARMAN, T. C., PARIS, B., MILLER, S. E., and GOERING, A. L. *J. Phys. Chem. Solids* **2**, 181 (1957)
5. LANGE, P. W. *Naturwissenschaften* **27**, 133 (1939)
6. See, for example, *Piezoelectricity* (H.M.S.O., London, 1957)
7. BUNN, C. W. *Chemical Crystallography*, p. 134 (Clarendon, Oxford, 1946)
8. VASENIN, E. I., and KONOVALOV, P. F. *J. tech. Phys., Moscow* **26**, 1406 (1956)

9. FRANCOMBE, M. H. *Brit. J. appl. Phys.* **9**, 415 (1958)
10. KOSTER, G. F. *Solid State Physics*, Vol. 5, p. 174 (Academic, New York, 1957)
11. MOOSER, E., and PEARSON, W. B. *Phys. Rev.* **101**, 1608 (1956)
12. MOOSER, E., and PEARSON, W. B. *Canad. J. Phys.* **34**, 1369 (1956)
13. LAGRENAUDIE, J. *J. Phys. Radium* **18** (Suppl.), 39 (1957)
14. KREBS, H. *Physica* **20**, 1125 (1954)
15. DRABBLE, J. R., and GOODMAN, C. H. L. *J. Phys. Chem. Solids* **5**, 142 (1958)
16. SUCHET, J. P. *J. Phys. Chem. Solids* **12**, 74 (1959)
17. AUSTIN, I. G., and SHEARD, A. *J. Electron.* **3**, 236 (1957)
18. TERAMOTO, I., and TAKAYANAGI, S. *J. Phys. Chem. Solids* **19**, 124 (1961)
19. HANEMAN, D. *Phys. Rev.* **119**, 567 (1960)
20. MOOSER, E., and PEARSON, W. B. *Progress in Semiconductors 5*, p. 103 (Heywood, London, 1960)
21. BLITZ, J., CLUNIE, D. M., and HOGARTH, C. A. *Proceedings of the International Conference on Semiconductors, Prague, 1960*
22. BLITZ, J. *Brit. J. Non-destr. Test.* **2**, 2 (1960)
23. BLACKMAN, M. *Proc. roy. Soc.* **A148**, 365, 385 (1935)
24. DRABBLE, J. R., and GOLDSMID, H. J. *Thermal Conduction in Semiconductors* (Pergamon, Oxford, 1961)
25. NYE, J. F. *Physical Properties of Crystals* (Clarendon, Oxford, 1957)
26. DRABBLE, J. R., GROVES, R. D., and WOLFE, R. *Proc. phys. Soc. Lond.* **71**, 430 (1958)
27. HERRING, C. *Bell Syst. tech. J.* **34**, 237 (1955)
28. HERRING, C., and VOGT, E. *Phys. Rev.* **101**, 944 (1956)
29. KEYES, R. W. *J. Electron.* **2**, 279 (1956)
30. DRABBLE, J. R. *Proc. phys. Soc. Lond.* **72**, 380 (1958)
31. GOLDSMID, H. J. *Ph.D. Thesis* (University of London, 1957)
32. DRABBLE, J. R. *J. Electron. Contr.* **5**, 362 (1958)
33. KANE, E. O. *J. Phys. Chem. Solids* **8**, 38 (1959)
34. YATES, B. *J. Electron. Contr.* **6**, 26 (1959)
35. SHIGETOMI, S., and MORI, S. *J. phys. Soc. Japan* **11**, 915 (1956)
36. BLACK, J., CONWELL, E., SEIGLE, L., and SPENCER, C. W. *J. Phys. Chem. Solids* **2**, 240 (1957)
37. MANSFIELD, R., and WILLIAMS, W. *Proc. phys. Soc. Lond.* **72**, 733 (1958)
38. GOLDSMID, H. J. Paper presented at *Conference on Thermoelectricity, Durham, 1961*
39. GOLDSMID, H. J. *Proc. phys. Soc. Lond.* **71**, 633 (1958)
40. WALKER, P. A. *Proc. phys. Soc. Lond.* **76**, 113 (1960)
41. SMITH, R. A. *Semiconductors*, p. 183 (Cambridge University Press, London, 1959)
42. BOWLEY, A. E., DELVES, R., and GOLDSMID, H. J. *Proc. phys. Soc. Lond.* **72**, 401 (1958)
43. GOLDSMID, H. J. *Proc. phys. Soc. Lond.* **72**, 17 (1958)
44. MACDONALD, D. K. C., MOOSER, E., PEARSON, W. B., TEMPLETON, I. M., and WOODS, S. B. *Phil. Mag.* **4**, 433 (1959)
45. BERMAN, R., NETTLEY, P. T., SPENCER, A. N., STEVENSON, R. W., SHEARD, F. W., and ZIMAN, J. M. *Proc. roy. Soc.* **A253**, 403 (1959)
46. GOLDSMID, H. J. *Proc. phys. Soc. Lond.* **B69**, 203 (1956)
47. AUSTIN, I. G. *Proc. phys. Soc. Lond.* **72**, 545 (1958)
48. AUSTIN, I. G. *J. Electron. Contr.* **6**, 271 (1959)
49. AUSTIN, I. G. *Proc. phys. Soc. Lond.* **76**, 169 (1960)
50. FAN, H. Y. *Rep. progr. Phys.* **19**, 107 (1956); *see also* Reference 41, Chap. 7
51. MCLEAN, T. P. *Progress in Semiconductors 5*, p. 53 (Heywood, London, 1960)
52. MACFARLANE, G. G., and ROBERTS, V. *Phys. Rev.* **97**, 1714 (1955)
53. MACFARLANE, G. G., MCLEAN, T. P., QUARRINGTON, J. E., and ROBERTS, V. *Phys. Rev.* **108**, 1377 (1957)
54. CARLSON, R. O. *J. Phys. Chem. Solids* **13**, 65 (1960)
55. ZENER, C. *Imperfections in Nearly Perfect Crystals*, p. 289 (Wiley, New York, 1951)
56. HANEMAN, D. *J. Phys. Chem. Solids* **11**, 205 (1959)
57. MANSFIELD, R. *Proc. phys. Soc. Lond.* **74**, 599 (1959)
58. GOLDSMID, H. J. *Proceedings of the International Conference on Semiconductors, Prague, 1960*, p. 1015 (Czechoslovak Academy of Sciences, 1961)

59. FROST, R. T., CORELLI, J. C., and BALICKI, M. Paper presented at *Symposium on Thermoelectric Energy Conversion, Dallas*, **1961**

60. TANTRAPORN, W. Paper presented at *Symposium on Thermoelectric Energy Conversion, Dallas, 1961*

61. TAYLOR, K. N. R. *Brit. J. appl. Phys.* **12**, 717 (1961)

62. EFIMOVA, KORENBLUM, NOVIKOV, and OSTROVMOV. *Fiz. Tverd. Tela* **3**, 2746 (1961), *Soviet Phys. Solid State* **3**, 2004 (1962)

63. LI, RUOFF, and SPENCER. *J. appl. Phys.* **32**, 1733 (1961)

64. ILISAVSHII, YU. V. *Fiz. Tverd. Tela* **3**, 1898 (1961), *Soviet Phys. Solid State* **3**, 1382 (1961)

THE INTERACTION OF IMPURITIES WITH DISLOCATIONS IN SILICON AND GERMANIUM

R. BULLOUGH, B.Sc., Ph.D.

and

R. C. NEWMAN, B.Sc., D.I.C., Ph.D.

*Associated Electrical Industries Ltd, Research Laboratory,
Aldermaston Court, Aldermaston, Berks*

MS. received March 1962

THE INTERACTION OF IMPURITIES WITH DISLOCATIONS IN SILICON AND GERMANIUM

1. INTRODUCTION

The first suggestion that the interaction between impurity atoms and dislocations should lead to observable effects on the properties of crystals was due to Cottrell.[1] He showed that impurity atmospheres should form round edge dislocations, and thus was able to provide an explanation for the sharp yield point observed in metals containing particular impurities. Cottrell and Bilby[2] developed this concept to explain the kinetics of strain ageing in steels containing carbon or nitrogen.[3, 4] More recently, strain ageing has been found in many systems, and in particular Pearson et al. have shown it to exist in silicon.[5] The presence of an enhanced concentration of impurities round dislocations automatically implies that these will be preferred sites for the nucleation of a second phase in a supersaturated solution.[6] Precipitation on dislocations in metals with a high dislocation density has been observed by transmission electron microscopy,[7, 8] and in transparent materials with a low dislocation density similar precipitation has been found by transmission optical microscopy.[9, 10] The former technique has not been applied so far to semiconductor materials, but the latter technique has provided a wealth of information on the precipitation of various impurities in silicon. In this context, silicon may be regarded as transparent,[11] since simple image converter tubes and photographic plates are available, both of which are sensitive to the transmitted infra-red radiation at wavelengths slightly greater than $1 \cdot 1$ microns. It has been shown[12, 13] that similar techniques can be employed for germanium, which transmits radiation at wavelengths greater than $1 \cdot 71$ microns. For these wavelengths, a scanning type of image converter is necessary and the technique has not been extensively used; in fact, there is only one publication describing such direct observations on germanium.[12] Thus the precipitation behaviour of impurities in silicon has been studied by visual methods, whereas in germanium the behaviour has had to be inferred from indirect measurements such as electrical conductivity and Hall effect. It would clearly be desirable to combine the direct and indirect methods for both silicon and germanium, since the former provides no quantitative data on the kinetics of the process and the latter cannot necessarily be interpreted in an unambiguous way with respect to location and density of precipitates.

Before reviewing the experimental observations on precipitation in silicon and germanium, we discuss the theory of the interaction of point defects with dislocations. The discussion of this interaction is restricted to a simple model where the crystal is replaced by an isotropic elastic medium; it may be possible in the future to refine this theoretical work when detailed information concerning the interatomic forces is known. Some results on the atomic configurations round point defects are already available from electron spin resonance studies.[14, 15] The dominant interaction, in general, arises as a result of the difference in size between the impurity atom and the available space in the solvent crystal. There are also other interactions arising from differences in elastic constants and electrical effects. In the experiments it will be seen that lattice vacancies play a very important role in the precipitation phenomena, and therefore some space is devoted to the interaction of vacancies with dislocations, which act as sources and sinks for these defects. A brief account is also given of some of the factors which influence the kinetics of precipitation. Although many of these theoretical results have not so far been correlated with experimental observations in silicon and germanium, their inclusion in this review is considered worth while if only to provide adequate background for the interpretation of future observations.

2. THEORY OF THE INTERACTION OF POINT DEFECTS WITH DISLOCATIONS

There are three possible contributions to the energy of interaction between a point defect and a dislocation:[16] (1) an elastic interaction arising from the difference in size between solute and solvent atoms, (2) a second order elastic interaction which appears if the solute atom behaves like a small region with different elastic constants from those of the matrix crystal, and (3) two electrical interactions, one resulting from a distortion of the band structure in the neighbourhood of the dislocation and the other from the presence of dangling bonds. Each of these contributions will now be examined in some detail.

2.1. ELASTIC INTERACTION DUE TO SIZE EFFECT

To deduce the form of this interaction, a solute atom, of radius $r_0(1 + \delta)$ in free space, is represented by an elastic sphere of the same size. The sphere is then inserted into a spherical cavity of radius r_0 in an infinite elastic medium, with the same elastic constants, representing the solvent crystal. The interaction energy then follows by consideration of the interaction between the stress field round the inclusion and that of a dislocation in the solvent crystal. The elastic fields of a dislocation and a spherical inclusion in an infinite isotropic elastic medium are known.[1, 17] The interaction energy E_1 between two elastic fields u_i^C and u_i^A is:

$$E_1 = \int_{\Sigma} (p_{ij}^C u_i^A - p_{ij}^A u_i^C) \, dS_j \qquad \ldots (1)$$

where u_i^C and u_i^A are the displacement fields produced by the inclusion and dislocation, respectively, p^C_{ij}, p^A_{ij} are the corresponding stresses, and Σ is any closed surface separating the inclusion from the dislocation.[18] Where repeated suffixes occur, summation is implied in the usual way. By taking Σ to be the surface S just inside the spherical inclusion, Eshelby[18] shows that:

$$E_1 = -\int_S p^A_{ij} u^T_i \, dS_j = -\int_V p^A_{ij} e^T_{ij} \, dv \qquad \ldots (2)$$

where the second integral follows from Gauss's theorem and the condition $p^A_{ij,j} = 0$, and where $V = \frac{4}{3}\pi r^3_0$ is the volume of the undeformed cavity. The stress-free strain:

$$e^T_{ij} = \delta \delta_{ij} \qquad \ldots (3)$$

is that uniform strain which transforms an elastic sphere of radius r_0 into one of radius $r_0(1+\delta)$, where δ_{ij} is the Kronecker delta and is unity if $i = j$ and zero otherwise. It is important to note[18] that expression (2) indicates that the interaction energy is independent of the final displacement field in the inclusion and matrix (denoted by the 'C' superscript). If equations (2) and (3) are combined, we obtain:

$$E_1 = -\delta \int_V p^A_{ii} \, dv \qquad \ldots (4)$$

It is rather surprising that E_1, given by equation (4), has the formal appearance of being simply the work done against the dislocation field p^A_{ij} by the expansion of a rigid inclusion from radius r_0 to $r_0(1+\delta)$. In reality the final constrained shape of the inclusion (given by u^C_i) may be quite complicated.

If a straight line dislocation with Burger's vector $\mathbf{b}$ lies through the origin of a system of rectangular Cartesian axes x_i ($i = 1, 2, 3$) parallel to the x_3 axis with x_2 normal to the slip plane, then[1] for a screw dislocation $\mathbf{b} = (0, 0, b)$:

$$\left.\begin{array}{l} p^A_{13} = -\dfrac{\mu b}{2\pi}\dfrac{x_2}{r^2} \\[3mm] p^A_{23} = +\dfrac{\mu b}{2\pi}\dfrac{x_1}{r^2} \end{array}\right\} \qquad \ldots (5)$$

where $r^2 = x^2_1 + x^2_2$ and μ is the shear modulus. For a positive edge dislocation, $\mathbf{b} = (b, 0, 0)$:

$$\left.\begin{array}{l} p^A_{11} = -\dfrac{\mu b}{2\pi(1-\nu)}\dfrac{x_2(3x^2_1 + x^2_2)}{r^4} \\[3mm] p^A_{22} = \dfrac{\mu b}{2\pi(1-\nu)}\dfrac{x_2(x^2_1 - x^2_2)}{r^4} \\[3mm] p^A_{33} = \nu(p^A_{11} + p^A_{22}) \\[3mm] p^A_{12} = \dfrac{\mu b}{2\pi(1-\nu)}\dfrac{x_1(x^2_1 - x^2_2)}{r^4} \end{array}\right\} \qquad \ldots (6)$$

103

where ν is Poisson's ratio. Thus for the screw dislocation:

$$p_{ii}^A = p_{11}^A + p_{22}^A + p_{33}^A = 0 \qquad \ldots (7)$$

and for the edge dislocation:

$$p_{ii}^A = -\frac{\mu b(1+\nu)}{\pi(1-\nu)}\cdot\frac{\sin\theta}{r} \qquad \ldots (8)$$

where $r\sin\theta = x_2$.

It follows immediately from equations (4) and (7) that there is zero size effect interaction between a solute atom and a screw dislocation.

For the edge dislocation, since p_{ii}^A, given by equation (8), is a potential function[19] (satisfying Laplace's equation), we have the exact result from equation (4):

$$E_1 = -\delta.\tfrac{4}{3}\pi r_0^3 p_{ii}^A(R,\psi) \qquad \ldots (9)$$

and thus from (8):

$$E_1 = \frac{4}{3}\frac{(1+\nu)}{(1-\nu)}\frac{\mu b \delta r_0^3 \sin\psi}{R} \qquad \ldots (10)$$

where (R, ψ) are the cylindrical polar co-ordinates of the centre of the inclusion. This expression is identical with that previously derived by Bilby,[20] since δ is related to ϵ, the corresponding parameter defining the *final* radius of the inclusion (assumed spherical in the embedded state) by:

$$\delta = 3\epsilon(1-\nu)/(1+\nu) \qquad \ldots (11)$$

The fact that equation (10), for the size effect interaction energy between a solute atom and an edge dislocation, is an exact result, valid both for $R \geqslant r_0$ and arbitrarily large r_0, appears to have been overlooked by previous investigators. Bilby[20] correctly evaluates the integral in equation (4) by expanding the integrand to $O(r_0/R)^2$, but thereby gives the erroneous impression that expression (10) is only an approximate result.

The above calculations of the size effect interactions with edge and screw dislocations are somewhat idealized, since there is no reason to suppose that a free impurity atom can be represented by a simple sphere. If an elastic ellipsoid is a better representation, then equation (2) becomes:

$$E_1 = -\frac{4\pi r_0^3}{3}p_{ij}^A e_{ij}^T \qquad \ldots (12)$$

at large enough distances from the dislocation to neglect the variation of p_{ij}^A over the volume of the inclusion, and where e_{ij}^T is the uniform stress-free strain that transforms the sphere into the ellipsoid. This means that, in general, the interaction energy between the solute atom and an edge dislocation will have a more complicated dependence on ψ than is indicated by equation (10), and furthermore there will be a non-zero interaction with a screw dislocation, which will be some function of ψ and vary inversely with R. This more general analysis has been done for carbon in iron by Cochardt et al.[21]

So far we have considered only the interaction between a solute atom and a long straight dislocation. The corresponding interaction with an edge dislocation loop may be easily obtained by substituting the relevant p_{ii}^A stress (see Bullough and Newman,[22] equation (6)) in equation (9), since it may be noted that the p_{ii}^A again satisfies Laplace's equation. In this case, however, the interaction is very short ranged, since p_{ii}^A is inversely proportional to the third power of the distance from the centre of the loop when this distance is large compared with the radius of the loop. However, the interaction energy of a solute atom close to the loop is comparable to that close to a straight dislocation. Similar remarks are equally applicable to dislocation arrays in the form of tilt boundaries, etc.

Estimates of the binding energy of various impurity atoms to an edge dislocation in germanium and silicon have been obtained by setting $R = b$ and $\psi = \pm \pi/2$ in equation (10), with δ given by equation (11), and are given in Tables 1 and 2. Values of the shear modulus for germanium and silicon have been taken from the results of McSkimmin[23] and extrapolated to temperatures of $700°$ C and $1,200°$ C, respectively. For substitutional impurities, the value of ϵ is taken as:

$$\epsilon = \frac{r_0 - r_i}{r_0}$$

where r_0 is now taken as the covalent radius of the host material (silicon or germanium) and r_i is the covalent radius of the impurity, values of which have been tabulated by Pauling.[24] We consider it more sensible to take the volume of the available space in the host material as $\frac{4}{3}\pi r_0^3$ and not the inverse of the number of atoms per unit volume in the crystal; this latter procedure would artificially double the interaction energy. This is the explanation of the discrepancy between our estimate in Table 1 and that of Queisser et al.[25] for the interaction energy of substitutional phosphorus atoms with dislocations in silicon. An estimate for the value of ϵ for substitutional boron in silicon has been deduced from the measurements of the variation of lattice parameter with boron concentration made by Horne.[26] The large value of ϵ thus deduced is in good agreement with the value calculated from the covalent radius, suggesting that the use of the covalent radius for determining ϵ is a good approximation for the other substitutional impurities.

We now consider interstitial impurities. In the diamond cubic structure, if the atoms are replaced by touching spheres of radius r_0, then it can easily be shown that a sphere of equal radius r_0 can fit in the centroid position of each tetrahedron thus formed. It follows that for an interstitial impurity we may adopt the covalent radius as the radius of the spherical region to be occupied. The choice of radius for the impurity presents some difficulty, since its radius must depend on the degree of ionization that occurs

105

Table 1. SIZE EFFECT INTERACTION FOR VARIOUS IMPURITIES IN SILICON AT A TEMPERATURE OF 1,200°C

Impurity element	Interstitial (i) substitutional (s)	Radius r_i of impurity atom (Å)	$-\epsilon$ $\dfrac{r_i - r_0}{r_0}$	E_1(max) eV	Capture radius where $E_1 = kT$ in Ångstrom
Boron	s	0·88	−0·25	0·75	24
Boron†	s	—	−0·28	0·80	25
Aluminium	s	1·26	0·077	0·23	7
Gallium	s	1·26	0·077	0·23	7
Indium	s	1·44	0·23	0·70	21
Phophorus	s	1·10	−0·060	0·18	5
Arsenic	s	1·18	0·009	0·03	8
Antimony	s	1·36	0·16	0·49	15
Carbon	s	0·77	−0·34	1·0	31
Germanium	s	1·22	0·086	0·26	9
Copper	s	1·35	0·15	0·47	14
Gold	s	1·5	0·28	0·85	26
Oxygen†	i	—	0·19	0·57	17
Copper	i	1·28	0·09	0·28	9
Gold, Silver	i	1·44	0·23	0·70	21
Nickel	i	1·24	0·06	0·18	5
Iron	i	1·26	0·08	0·23	7

† Estimates of ϵ from X-ray data (see text).

TABLE 2. SIZE EFFECT INTERACTION FOR VARIOUS IMPURITIES IN GERMANIUM AT A TEMPERATURE OF 700°C

Impurity element	Interstitial (i) substitutional (s)	Radius r_i of impurity atom (Å)	$-\epsilon$ $\dfrac{r_i - r_0}{r_0}$	E_1(max) eV	Capture radius where $E_1 = kT$ in Ångstrom
Boron	s	0·88	−0·28	0·79	38
Aluminium	s	1·26	0·03	0·09	4
Gallium	s	1·26	0·03	0·09	4
Indium	s	1·44	0·18	0·51	24
Phosphorus	s	1·10	−0·10	0·28	13
Arsenic	s	1·18	0·03	0·09	4
Antimony	s	1·36	0·12	0·33	16
Silicon	s	1·17	0·04	0·12	6
Copper	s	1·35	0·11	0·30	14
Gold	s	1·5	0·23	0·65	31
Oxygen	i	1·39†	0·14	0·40	19
Copper	i	1·28	0·05	0·14	7
Gold, Silver	i	1·44	0·18	0·51	24
Nickel	i	1·24	0·02	0·05	2
Iron	i	1·26	0·03	0·09	4

† Estimated from X-ray data for oxygen in silicon.

on its insertion in the matrix. The radii used in Tables 1 and 2 for interstitial impurities are simply half the closest distance of approach of these
atoms in their elemental form. This procedure was previously adopted by
Kulin and Kurtz.[27] An estimate for the values of ϵ for interstitial oxygen in
silicon has been deduced from the measurements of the variation of lattice
parameter with oxygen content made by Bond and Kaiser.[28] However, the
interpretation of these results is open to some criticism, since no account was
taken of the possibility that the crystals may have contained carbon (see sub-
section 3.3) in concentrations as great as that of the oxygen (10^{18} atoms cm^{-3}).
The radius associated with interstitial oxygen in germanium (Table 2) has
been deduced from the value of ϵ for oxygen in silicon, since infra-red
spectrographic techniques indicate that it occupies the same type of site in
both silicon and germanium.[29, 30]

2.2. ELASTIC INTERACTION DUE TO DIFFERENCE IN ELASTIC CONSTANTS

A detailed treatment of this problem has been given by Eshelby.[18] The
spherical inhomogeneity, with shear modulus μ_1 and bulk modulus K_1, is
replaced by an equivalent elastic inclusion, and the stress-free strains e_{ij}^T
associated with this inclusion are functions of the dislocation strain field e_{ij}^A.
Eshelby shows that for a spherical inhomogeneity:

$$\left. \begin{array}{l} e_{ii}^T = Ae_{ii}^A \\ 'e_{ij}^T = B'e_{ij}^A \end{array} \right\} \qquad \ldots (13)$$

where the constants A and B are given by:

$$\left. \begin{array}{l} A = \dfrac{K_1-K}{(K-K_1)\alpha - K} \\[2mm] B = \dfrac{\mu_1-\mu}{(\mu-\mu_1)\beta-\mu} \end{array} \right\} \qquad \ldots (14)$$

and

$$\alpha = (1+v)/3(1-v)$$
$$\beta = 2(4-5v)/15(1-v)$$

K, μ, and v are the elastic constants of the matrix material. In equations (13),
$'e_{ij}$ is the deviatoric part of the tensor e_{ij}; thus:

$$e_{ij} = 'e_{ij}+\tfrac{1}{3}e_{pp}\delta_{ij}$$

In Eshelby's theory, e_{ij}^T must be a uniform strain, and therefore any
variation of e_{ij}^A through the volume of the equivalent inclusion must be
neglected. Under these circumstances, equation (2) becomes:

$$E_2 = -Vp_{ij}^A e_{ij}^T$$

8

and thus from equations (13) we obtain:

$$E_2 = -V\left(\frac{A}{9K} p_{ii}^{\Lambda} p_{ii}^{\Lambda} + \frac{B}{2\mu} {}'p_{ij}^{\Lambda} {}'p_{ij}^{\Lambda}\right) \qquad \ldots (15)$$

where A and B are given by equations (14).

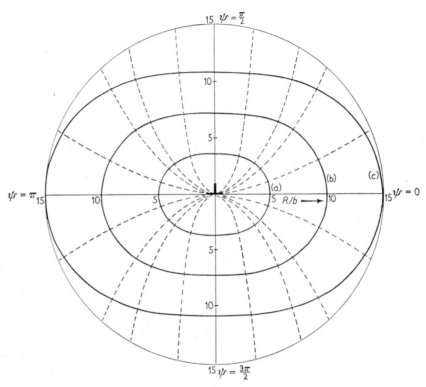

Figure 1. *A polar plot of the equipotentials from equation (16) for the interaction of a vacancy with an edge dislocation with $\nu = 1/3$. Full curves: (a) $E_2 = -E_{max}/25$, (b) $E_2 = -E_{max}/100$, and (c) $E_2 = -E_{max}/225$, where E_{max} is the value of E_2 at $R = b, \psi = 0$. The broken curves are the orthogonal trajectories and represent the flow lines in the absence of flow; they are given by*

$$R = const.|\tan\psi|s|\cos\psi|$$

where $s = 5(1 + 6\nu - 5\nu^2)^{-1}$

Since, in general, the elastic properties of an impurity atom will be different from those of the matrix, equation (15) indicates that there will be an interaction between the impurity atom and the dislocation varying as the inverse square of the distance between them. In particular, it is to be noted that this interaction is non-zero for a screw dislocation. In estimating a binding energy contribution from E_2, it must be emphasized that equation (15) is only an approximate result.

Expression (15) can be used to calculate the interaction energy between a dislocation and a vacancy[31] ($\mu_1 = K_1 = 0$), and we find:

$$E_2(\text{edge}) = -\frac{5\mu b^2 r_0^3}{\pi(1-\nu)(7-5\nu)} \frac{1}{R^2} \left(1 - \frac{(1+6\nu-5\nu^2)}{5} \sin^2\psi\right) \quad \dots (16)$$

and

$$E_2(\text{screw}) = -\frac{5\mu b^2 r_0^3(1-\nu)}{\pi(7-5\nu)} \cdot \frac{1}{R^2} \quad \dots (17)$$

where r_0 is the radius of a vacant lattice site. An attractive interaction is indicated by both equations (16) and (17). As might be expected, there is no ψ dependence for the screw dislocation, while for the edge dislocation the attraction is a maximum in the slip plane ($\psi = 0$), as shown in Figure 1. The interactions E_2 above have not been widely applied, and in fact several authors[32-34] have erroneously used only the size effect formula given by equation (10) to describe the interaction between vacancies and dislocations. The latter contribution can arise only if there is a dilatation present round the vacancy in the absence of an applied stress field. The enhanced concentration of vacancies round dislocations has been invoked to explain, in part, the enhanced diffusion rate of impurities along the dislocations in low-angled tilt boundaries in silicon.[25] Similar observations in germanium have been reported by Karstensen.[35]

Expressions (16) and (17) have been used to evaluate the binding energy between a vacancy and edge and screw dislocations in germanium and silicon. To obtain the binding energy, we set $R = b$ and derive an approximate value for Poisson's ratio from the data given by Mcskimin;[23] these are displayed in Table 3. The results are clearly sensitive to the choice of $R = b$, and several authors[1, 16] have assumed values as small as $2b/3$, which leads to a doubling of the values in the table. It is usually assumed that the maximum binding energy between a vacancy and a pure edge dislocation occurs[16] at $\psi = \pm\pi/2$, whereas expression (16) indicates that the binding energy in these positions is only one-half of the maximum which occurs in the positions of maximum shear stress ($\psi = 0, \pi$).

2.3. Electrical Interactions

In homopolar semiconductor crystals, the electrical interaction between impurities and dislocations is a very complex phenomenon and no complete theory exists. Two distinct effects have been described.

The presence of an asymmetrical distribution of dilatation round an edge dislocation has led Kulin and Kurtz[27] to postulate that in germanium the energy gap is increased in the compressed region and decreased in the tensile region, above and below the slip plane, respectively. In an N-type crystal, a higher concentration of conduction electrons is expected to be present in the tensile region compared with regions away from the dislocation, and a correspondingly reduced concentration is expected in the compression region. Thus a weak electric dipole field is created; in P-type material, the polarity of the dipole is reversed. In silicon, where compression will result in a reduction of the energy gap,[36] a similar dipole effect will arise but with reversed polarity compared with germanium. On the basis of this model, a positively charged impurity atom should be attracted to the region of negative polarity, and vice versa. The precise spatial form and magnitude of this interaction do not appear to have been investigated. It is worth remarking, however, that the concept of a distortion of the energy bands in a direction orthogonal to the dislocation line is somewhat dubious in view of the localized nature of the disturbance in this direction.

TABLE 3. VALUES OF BINDING ENERGIES OF
VACANCIES TO EDGE AND SCREW
DISLOCATIONS IN ELECTRON-VOLTS

Element	Edge		Screw
	E_2 (max) $\psi = 0$	E_2 $\psi = \dfrac{\pi}{2}$	E_2 (max)
Silicon $T = 1,200°C$ $\nu = 0\cdot22$	0·26	0·15	0·16
Germanium $T = 700°C$ $\nu = 0\cdot21$	0·25	0·15	0·16

The second electrical interaction was suggested by Shockley[37] as a result of the presence of dangling bonds, along the core of a dislocation with an edge component; these bonds are thought to act as localized acceptor states. In N-type material, it is shown that the dangling bonds capture electrons from the conduction band until a steady state is achieved; further electron capture is prevented by the electrostatic repulsion arising from the negative line charge on the dislocation.[38] At this stage the dislocation is surrounded by a cylindrical region of positive space charge extending out to a radius R_s. At the absolute zero of temperature, Read[38] has shown that the electrostatic potential distribution ϕ is given by:

$$\phi = -\frac{fq}{\kappa a}\left(\ln\frac{R_s^2}{r^2} + 1 - \frac{r^2}{R_s^2}\right), \quad a < r \leqslant R_s \qquad \ldots (18)$$

where f is the fraction of available dangling bonds, spaced a distance a apart along the dislocation, which have captured an electron, κ is the dielectric constant, q is the electronic charge, and r is the distance from the dislocation. f is a function of the net donor concentration $(N_D - N_A)$ and temperature; for $N_D - N_A = 10^{15}\,\mathrm{cm}^{-3}$; Read calculates values of f of about $0 \cdot 1$ at $T = 0°\,\mathrm{K}$ and $0 \cdot 02$ at $T = 300°\,\mathrm{K}$. At temperatures above absolute zero, the outer boundary of the space charge region becomes somewhat diffuse, but nevertheless the form of ϕ should not be drastically altered. Thus a positive ion present in the space charge region will experience a force of $-q\,\mathrm{grad}\,\phi$ towards the dislocation. For the donor concentration above, the value of R_s is about $10^{-5}\,\mathrm{cm}$, and thus the maximum binding energy for a singly-charged positive ion (when $r = a = 4\,\text{Å}$) is given approximately by:

$$E_{max} = -\frac{11fq^2}{\kappa a} \simeq 0 \cdot 04\,\mathrm{eV}\,(T = 300°\,\mathrm{K}) \qquad \ldots (19)$$

for germanium with $\kappa = 16$.

This effect is not present in P-type material, and in N-type material the effect becomes negligible at temperatures much above $300°\,\mathrm{K}$. This interaction can thus be important only for rapidly diffusing impurities which have a high mobility at low temperatures; an impurity with these properties in both silicon and germanium is lithium.[39] In previous studies of the precipitation of lithium in germanium and silicon, this particular interaction has not been invoked in the interpretation of the results.

Further details of the electrical effects due to dangling bonds are to be found in review articles by Bardsley[40] and van Bueren.[34]

2.4. TOTAL BINDING ENERGY AT THE DISLOCATION

The total binding energy for an impurity atom a short distance away from a dislocation is given by the direct sum of the various contributions discussed above. It may be noted that the contributions are not necessarily in the same sense; thus a large 'rigid' atom would be attracted by the size effect and repelled as a result of the difference in elastic constants. In the actual core region we envisage two distinct possibilities:[41] (a) the impurities remain mobile and the equilibrium state is a Maxwellian concentration distribution,† that is:

$$c(r, \theta) = c_0 \exp[-E_t(r, \theta)/kT] \qquad \ldots (20)$$

where E_t is the total interaction energy and c_0 is the concentration of impurity atoms at large distances from the dislocation, or (b) the impurities interact with one another or with the dangling bonds on the dislocation and are rendered immobile. Under the latter conditions, the binding energy

---

† This result is true only if the concentration remains dilute everywhere, otherwise the detailed occupation statistics of available lattice sites must be taken into account[42-44].

estimate above must be increased by an additional amount arising from the chemical binding. For example, an oxygen atom in the core of an edge dislocation in silicon may bridge two adjacent dangling bonds and thus complete the electronic configuration.[34]

2.5. KINETICS OF MIGRATION OF IMPURITIES TO DISLOCATIONS

The migration of impurities to dislocations will be controlled by diffusion processes assisted by drift flow resulting from the interactions discussed in the previous section. The concentration of impurities $c(r, \theta, t)$ in the neighbourhood of a long straight dislocation line lying along the x_3 axis must satisfy the differential equation:[45]

$$\frac{1}{D}\frac{\partial c}{\partial t} = \Delta^2 c + \frac{\Delta.(c\Delta E_t)}{kT} \qquad \ldots (21)$$

where $E_t = E_t(r, \theta)$ is the total interaction energy, and D is the diffusion coefficient of the solute. For most impurities substantial migration can occur only at elevated temperatures where the electrical interaction is negligible. Since E_2, the interaction due to differences in elastic constants between solute and matrix, is short ranged, the main contribution to E_t will, in general, be E_1, the size effect interaction. However, an example of an exception to this may be arsenic in silicon (see Table 1). Detailed theoretical studies of the migration kinetics have been made using only the size effect interaction,[2, 41, 45-47] and in view of the above comments there appears little point in incorporating the other interactions into a general theory.

If the initial impurity concentration is dilute and uniform, then the subsequent growth of the impurity atmospheres round the dislocations will be due entirely to the presence of a non-zero $E_t = E_1$ in equation (21). The relevant boundary conditions for such an atmosphere solution of equation (21) are zero flow across the surface through points midway between adjacent dislocations, and overall conservation of impurity.[45] Clearly, the latter condition is not possible with the singular potential E_1, given by equation (10). The singularity is in any case physically unreasonable in view of the inapplicability of linear elasticity in a dislocation core, and hence the form of E_1 must be modified so as to limit its maximum value to the value of the binding energy.[46] This general transient atmosphere problem has never been solved, although the relevant steady state solution is given by equation (20) with $E_t = E_1$. However, detailed analytic and numerical solutions have been obtained when the angular term in E_1 is omitted, the analytic solution being valid when E_1 is everywhere small.[45, 46] An important result which emerges from these kinetic studies is that they indicate the time required to establish the equilibrium atmosphere configuration from an initially uniform concentration. It can be seen from Figure 2 that equilibrium is achieved in a time given by $\sqrt{Dt} \simeq 3 \times 10^{-6}$ cm; the concentration in the dislocation core regions attains about 70 per cent of its final maximum value in a time given by $\sqrt{Dt} \simeq 10^{-6}$ cm.

We now discuss the solutions of equation (21) when a second phase nucleates and grows along the dislocations. Under such conditions, the final steady state is achieved when the concentration of free solute drops to a value c_s^{47}, related to the equilibrium concentration c_s' in the matrix at the precipitate matrix interface by:

$$c_s' = c_s \exp\left(-E_t^i/kT\right) \qquad \ldots (22)$$

where E_t^i is the value of E_t at the position of the interface. In general, there will be a finite velocity of transfer v of impurity atoms across the precipitate

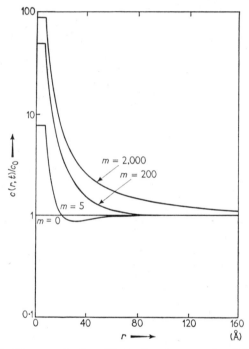

Figure 2. *The concentration of impurity atoms round a dislocation at various values of the reduced time $m = Dt/r_c^2$ during atmosphere formation resulting from the size effect interaction when the crystal contains a low dislocation density. A radial potential E_1 has been used with some allowance for the non-Hookean core region*[46]

matrix interface; the general boundary condition on this surface will have the form:[41, 46]

$$D\Delta c + \frac{D}{kT}c\Delta E_t^i = v(c - c_s') \qquad \ldots (23)$$

113

The simplest condition that can be envisaged is that there is no rate limitation at the precipitate matrix interface; that is, v can be regarded as infinite and the boundary condition (23) reduces to:[41, 46, 47]

$$c = c'_s \qquad \dots (24)$$

A numerical solution of equation (21) subject to the boundary condition (24) has been given by Ham[47] for a crystal with a high dislocation density. If, however, the dislocation density is low, say 10^4 lines cm^{-2}, then the effect of the drift flow will be negligible, since the volume of the crystal, throughout which the interaction energy is appreciable, is a negligible fraction of the total volume. For relatively short diffusion times, one can regard each dislocation as being isolated, and if the drift flow is ignored and the boundary condition (24) applied on a stationary cylindrical surface $r = r_c$ around the dislocation, we have :[48]

$$\frac{c(r, t) - c'_s}{c_0 - c'_s} = \frac{2}{\pi} \int_0^\infty \frac{\exp(-mu^2)}{u} \frac{[J_0(u) Y_0(u\gamma) - J_0(u\gamma) Y_0(u)]}{J_0^2(u) + Y_0^2(u)} du \qquad \dots (25)$$

where $m = Dt/r_c^2, \gamma = r/r_c$, and J_0, Y_0 are Bessel functions of real argument. If $\sqrt{Dt} \gg r_c$, then it may be shown that the solution (25) is insensitive to the choice of r_c and the approximation of a stationary interface at $r = r_c$ is reasonable; it may be noted that frequently the precipitate particles grow at discrete points along the dislocations, in which case the surface $r = r_c$ would define the core region of the dislocations. If, however, the precipitate grows as a uniform cylindrical rod along the dislocations, then the 'moving interface' solution would be more applicable; this has been given by Frank[49] and Ham[50] and used to interpret certain observations of precipitation in silicon.[51]

Expression (25) is applicable only to the early stages of precipitation, and at later times, when $\sqrt{Dt}$ becomes comparable to the distance between adjacent dislocations, equal to $2R_0$, the corresponding finite body solution, with zero flow across the cylindrical surfaces $r = R_0$, must be used.[41, 50] It has been shown[50] that over most of the period during which precipitation occurs the fraction of available solute F remaining in solution is given by:

$$F = \exp(-t/\tau) \qquad \dots (26)$$

where τ is a characteristic time depending on the diffusion coefficient and the dislocation density; if the dislocation density is high, then τ also depends on the magnitude and form of the interaction energy E_1.

Under certain circumstances, there may be a large rate limitation controlling the incorporation of solute into the precipitates (v small). The drift flow may now be important, even when the dislocation density is low, since the rate of incorporation of solute atoms into the impurity atmospheres around each dislocation can exceed their rate of removal by transfer into the second phase,[46, 52] as indicated in Figure 3. Furthermore, there is no reason why v should remain constant, and one might expect v to be large in the early stage of precipitate growth and to decrease gradually as the precipitates grow if there is a local increase in volume on formation of the second phase.[46]   When the value of v is small and constant, the fraction of available solute remaining in solution again has the form of equation (26)

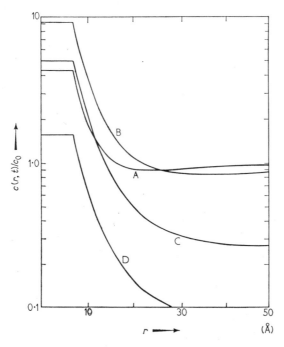

Figure 3. Concentration distributions at various reduced times $m = Dt/r_c^2$ ($r_c = 7\,\text{Å}$) with a small transfer velocity v and a large interaction potential E_1 which illustrate the growth of precipitate particles immersed in a dilute impurity atmosphere. The dislocation density is 10^{11} lines cm^{-2}. Curve A ($m = 2$), curve B ($m = 10$), curve C ($m = 500$), curve D ($m = 1,000$); initially at $m = 0, 0(r, 0) = c_0$. (Reproduced by permission of The Royal Society, after Bullough and Newman[46])

with a larger value of τ.[41] If, however, v decreases with time, as discussed above, then it has been shown[46] that kinetics of the form:

$$F = \exp\left[-\left(\frac{t}{\tau}\right)^n\right] \qquad \qquad \ldots (27)$$

can be obtained, where n may be less than unity.

The general considerations of precipitation on straight dislocations are also applicable to nucleation and growth of precipitates on small dislocation loops, which may be present as a result of the aggregation of vacancies.

Because there is now three-dimensional diffusion flow, the kinetics of precipitation are modified, the form of equation (26) being valid only in the later stages;[50] in the early stages, F is given by:

$$1 - F = (\tau/\tau')^{3/2} \qquad \qquad \dots (28)$$

3. PRECIPITATION IN SILICON CRYSTALS CONTAINING OXYGEN

3.1. UNDOPED CRYSTALS

It is now well established that silicon crystals grown from a quartz crucible contain about 2×10^{18} atoms cm^{-3} of oxygen.[53] Detailed spectroscopic studies have shown that dissolved oxygen leads to several infra-red absorption bands, the principal one being at $9 \cdot 1$ microns, and it is deduced that oxygen occupies interstitial sites.[54] The magnitude of the absorption at $9 \cdot 1$ microns is taken as a measure of the concentration of free oxygen in the crystal, and this technique has been used to study the precipitation of oxygen[55] in the temperature range 900° C to 1,350° C. Annealing at the highest temperature leads to no decrease in the concentration of free oxygen, while heating at 1,000° C reduces the oxygen concentration to about 10 per cent of its initial value, owing to the formation of precipitate particles of silica.[55]

It has been reported that in samples containing the same concentrations of electrically active impurities the rate of depletion of free oxygen varies from one sample to another; the presence of varying densities of structural defects was invoked to explain the observations.[56] To confirm this, the rate of depletion was examined as a function of dislocation density, the dislocations being introduced by plastic deformation at 950° C. As expected, it was found that the rate of depletion increased with increasing dislocation density,[56] as shown in Figure 4. Light scattering experiments suggested that the oxygen had precipitated along the dislocation lines, although the precipitates were not detected by infra-red microscopy.[56] This increased rate of precipitation may not, however, be due entirely to the increase in the number of nucleation sites provided by the dislocations, since during the actual plastic deformation vacancies will be produced. In view of the fact that a large local volume increase occurs on the formation of silica precipitates from interstitial oxygen, their rate of growth might be expected to depend on the rate of arrival of vacancies to accommodate the volume change. It may not be possible to supply these vacancies from the dislocations on which the precipitates are growing, since the climb of such dislocations will be hindered by the presence of the precipitates; some evidence for this is provided by the observations of Dash[57] (see sub-section 4.2). Thus the vacancies introduced by the plastic deformation may play a significant role in the precipitation process. Further support for this suggestion is provided by Willis[58] who found that heating as-grown crystals at 1,000° C for long periods up to 300 hr, followed by either slow cooling or quenching, never reduced the oxygen concentration by more than 20 per cent, and the reduction could not be correlated with dislocation content. However, if the samples were first heated at 1,350° C and quenched, and then heated at 1,000° C, the reported drop[59] in the 9·1 micron band was always observed. This pretreatment would again introduce an excess concentration of vacancies which would be available to facilitate the growth of precipitates on dislocations and elsewhere.

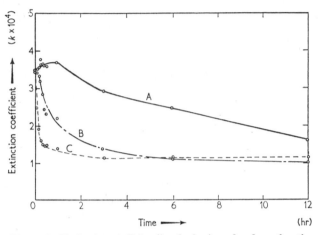

Figure 4. *Extinction coefficient for the 9 micron band as a function of annealing time at 1,000° C for various silicon samples. Curve A, as-grown crystal, dislocation density* $\rho = 2 \times 10^4$ *lines* cm^{-2}; *curves B and C for plastically deformed crystals with* $\rho = 3 \times 10^6$ *and* 2×10^7 *lines* cm^{-2}, *respectively. (Reproduced by permission of* The Physical Review, *after Lederhandler and Patel[56])*

3.2. Crystals Containing Aluminium

It has been shown that the chemical bonding between aluminium and oxygen is greater than the bonding between silicon and oxygen,[51, 60] and hence if precipitate particles of silica are formed, any aluminium present would be expected to be preferentially incorporated into such particles and local depletion of aluminium should result.[51, 61] A simple etching technique has been developed to demonstrate such local depletion of aluminium[48] in crystals doubly doped with aluminium to a level of 10^{17} atoms cm^{-3}, and a suitable N-type dopant, such as phosphorus or antimony, the concentration of the N-type material being slightly less than that of the aluminium. Thus initially the whole crystal is P-type, and on annealing conversion to N-type occurs in the regions where the aluminium has depleted; the resulting P–N junctions are delineated by a simple acid etch. On annealing such doubly doped crystals, containing about 10^{18} oxygen atoms cm^{-3}, at a temperature of about 1,200° C to 1,250° C, it is found that cylindrical P–N junctions are formed round individual dislocations, the position of the emergent dislocation within the N-type region being revealed by the Dash etch.[11] The depletion effect is shown schematically in Figure 5, and a micrograph is shown in Plate I. The observed radii of such cylindrical P–N junctions agree with the value predicted from a knowledge of the ratio of the concentrations of aluminium and phosphorus present and the drop in aluminium concentration calculated from equation (25). In the evaluation of this expression (as depicted in Figure 5), the usual value is taken for the

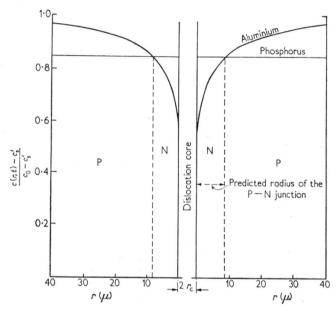

Figure 5. *The concentration distribution of aluminium round a dislocation, illustrating the formation of cylindrical P–N junctions. $T = 1,250°C$, $t = 16$ hr, $c_0 = $ initial concentration of aluminium, and $c_s' = $ concentration of aluminium at $r = r_c$. (Reproduced by permission of* The Journal of Applied Physics, *after Bullough et al.[48])*

diffusion coefficient of aluminium, and c_s' has been taken[48] as 10^{16} atoms cm^{-3}. Similar P–N junctions are observed to be associated with groups and arrays of dislocations (see Plate I); if the local dislocation density exceeds a certain value, the N-type regions associated with the individual dislocations overlap and large N-type regions may be produced. In particular, an N-type sheet of material is produced about a planar boundary with high defect density, and, in fact, Kirton[62] has verified, by Hall effect measurements, that the conductivity of such a region is definitely N-type.

If the oxygen concentration is reduced to about 5×10^{17} atoms cm^{-3}, the size of the N-type regions produced around the crystal defects is substantially reduced[63] and P–N junctions are observed only in regions of the crystal where the initial concentration of aluminium is only slightly in excess of that of the phosphorus. No P–N junctions are formed on annealing oxygen-free crystals.[63] It is therefore concluded that the aluminium will precipitate only in association with oxygen, and that at temperatures of about 1,200° C the dislocations provide preferred sites for such precipitation. No depletion of aluminium is observed at temperatures greater than 1,300° C, consistent with the observations, using infra-red spectroscopy,[55] that no precipitation of oxygen occurs at such high temperatures.

When crystals containing oxygen are annealed at temperatures below 1,200° C, the N-type regions round dislocations are larger, and at 1,000° C extensive regions not directly associated with the crystal defects may be converted. All these observations may be correlated with the form and distribution of precipitate particles observed internally in the crystal by transmission infra-red microscopy.[48, 63] It may also be noted that converted N-type regions may be reconverted to P-type by annealing the sample at 1,375° C.[63]

The direct optical observations are now briefly reviewed as a function of annealing temperature.[48] Above 1,300° C, no precipitation is observed; between 1,200° C and 1,250° C, discrete precipitate particles are observed along the dislocation lines; at 1,100° C, continuous rod-like precipitates grow along the dislocations surrounded by a localized cloud of globular particles; at lower temperatures, dislocations are still decorated but in addition there is a high density of random precipitate particles. These observations are consistent with the P–N junction observations, and can be explained by an increasing supersaturation of oxygen as the temperature is reduced, which leads to the formation of a higher density of nucleation sites.

It has been shown by Southgate[64] that the presence of free oxygen in silicon can be detected by internal friction measurements; he has used this technique to study the precipitation kinetics of oxygen in crystals which also contain aluminium at a concentration of 5×10^{15} atoms cm^{-3}. Annealing the samples for several hours at a temperature of 1,030° C leads to oxygen precipitation, and the kinetics are found to have the form given by equation (27). In an as-grown sample, the value of n in equation (27) is $0 \cdot 69$, and in a similar sample, plastically deformed by twisting at 1,000° C, n has the value of $0 \cdot 54$; the time scale of the ageing is not significantly affected as a result of the plastic deformation. Southgate concludes that the aluminium atoms act as preferential nucleation sites compared with dislocation sites, and that the form of his observed kinetics can be interpreted only in terms of a build-up of stresses around the growing precipitate particles. These results are thus consistent with the theoretical concepts outlined in sub-section 2.5 and with the observations of random precipitation at similar temperatures by Bullough et al.,[48] as described above. Southgate finds that precipitated oxygen can be returned to solution by annealing the sample at 1,280° C for about 10 min; this is again consistent with the above observations using the P–N junction technique. The influence of aluminium on the precipitation of oxygen is again indicated by Southgate's observation that the rate of oxygen precipitation is considerably reduced when aluminium is not present.

There is now considerable evidence that the dislocations present in as-grown silicon crystals containing oxygen are contaminated with impurity atoms;[57, 65] these impurities can then act as nucleating sites for precipitation during a subsequent anneal. Dislocations introduced by plastic deformation are expected to be 'clean', and can act as sites for precipitation only when nuclei have formed along their length; this process is obviously more difficult than on the dislocations in the as-grown material. This is substantiated by the observations on the formations of P–N junctions around dislocations in plastically deformed crystals doubly doped with aluminium and phosphorus. No junctions are produced on annealing such crystals at temperatures above about 1,200° C, and there is no observable precipitation on the dislocations, in contrast to the underformed samples.[48] When deformed samples are heated at lower temperatures the dislocations are decorated and the usual N-type conversion occurs around the dislocations; thus spontaneous nucleation of precipitates can occur on the dislocations at temperatures below about 1,200° C.[63] Nucleation of precipitates may also occur on vacancy or interstitial loops created as a result of the generation of point defects during the plastic deformation. It is difficult to reconcile these observations, and also the results of Lederhandler and Patel,[56] with the apparent unimportance of plastic deformation in the experiments of Southgate.[64]

Further evidence for the interaction of an impurity with dislocations is afforded by the results on the strain ageing of silicon described by Pearson et al.[5] They observed a discontinuous yield point which could be recovered by subsequent annealing at temperatures between 800° C and 1,200° C; these observations are similar to the results of Thomas and Leak[4] for the iron–carbon system. By assuming that the impurity concerned was oxygen, present in a concentration of 10^{18} atoms cm^{-3}, and in view of the fact that there was no variation of the yield point over the above temperature range, they deduced[5] a binding energy of greater than $1 \cdot 4$ eV between the impurity (oxygen) and a dislocation. They remark that this large value is probably a result of a chemical interaction with the dangling bonds on the dislocation rather than a simple size effect interaction, the estimated contribution to the binding energy from the latter interaction being about $0 \cdot 6$ eV (see Table 1). The activation energy for the migration of the impurity was estimated to be $3 \cdot 3$ eV. Although this estimate of the activation energy is of necessity somewhat crude, it appears to be significantly larger than the now known activation energy of $2 \cdot 55$ eV[66] for the diffusion of oxygen in silicon. The conclusion that oxygen alone was responsible for the observed strain ageing is perhaps somewhat doubtful, since the crystals may have contained carbon which interacts very strongly with dislocations (see Table 1 and the following section); moreover, the most recent estimate of $3 \cdot 16$ eV[67] for the activation energy for the diffusion of carbon in silicon is closer to their value.[5]

3.3. THE INFLUENCE OF CARBON

Although the mode of precipitation of aluminium may be successfully correlated with the known behaviour of oxygen,[48] the situation must be more complicated than that discussed above, since it is now known that co-precipitation of carbon occurs during the annealing of such samples.[68] Precipitate particles may be exposed in the converted N-type regions by etching the sample in a mixture of hydrofluoric and nitric acids, and these particles may then be examined by reflection electron diffraction. Composite diffraction patterns are found corresponding to the parent silicon and a material with a basically face centred cubic lattice with $a_0 = 4 \cdot 37 \pm 0 \cdot 03$ Å. This material was thus identified as β-silicon carbide, which has a zinc blende structure with $a_0 = 4 \cdot 35$ Å. In some cases, extra diffraction spots were observed which could be interpreted as due to γ-aluminium oxide. Since any precipitate particles of silica would be dissolved by the etchant, the absence of any diffraction pattern corresponding to silica was not unexpected. These observations indicate that a large proportion of the precipitated material consists of silicon carbide; this requires the crystal initially to contain a high concentration of carbon. In fact, mass spectrographic[69] and chemical analyses[70] confirm that the crystals contain between 10^{18} and 10^{19} atoms cm^{-3}, in agreement with some earlier carbon determinations by Papazian and Wolsky.[71] The diffusion coefficient of carbon in silicon has been measured in the temperature range $1,000°$ C to $1,400°$ C by a radio tracer technique;[67] these results, together with further unpublished measurements, give a value:

$$D = 2 \cdot 0 \exp\left(\frac{-3 \cdot 16 \pm 0 \cdot 18\,\text{eV}}{kT}\right) \text{cm}^2\,\text{sec}^{-1}$$

With this value of D and an initial carbon concentration of 3×10^{18} atoms cm^{-3}, it is possible to show (with the aid of expression (25)) that sufficient carbon will arrive at the dislocations to account for a significant proportion of the observed precipitated material. Similar precipitation of carbon is thought to occur in undoped crystals containing oxygen, since the visual appearance of the precipitates is very similar to those in the doped specimens. However, it has not been possible to identify these particles, since the etching technique fails in the absence of localized P–N junctions.[68]

Any detailed explanation of the precipitation phenomona associated with the presence of carbon necessitates knowing whether carbon occupies substitutional or interstitial sites in the silicon lattice. From the value of $3 \cdot 16$ eV for the activation energy of diffusion of carbon, it might be reasonable to conclude that it occupied substitutional sites. If this is so, then a large decrease in volume is to be expected on the formation of silicon carbide particles with a consequent generation of vacancies at the precipitate matrix interface. The aggregation and collapse of such vacancies could provide an explanation for the formation of the large circular dislocation loops on (111) planes observed round straight dislocations on which heavy precipitation of silicon carbide occurs.[72] Similar large loops on (111) planes have also been found round isolated precipitate particles, and there is good evidence for the segregation of oxygen into such loops, since in doubly doped crystals P–N junctions are found to be associated with the loops.[63] In the case of loops round straight dislocations, such P–N junctions have *not* been observed, and it can only be concluded that any oxygen which diffuses into these loops is then preferentially attracted towards the straight dislocation line which *is* surrounded by an N-type region.

However, the possibility that carbon occupies interstitial sites cannot be ignored in view of the fact that carbon has a tetrahedral radius of only $0 \cdot 77$ Å. In fact, it has been recently reported[73] that when the carbon concentration exceeds $2 \cdot 5 \times 10^{20}$ cm^{-3}, the mean spacing of the silicon lattice increases with increasing carbon content; at lower concentrations no definite correlation has been established. Such a high concentration of carbon in free solution seems unreasonable in view of other reported observations on the solubility.[67] If carbon does, however, occupy interstitial sites, its precipitation to form silicon carbide would involve a negligible volume increase, and hence, in contrast to oxygen, no significant rate limitation would be expected at the precipitate matrix interface. The large dislocation loops could then be interpreted as due to the growth of silicon carbide in the form of a planar sheet on (111) planes. If this is so, it is difficult to explain the observations concerning P–N junctions round such loops. It is clear that the presence of carbon in silicon is important, but the detailed interpretation of its behaviour in relation to precipitation phenomena must await definitive experiments to decide whether it occupies substitutional or interstitial sites.

4. PRECIPITATION IN SILICON RESULTING FROM RETROGRADE SOLUBILITY

Up to now we have only discussed impurities which precipitate during the heat treatment, and since these impurities have low diffusion coefficients, little migration would be expected during the actual period of cooling. An entirely different situation arises in the case of rapidly diffusing impurities which exhibit retrograde solubility. If such a material is diffused into silicon, its concentration rapidly attains the equilibrium value appropriate to the particular temperature of heating. On cooling the sample a super-saturated solution is produced and the impurity tends to diffuse out of the crystal; on fast cooling, there is insufficient time for the impurity to reach the

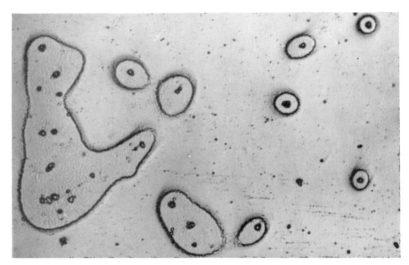

Plate I. *P–N junctions round isolated and groups of dislocations as revealed by etching*

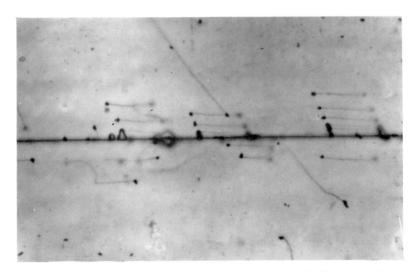

Plate II. *Precipitation on dislocations in an aluminium doped silicon crystal after annealing at 1,250°C for 18 hr. Dislocation pile-ups against a coherent (111) twin boundary are shown and internal decoration with chemical etch pits are also correlated*

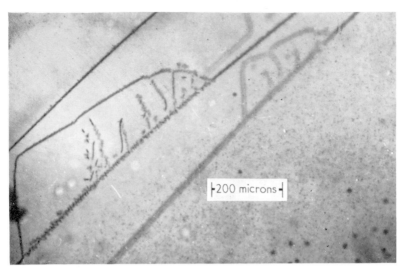

Plate III. *Trails behind moved portion of a grown-in dislocation. Original location is marked by large precipitates, presumably associated with oxygen on dislocation before deformation. (Reproduced by permission of* The Journal of Applied Physics, *after Dash[65])*

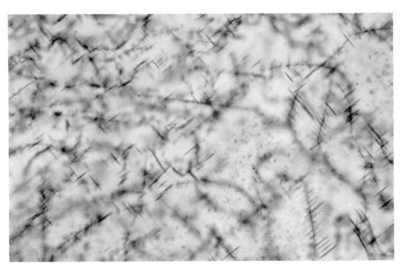

Plate IV. *Precipitation of iron in a silicon crystal. (Magnification × 170)*

external surfaces and precipitation of a second phase occurs on any internal structural defects which can act as nucleating sites. This general behaviour does not depend on the presence of other chemically active impurities, such as oxygen, but the detailed mode of precipitation can be influenced by the presence of such additional impurities.

4.1. COPPER PRECIPITATION

The solubility of copper in silicon is retrograde[74] with a maximum value of about 10^{18} atoms cm^{-3} at $1,300°$ C, reducing to a value of 10^{16} atoms cm^{-3} at $700°$ C. The diffusivity is very large over this temperature range and is given by[75]

$$D = 4 \cdot 10^{-2} \exp\left(\frac{-1 \cdot 0 \, eV}{kT}\right) cm^2 sec^{-1}$$

This value indicates motion by an interstitial process, but in fact it is considered that a certain proportion of the copper atoms occupy substitutional sites[76] depending on the local concentration of vacancies. Precise details of this dissociative mechanism of diffusion for copper in silicon have not been obtained, but the process is considered to be analogous to that of copper in germanium (see sub-section 5.2).

Thus diffusion of copper into silicon at temperatures above about $900°$ C, followed by a rapid quench of the sample, leads to precipitation on internal defects. By means of this technique, Dash[11] was able, for the first time, to establish conclusively the correlation between chemical etch pits and emergent dislocations. Dislocations generated by the operations of internal Frank–Read sources were observed, an interesting feature being the absence or near absence of precipitation on the pure screw components of the loops. This observation emphasizes the importance of the size effect interaction potential (equation (10)) in the nucleation of such precipitates; in the initial stage of cooling, a dense impurity atmosphere, which can subsequently condense to form precipitate nuclei, will grow in the neighbourhood of dislocations with an edge component, whereas only relatively dilute atmospheres would be expected to grow round pure screw dislocations. Dash[77] has also observed decorated isolated dislocation loops and dislocations held up by a coherent twin boundary, although the boundary itself is not decorated. The latter observation is in accord with the observations on precipitation in silicon crystals containing oxygen and aluminium,[48] as shown in Plate II.

The presence of an oxide phase on dislocations in silicon crystals grown from a quartz crucible has been suggested by Dash to explain certain observations on lightly deformed crystals.[65] As a result of the deformation, portions of the grown-in dislocations were displaced from their original positions and precipitation of copper was observed both on the original and

9 123

final positions of the dislocations, as shown in Plate III; decoration of the original positions was attributed to the presence on the grown-in dislocations of a precipitated phase, presumed to be oxide. Alternatively, the observed decoration could conceivably be due to the formation of small vacancy aggregates which are nucleated when the dislocation is torn away from its equilibrium vacancy atmosphere during the deformation. The decoration by copper and the preferential etching of small vacancy or interstitial aggregates was also demonstrated in this work. These defects appear as trails between the old and new locations of the dislocations and were attributed to the non-conservative motion of jogs present on the grown-in dislocations.

Schwuttke[78] has studied the location and shape of copper precipitates in silicon crystals as a function of their oxygen content. In vacuum floating-zone-refined crystals, all the precipitates are on dislocations and take the form of a single set of parallel needles lying along a $\langle 110 \rangle$ direction. When oxygen is present, however, some random precipitates, often coincident with the growth striations, are observed and the precipitates on the dislocations have a complex 'dendritic' form. In these latter crystals some hollow cylindrical defects, assumed to be screw dislocations, were observed. If these defects are helical dislocations, derived from pure screw dislocations, then it may be inferred that dislocation climb has occurred (see sub-section 4.2). It has been further suggested that much of the interstitial copper which precipitates was originally in substitutional sites during the heat treatment; the fact that vacancies are generated throughout the volume of the crystal upon cooling[14] is cited as evidence for the transfer from substitutional to interstitial sites.

4.2. Gold in Silicon

The solubility of gold in silicon[79] has a maximum value of 10^{17} atoms cm^{-3} at 1,300° C, falling to 10^{16} atoms cm^{-3} at 1,000° C; from electrical measurements[79] it is considered that a substantial fraction of the dissolved gold occupies substitutional sites. The diffusion constant is given by[80]

$$D = 0 \cdot 0011 \exp(-1 \cdot 12 \, eV/kT) \, \text{cm}^2 \text{sec}^{-1}$$

and it is seen that the activation energy is very similar to that for copper in silicon and its magnitude would indicate diffusion by an interstitial mechanism. However, the pre-exponential factor is fifty times smaller than that for copper, suggesting that the proportion of gold atoms occupying interstitial sites is correspondingly reduced; the atoms occupying substitutional sites are assumed to be relatively immobile. The difference between the proportions of copper and gold which occupy interstitial sites is not inconsistent with the relative values of ϵ in Table 1, which give some measure of the lattice distortion around the solute atom.

The interaction of gold with internal defects has been studied by Dash,[57] who diffused gold into silicon in the temperature range 1,000° C to 1,300° C. Autoradiographs taken on samples after the in-diffusion of gold-198 showed that there was an enhanced concentration in the neighbourhood of the dislocations, not localized to the core regions. This evidence for lack of precipitation on the dislocations is consistent with the fact that no observable precipitate particles could be detected by transmission infra-red microscopy and with the observation by Collins et al.[79] that the concentration of gold determined by electrical measurements after heat treatment is equal to the total concentration of gold present in the crystal. This is in contrast to similar experiments[76] on the electrical properties of copper diffused silicon when it is found that the concentration of electrically active copper remaining in solution is a small fraction of the total concentration of copper present in the crystal, indicating that most of the copper precipitates on cooling.

It was found[57] that when the gold diffused samples were etched, pits characteristic of helical dislocations were produced similar to those found by Tweet[81] in as-grown germanium and considered by Tweet to be due to the absorption of vacancies on screw dislocations (see sub-section 5.2). The presence of helices in gold diffused silicon was confirmed by the copper decoration technique. It is clear from subsequent work by Dash[57] that the simple explanation suggested by Tweet for the formation of the helices in germanium is not appropriate here. By very careful indentation experiments, Dash was able to introduce a small number of left-hand screw dislocations into an initially dislocation-free crystal. Upon gold in-diffusion it was observed that these dislocations were transformed into right-hand helices, indicating that the screw dislocations had climbed by *generating* and not by absorbing vacancies.

It is concluded that the rapid in-diffusion of interstitial gold will result in the annihilation of most of the thermal vacancies present throughout the crystal so as to produce the equilibrium ratio of substitutional to interstitial gold atoms. This depletion of vacancies is the driving force for their further generation at the dislocations (and at the external surface); in addition, we expect an atmosphere of gold to form in the vicinity of the dislocations (see Table 1) which would further enhance the climb mechanism. The above explanation thus accounts satisfactorily for the observed enhanced concentration of gold in the neighbourhood of the dislocations found in the experiments with radioactive gold.

The diameters of the helices were found to increase with increasing periods of heat treatments at a given temperature and with increasing temperature for a given period of heating. It was concluded from these observations and the fact that the size of the helices was independent of cooling rate that climb occurs during the heat treatment and not during the cooling. Dash[82] observed circular prismatic loops lying in a (110) plane which had been punched off[83] from the extremities of a short length of helical dislocation due to the mutual repulsive force between adjacent turns of the helix. In view of the observation of Dash[57] discussed above, these loops must be 'interstitial' loops rather than vacancy loops as originally suggested by Dash.[82] The spacing between these loops increases with increasing distance from their source, in agreement with the theoretically expected spacings for a row of glissile loops.[22]

So far, the discussion has been limited to oxygen-free crystals. In crucible-grown silicon, much more complicated effects due to dislocation climb are observed[57] and the complexity is thought to be introduced as a result of the pinning of the dislocations by oxide complexes. In addition, dislocation loops on (111) planes are observed; such loops can only be produced in oxygen-free crystals by the introduction of other impurities prior to the in-diffusion of gold. Thus it is thought that oxygen clusters can nucleate the loops, and their subsequent growth will be controlled by a similar mechanism to that controlling the climb of straight dislocations. Samples containing such loops, not decorated by copper, have recently been thinned by a polishing technique and examined by transmission electron microscopy.[84] Fringes, characteristic of those expected from the presence of a stacking fault,[85] were found across the loops, and it was concluded that the loops consist of an extra plane of silicon atoms and not a coherent gold platelet.

4.3. OTHER IMPURITIES

Direct evidence of precipitation in silicon crystals containing silver, cobalt, iron, manganese, nickel, uranium, and zinc has been obtained by Dash (as reported by Collins and Carlson[76]) using transmission infra-red microscopy. Most of these elements are known to have high diffusion coefficients and exhibit retrograde solubility[86] and hence, by comparison with the behaviour of copper, such precipitation is not unexpected. Similar infra-red observations on the precipitation of nickel have been published by Shattes and Wegener,[87] who suggest that such precipitates which are found to nucleate on the dislocations may act as getters for other rapidly diffusing impurities. When present in free solution these latter impurities are known to have a deleterious effect on the minority carrier lifetime. Needle-like iron precipitates with $\langle 110 \rangle$ axes, produced in a silicon crystal quenched from 1,200°C, are shown in Plate IV; it can be seen that most of the precipitation occurs on the dislocations.[58] The effect of oxygen on the precipitation behaviour of these impurities has not been studied. Evidence derived from electron spin resonance by Woodbury and Ludwig[14] indicates that both manganese and chromium can occupy both substitutional and interstitial sites; it follows that the diffusion of such elements into silicon at high temperatures may lead to vacancy absorption with the subsequent dislocation climb reactions as produced by gold.

The behaviour of lithium in silicon has been extensively studied and reviewed,[88] and it is found that the precipitate particles grow at random sites. It has been shown that lithium interacts strongly with dissolved oxygen,[89] and thus, in view of the evidence for the preferential segregation of oxygen on the dislocations, it is to be expected that some precipitation of lithium also occurs on dislocations in crucible-grown material. Some evidence for the interaction of lithium with dislocations, even in the absence of oxygen, has been reported by Pell.[90] In specimens given a 15 degree twist (resulting in a dislocation density of about 3×10^7 lines cm^{-2}) it was found that the rate of ion drift at room temperature was reduced to less than 10 per cent of that in undeformed samples; this effect could be due in part to the electrical interaction discussed in sub-section 2.3.

It can be seen from Table 1 that the value of ϵ for boron is rather large, and thus a strong interaction with dislocations is to be expected. Silicon whiskers containing $0 \cdot 1$ per cent of boron exhibit strain ageing which is interpreted by Pearson et al.[5] to be due to the interaction of boron with dislocations. The ageing behaviour in these boron doped samples was different from that in the undoped samples discussed in sub-section 3.2.

After the in-diffusion of phosphorus into silicon, a proportion of the phosphorus atoms near the surface, in the region of high concentration, is found to be in an electrically inactive state.[91] This effect could be due, in part, to the formation of precipitates or impurity atmospheres of phosphorus on dislocations in the surface region. Furthermore, it has been demonstrated[92] that dislocations are actually created in the surface region to accommodate the change in lattice parameter with impurity content. The effect is most marked for boron but is still detectable for phosphorus with a relatively small value of ϵ (see Table 1).

5. PRECIPITATION IN GERMANIUM

5.1. Lithium in Germanium

The behaviour of lithium in germanium has been extensively studied, particular effort being devoted to an understanding of the kinetics and equilibrium of ion pairing reactions with other impurities.[93] Dislocations do not appear to play a significant role in these reactions and they will not be discussed here. We shall concern ourselves only with the precipitation phenomena observed in intrinsic material where it has been shown that dislocations are directly involved.

The solubility of lithium in germanium is retrograde, exceeding 10^{18} atoms cm^{-3} at 500° C and only 10^{14} atoms cm^{-3} at room temperature.[94, 95] The diffusion coefficient is very high, and precipitation from a supersaturated solution is feasible in a reasonable time even at room temperature; the diffusion coefficient is given by[39, 96]

$$D = 2 \cdot 5 \times 10^{-3} \exp(-0 \cdot 51 \, eV/kT) \, cm^2 \, sec^{-1}$$

127

The kinetics of the precipitation of lithium can be followed by electrical conductivity measurements, since each lithium atom in free solution acts as a donor,[97] and in addition it has been found that etching techniques can be used to reveal the location of the precipitate particles.[98]

Tyler and Dash[98] have studied the precipitation of lithium at room temperature in samples saturated with lithium at various higher temperatures. It was found that the kinetics of precipitation were independent of dislocation density when the diffusion temperature was 575° C. However,

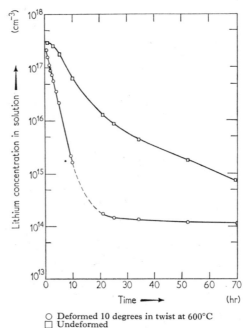

○ Deformed 10 degrees in twist at 600°C
□ Undeformed

Figure 6. *Precipitation of lithium as a function of time at 300° K. Lithium diffusion was for 91 hr at 400°C. (Reproduced by permission of* The Journal of Applied Physics, *after Tyler and Dash[98])*

when a lower diffusion temperature of 400° C was used it was found that the rate of precipitation was considerably greater in the plastically deformed sample containing between 10^6 and 10^7 dislocation lines cm^{-2} (see review articles by Reiss[99]) compared with an undeformed sample containing less than 10^3 dislocation lines cm^{-2}. In the former sample, the kinetics were found to have the form of expression (26), as shown in Figure 6, indicating substantial precipitation on line sinks (i.e. the dislocations), whereas the latter kinetics were complicated and were not interpreted in detail. Parallel etching studies confirm that precipitation on dislocations does occur, and in the undeformed samples there were random precipitate particles with an estimated density of 10^9 particles cm^{-3}. Some evidence was obtained which indicated that screw dislocations provide less favourable sites for precipitation than dislocations with an edge component (cf. copper in silicon). In addition to the precipitation on the dislocations, there was some decoration of trails behind the dislocations which were thought to be the sites of aggregates of point defects generated during the deformation as a result of the non-conservative movement of jogs present on the dislocations (again, cf. copper in silicon). Direct evidence for the precipitation of lithium on dislocations has been obtained by Deutschbein and Bernard[12] using an infra-red microscope together with a special television pick-up tube sensitive to wavelengths greater than $1 \cdot 7$ microns; these observations of precipitates were correlated with chemical etch pits. In some samples, groups of needle-like precipitates along $\langle 110 \rangle$ directions were found. In this work there was no evidence for small random precipitates as found by Tyler and Dash,[98] but it is doubtful whether such particles could have been resolved with the technique employed.

Complementary to the above work is the very comprehensive study of the precipitation kinetics of lithium by Morin and Reiss.[97] The observed kinetics had the form of equation (27) with $n = 3/2$, and this led the authors to conclude that most of the precipitate particles should be approximately spherical in shape and located at random sites throughout the crystal. This exponential variation was observed to hold until the precipitation was more than 90 per cent complete. Ham[50] has shown that for the growth of random spherical particles such kinetics should only occur until 50 per cent of the available solute has precipitated. Thus it may be inferred that the precipitation process is more complex than Morin and Reiss suggest. For example, the possibility of precipitation on dislocations was completely discounted. It seems certain that the majority of precipitate particles will grow at random sites because of the relatively short time required to complete the process, but in view of the observations of Tyler and Dash the effect on the kinetics of precipitation on dislocations should not be completely ignored. Considerable evidence was given to show that the nucleation sites for the random precipitates were lithium vacancy pairs, the vacancies being generated from the dislocations during the diffusion used to saturate the sample with lithium. In samples diffused at a temperature of 425° C for a time sufficiently long to ensure that equilibrium is attained, the density of precipitate particles, which was independent of the precipitation temperature, was estimated to be about 10^{12} cm^{-3} from the kinetics. This value is about three orders of magnitude greater than that observed by Tyler and Dash for a diffusion temperature of 400° C; the difference in temperature of 25° C leads to a negligible reduction in the concentration of lithium vacancy pairs if the heat of formation of this complex is taken as $1 \cdot 6$ eV.[97] Thus although the initial number of nucleation sites may be equal to the number of lithium vacancy pairs present, it should not be assumed that this will necessarily be the final density of precipitate particles. Because of the surface energy considerations the larger particles will grow at the expense of smaller ones, and, furthermore, particles nucleated in the vicinity of dislocations will tend to evaporate with a transfer of the lithium to the dislocations. A further possible complication in deciding the nature of the precipitate nuclei is the possibility that the crystals used by Morin and Reiss may have contained oxygen in a concentration in excess of the number of lithium vacancy pairs. In fact it has been shown by Carter and Swalin[100] that the presence of oxygen in germanium modifies the kinetics in a gross manner; the rate of precipitation is much faster, and the final concentration of unprecipitated lithium was stated to be equal to the oxygen concentration. This last observation suggests that lithium–oxygen pairs in germanium act as donors in a similar fashion to that reported by Pell[89] for such complexes in silicon.

Carter and Swalin[100] also investigated the effect of simultaneously diffusing copper and lithium and found that under these conditions the precipitation rate of lithium is much reduced. The obvious interpretation of this observation is that vacancies generated from dislocations during the diffusion are immediately removed as a result of converting interstitial copper to substitutional sites; thus if vacancies are involved in the formation of nuclei for lithium precipitation, the density of such sites will be automatically reduced. Further details concerning copper in germanium will now be discussed.

5.2. COPPER AND NICKEL IN GERMANIUM

This topic has been dealt with in detail in several recent review articles,[80, 99, 101] and hence we shall confine ourselves here to a short survey of the observations, the interpretations of which involve the presence of dislocations.

Both these elements diffuse in germanium by the now well understood dissociative mechanism;[102] briefly, very rapidly diffusing interstitials combine with vacancies generated from dislocations or from the surface and are converted to substitutional sites. It follows that the rate of diffusion is more rapid in regions of high dislocation density than in regions of perfect crystals.[103-105] The equilibrium solubility, which is found to be retrograde,[106-109] is determined by measuring the amount of element in free solution by electrical measurements after quenching from various temperatures; radio tracer techniques have also been employed for copper.

To study the precipitation phenomena, samples are usually saturated at about 800° C and then annealed for various times at temperatures between 300° C and 700° C.[110, 111] The amount of copper or nickel in free solution at a given time is determined by resistivity or Hall effect measurements, since both these elements are acceptors in germanium.[112-114] In samples containing a high density of dislocations, Tweet[110] finds that kinetics for copper precipitation have the form of equation (26), suggesting precipitation on dislocations; the characteristic time τ is found to vary in the expected way with dislocation density at the higher annealing temperatures. At lower temperatures τ is found to be independent of dislocation density, and the rate limiting process for precipitation is dissociation of substitutional copper into interstitial copper and a vacant lattice site. Penning[115] has further interpreted the high temperature results, and has shown that the rate of removal of copper is equal to the rate of annihilation of vacancies at the dislocations. Penning is thus able to deduce the self-diffusion coefficient which agrees with the directly measured values[116] extrapolated to the range of precipitation temperatures employed. The co-precipitation of the vacancies is clearly necessary, since each vacancy itself acts as an acceptor,[111] and hence the removal of substitutional copper in itself would not reduce the overall carrier concentration if an equal number of vacancies remained in solution. Some additional evidence that the precipitates grow on dislocations is provided by the internal friction studies of Teutonico, Granato, and Truell.[117]

Direct evidence from Hall effect measurements over a wide temperature range for the initial generation of vacancies followed by their co-precipitation on dislocations in germanium containing nickel has been obtained by Penning.[111] In this case the ionization energy levels for the two acceptors present (i.e. nickel $0 \cdot 23$ eV and vacancy $0 \cdot 02$ eV) are sufficiently different for the concentration of each to be determined unambiguously as a function of the time of annealing. The kinetics found for the precipitation of nickel are similar to those described above for copper, having again the form of equation (26).

Tweet[81] has used an etching technique to study as-grown germanium crystals containing a low density of dislocations. He finds that the rate of etching is greatly enhanced in the regions away from the external surface and dislocations; this effect is attributed to the presence of small vacancy clusters which have formed during cooling from the melting temperature. In the regions of relatively low etch rate, spiral dislocations[57, 118] are observed and their formation is attributed to the climb of simple screw dislocations by the absorption of vacancies from the region of the crystal in the neighbourhood of the dislocations. After annealing such crystals at 800° C for 10 hr the enhanced etching effect disappears, there is no evidence for spiral dislocations, and a low density of etch pits (not characteristic of dislocations) is observed. Tweet suggests that large vacancy aggregates form during the anneal and that these are responsible for the observed featureless etch pits. The disappearance of the spiral dislocations is not commented on, and presumably vacancies have been regenerated from the spirals and subsequently incorporated in the large aggregates. Diffusion of copper at 800° C for 10 min reproduces the effects found after the prolonged anneal. Tweet suggests that the vacancies combine with interstitial copper atoms and are thereby removed (see above). It is difficult to understand why the spiral dislocations unwind to generate vacancies and then this process ceases as

131

soon as the dislocations are straight. In view of the observation of helix formation in gold doped silicon[57] (sub-section 4.2), it might be expected that further dislocation climb would occur to yield helices in the opposite sense.

ACKNOWLEDGEMENTS

The authors wish to thank D. P. R. Petrie, R. L. Rouse, J. Wakefield, and J. B. Willis for useful comments on the manuscript, and Dr. T. E. Allibone, C.B.E., F.R.S., Director of the Laboratory, for permission to publish this paper.

REFERENCES

1. COTTRELL, A. H. *Dislocations and Plastic Flow in Crystals* (Oxford University Press, 1953)
2. COTTRELL, A. H., and BILBY, B. A. *Proc. phys. Soc. Lond.* **62**, 49 (1949)
3. DAVENPORT, E. S., and BAIN, E. C. *Trans. Amer. Soc. Metals* **23**, 1047 (1949)
4. THOMAS, W. R., and LEAK, G. M. *J. Iron Steel Inst.* **180**, 155 (1955)
5. PEARSON, G. L., READ, W. T., and FELDMANN, W. L. *Acta Met.* **5**, 181 (1957)
6. CAHN, J. W. *Acta Met.* **5**, 169 (1957)
7. HULL, D., and MOGFORD, I. L. *Phil. Mag.* **6**, 535 (1961)
8. THOMAS, G. *Phil. Mag.* **4**, 606 (1959)
9. HEDGES, J. N., and MITCHELL, J. W. *Phil. Mag.* **44**, 223 (1953)
10. AMELINCKX, S. *Dislocations and Mechanical Properties of Crystals*, p. 3 (Wiley, New York, 1957)
11. DASH, W. C. *J. appl. Phys.* **27**, 1193 (1956)
12. DEUTSCHBEIN, O., and BERNARD, M. *Solid State Physics in Electronics and Tele-communications*, Vol. 1, p. 117 (Academic, New York, 1960)
13. OSHCHEPKOV, P. K. *J. Acad. Sci. U.S.S.R.* **10**, 64 (1958)
14. WOODBURY, H. H., and LUDWIG, G. W. *Phys. Rev. Lett.* **5**, 96 (1960) ; *Phys. Rev.* **117**, 102 (1960)
15. WATKINS, G. D., and CORBETT, J. W. *Phys. Rev.* **121**, 1001 (1961)
16. FRIEDEL, J. *Les Dislocations* (Gauthier-Villars, Paris, 1956)
17. ESHELBY, J. D. *Phil. Trans.* **A244**, 87 (1951)
18. ESHELBY, J. D. *Proc. roy. Soc.* **A241**, 376 (1957)
19. JEANS, J. H. *The Mathematical Theory of Electricity and Magnetism* (5th Edn) p. 42 (Cambridge University Press, 1948)
20. BILBY, B. A. *Proc. phys. Soc. Lond.* **A63**, 191 (1950)
21. COCHARDT, A., SCHOEK, G., and WIEDERSICH, H. *Acta Met.* **3**, 533 (1955)
22. BULLOUGH, R., and NEWMAN, R. C. *Phil. Mag.* **5**, 921 (1960)
23. McSKIMMIN, H. J. *J. appl. Phys.* **24**, 988 (1953)
24. PAULING, L. *Nature of the Chemical Bond* (3rd Edn) p. 246 (Cornell University Press, 1960)
25. QUEISSER, H. J., HUBNER, K., and SHOCKLEY, W. *Phys. Rev.* **123**, 1245 (1961)
26. HORNE, F. H. *Phys. Rev.* **97**, 1521 (1955)
27. KULIN, S. S., and KURTZ, A. D. *Acta Met.* **2**, 354 (1954)
28. BOND, W. L., and KAISER, W. *J. Phys. Chem. Solids* **16**, 44 (1960)
29. KAISER, W., KECK, P. H., and LANGE, C. F. *Phys. Rev.* **101**, 1264 (1956)
30. BLOEM, J., HAAS, C., and PENNING, P. *J. Phys. Chem. Solids* **12**, 22 (1959)
31. BULLOUGH, R., and NEWMAN, R. C. *Phil. Mag.* **7**, 529 (1962)
32. KESSLER, J. O. *Phys. Rev.* **106**, 654 (1957)
33. STURGE, M. D. *Proc. phys. Soc. Lond.* **73**, 297 (1959)
34. VAN BUEREN, H. G. *Imperfections in Crystals*, p. 190 (North-Holland, Amsterdam, 1960)
35. KARSTENSEN, F. *Z. Naturforsch.* **14a**, 1031 (1959)

36. CHYNOWETH, A. G., and PEARSON, G. L. *J. appl. Phys.* **29**, 1103 (1958)
37. SHOCKLEY, W. *Phys. Rev.* **91**, 228 (1953)
38. READ, W. T. *Phil. Mag.* **45**, 775 (1954); **45**, 1119 (1954)
39. FULLER, C. S., and SEVERIENS, J. C. *Phys. Rev.* **92**, 1322 (1953); **96**, 21 (1954)
40. BARDSLEY, W. *Progress in Semiconductors 4*, p. 155 (Heywood, London, 1960)
41. BULLOUGH, R., and NEWMAN, R. C. *Phil. Mag.* **6**, 403 (1961)
42. CRUSSARD, C. *Métaux et Corros.* **25**, 203 (1950)
43. LOUAT, N. *Proc. phys. Soc. Lond.* **B69**, 459 (1956)
44. SUZUKI, H. *Dislocations and Mechanical Properties of Crystals*, p. 363 (Wiley, New York, 1956)
45. BULLOUGH, R., and NEWMAN, R. C. *Proc. roy. Soc.* **A249**, 427 (1959)
46. BULLOUGH, R., and NEWMAN, R. C. *Proc. roy. Soc.* **A266**, 198, 209 (1962)
47. HAM, F. S. *J. appl. Phys.* **30**, 915 (1959)
48. BULLOUGH, R., and NEWMAN, R. C., WAKEFIELD, J., and WILLIS, J. B. *J. appl. Phys.* **31**, 707 (1960)
49. FRANK, F. C. *Proc. roy. Soc.* **A201**, 586 (1950)
50. HAM, F. S. *J. Phys. Chem. Solids* **6**, 335 (1958)
51. BULLOUGH, R., NEWMAN, R. C., and WAKEFIELD, J. *Proc. Inst. elect. Engrs.* **106B**, Suppl. 15, 277 (1959)
52. BULLOUGH, R., NEWMAN, R. C., WAKEFIELD, J., and WILLIS, J. B. *Proc. International Conf. on Semiconductor Physics*, p. 811 (Czechoslovak Academy of Science, Prague, 1961)
53. KAISER, W., and KECK, P. H. *J. appl. Phys.* **28**, 882 (1957)
54. HROSTOWSKI, H. J., and KAISER, R. H. *Phys. Rev.* **107**, 966 (1957)
55. HROSTOWSKI, H. J., and KAISER, R. *J. Phys. Chem. Solids* **9**, 214 (1959)
56. LEDERHANDLER, S., and PATEL, J. R. *Phys. Rev.* **108**, 239 (1957)
57. DASH, W. C. *J. appl. Phys.* **31**, 2275 (1960)
58. WILLIS, J. B. Unpublished work
59. KAISER, W. *Phys. Rev.* **105**, 1751 (1957)
60. FULLER, C. S. *Chem. Rev.* **59**, 65 (1959)
61. BULLOUGH, R., NEWMAN, R. C., WAKEFILED, J., and WILLIS, J. B. *Nature, Lond.* **183**, 34 (1959)
62. KIRTON, J. Unpublished work
63. NEWMAN, R. C., WAKEFIELD, J., and WILLIS, J. B. Unpublished work
64. SOUTHGATE, P. D. *Proc. phys. Soc. Lond.* **74**, 398 (1960)
65. DASH, W. C. *J. appl. Phys.* **29**, 705 (1958)
66. HAAS, C. *J. Phys. Chem. Solids* **15**, 108 (1960)
67. NEWMAN, R. C., and WAKEFIELD, J. *J. Phys. Chem. Solids* **19**, 230 (1961)
68. NEWMAN, R. C. *Proc. phys. Soc. Lond.* **74**, 993 (1960)
69. WALDRON, J. Private communication
70. BUSH, G. H. Private communication
71. PAPAZIAN, H. A., and WOLSKY, S. P. *J. appl. Phys.* **27**, 1561 (1956)
72. NEWMAN, R. C., and WAKEFIELD, J. *Proc. of the Conf. on Metallurgy of Semiconductor Materials* (A.I.M.E. Met. Soc., Los Angeles, 30 August–1 September, 1961) In press
73. BURGEAT, J. Private communication from Bernard, G. A.
74. STRUTHERS, J. D. *J. appl. Phys.* **27**, 1560 (1956)
75. BOLTAKS, B. I., and SOZINOV, I. I. *J. tech. Phys., Moscow* **28**, 679 (1958)
76. COLLINS, C. B., and CARLSON, R. O. *Phys. Rev.* **108**, 1409 (1957)
77. DASH, W. C. *J. appl. Phys.* **30**, 459 (1959)
78. SCHWUTTKE, G. H. *Trans. Electrochem. Soc.* **108**, 163 (1961)
79. COLLINS, C. B., CARLSON, R. O., and GALLAGHER, C. J. *Phys. Rev.* **105**, 1168 (1957)
80. REISS, H., and FULLER, C. S. *Semiconductors*, p. 244 (Reinhold, New York, 1959)
81. TWEET, A. G. *J. appl. Phys.* **29**, 1520 (1958)
82. DASH, W. C. *Phys. Rev. Lett.* **1**, 400 (1958)
83. JONES, D. A., and MITCHELL, J. W. *Phil. Mag.* **3**, 1 (1957)
84. PHILLIPS, V. A., and DASH, W. C. *J. appl. Phys.* **33**, 568 (1962)
85. HIRSCH, P. B., HOWIE, A., and WHELAN, A. J. *Phil. Trans.* **A252**, 499 (1960)
86. TRUMBORE, F. A. *Bell Syst. Tech. J.* **39**, 205 (1960)

87. SHATTES, W. J., and WEGENER, H. A. R. *J. appl. Phys.* **29**, 866 (1958)
88. TWEET, A. G. *J. appl. Phys.* **30**, 1244 (1959)
89. PELL, E. M. *Solid State Physics in Electronics and Telecommunications*, Vol. 1, p. 261 (Academic, New York, 1960)
90. PELL, E. M. *Phys. Rev.* **119**, 1222 (1960)
91. TANNENBAUM, E. *Solid State Electron.*, **2**, 123 (1961)
92. QUEISSER, H. J. *J. appl. Phys.* **32**, 1776 (1961)
93. FULLER, C. S. *Semiconductors*, p. 192 (Reinhold, New York, 1959)
94. REISS, H., and FULLER, C. S. *J. Phys. Chem. Solids* **4**, 58 (1958)
95. PELL, E. M. *J. Phys. Chem. Solids* **3**, 74 (1957)
96. FULLER, C. S. and DITZENBERGER, J. A. *Phys. Rev.* **91**, 193 (1953)
97. MORIN, F. J., and REISS, H. *J. Phys. Chem. Solids* **3**, 196 (1957)
98. TYLER, W. W., and DASH, W. C. *J. appl. Phys.* **28**, 1221 (1957)
99. REISS, H. *J. appl. Phys.* **30**, 1141 (1959)
100. CARTER, J. R., and SWALIN, R. A. *J. appl. Phys.* **31**, 1191 (1960)
101. VAN BUEREN, H. G. *Imperfections in Crystals* (2nd Edn) p. 647 (North-Holland, Amsterdam, 1961)
102. FRANK, F. C., and TURNBULL, D. *Phys. Rev.* **104**, 617 (1956)
103. LOGAN, R. A. *Phys. Rev.* **100**, 615 (1955)
104. FULLER, C. S., and DITZENBERGER, J. A. *J. appl. Phys.* **28**, 40 (1957)
105. TWEET, A. G., and GALLAGHER, C. J. *Phys. Rev.* **103**, 828 (1956)
106. TYLER, W. W. *J. Phys. Chem. Solids* **8**, 59 (1959)
107. WOLFSTIRN, K. B., and FULLER, C. S. *J. Phys. Chem. Solids* **7**, 141 (1958)
108. VAN DER MAESEN, F., and BRENKMAN, J. A. *Philips Res. Rep* **9**, 225 (1954)
109. WERTHEIM, G. K. *Phys. Rev.* **115**, 37 (1959)
110. TWEET, A. G. *Phys. Rev.* **106**, 221 (1957)
111. PENNING, P. *Philips Res. Rep.* **13**, 17 (1958)
112. WOODBURY, H. H., and TYLER, W. W. *Phys. Rev.* **102**, 647 (1956); **105**, 84 (1957)
113. BURTON, J. A., HULL, G. W., MORIN, F. J., and SEVERIENS, J. C. *J. phys. Chem.* **57**, 853 (1953)
114. TYLER, W. W., NEWMAN, R., and WOODBURY, H. H. *Phys. Rev.* **98**, 461 (1955)
115. PENNING, P. *Phys. Rev.* **110**, 586 (1958)
116. LETAW, H., PORTNOY, W. M., and SLIFKIN, L. *Phys. Rev.* **102**, 636 (1956)
117. TEUTONICO, L. J., GRANATO, A., and TRUELL, R. *Phys. Rev.* **103**, 832 (1956)
118. BONTINCK, W., and AMELINCKX, S. *Phil. Mag.* **2**, 94 (1957)

EFFECT OF PRESSURE ON THE PROPERTIES OF GERMANIUM AND SILICON

W. PAUL, M.A., Ph.D.
Associate Professor of Applied Physics,
Division of Engineering and Applied Physics,
Harvard University, Cambridge, Mass., U.S.A.

and

H. BROOKS, A.B., Ph.D.
Dean of Engineering and Applied Physics,
Harvard University, Cambridge, Mass., U.S.A.

MS. received July 1962

EFFECT OF PRESSURE ON THE PROPERTIES OF GERMANIUM AND SILICON

1. INTRODUCTION

The purpose of this article is to review theoretical and experimental work on the effect of small changes in lattice constant on the electronic band structure of simple semiconductors. This examination will be concerned mostly with the effect of hydrostatic pressure on the band structure of the Group IV semiconductors, germanium and silicon, and, to a certain extent, some related intermetallic compounds such as indium antimonide. It will appear that there is a certain correlation between the properties of the covalent germanium and silicon and those of the partly ionic compounds. Whether this correlation extends beyond the III–V compounds to II–VI compounds such as zinc sulphide is not yet known. The measurements to be reviewed give us some idea of the types of variation in physical properties that can occur and of the order of magnitude of the changes in electronic band structure.

In this first section the experimental measurements that have been made will be discussed. This will be followed by a brief review of the properties of germanium, silicon, and the intermetallics at atmospheric pressure, with particular attention to the band structures of these materials. Theoretical and experimental methods of determining the band structure near the extrema of allowed energy values and at particular positions in the Brillouin zone away from the extrema will be reviewed. The experiments appropriate to determine the variation in the band structure with pressure will then become evident and some comparison of the relative merits of the different approaches will be made. We shall also discuss in this section the purely theoretical approach to the calculation of the effect of volume changes on the band structure.

In the second section, we shall discuss briefly the apparatus and techniques used in the different types of experiment.

The third section will be concerned with a report of the results of electrical transport measurements on germanium. The experiments of earlier workers and of the present authors will be reviewed and a theory of the behaviour of germanium discussed in detail. This theory will necessitate a pheno-menological approach to the scattering of electrons between states of different symmetry in the conduction band of germanium. The fit of this theory to experimental results obtained by Nathan will then be reported. The postulates of this theory are further verified by measurements of magnetoconductance in germanium to 20,000 $\mathrm{kg\,cm^{-2}}$ pressure carried out by Howard, which demand the above-mentioned interband scattering, and also, incidentally, explain the effect of impurity scattering on the galvanomagnetic properties in a very clear way. Howard's work supersedes and justifies earlier results of Benedek, Paul, and Brooks on the Hall effect and magnetoresistance, determined to pressures up to $10,000 \text{ kg cm}^{-2}$.

In the fourth section, work on the indirect and direct optical energy gaps in germanium will be reported.

In the fifth section, results on the dielectric constant and refractive index variations with pressure will be presented. These variations depend on the changes of all of the energy levels in the conduction and valence bands with change of volume and so can be compared only indirectly with other measurements of the changes of band structure. Several salient features of this variation will, however, emerge, primary among them being the large explicit temperature dependence of the dielectric constant. The existence of this large explicit dependence is not unexpected in view of the existence of explicit temperature dependences of the effective masses and energy gaps in semiconductors.

In the sixth section, results parallel to the above on the conduction properties, optical gaps, and dielectric constants of silicon will be given.

The seventh section will discuss the early work of Long and of Keyes on indium antimonide and more recent investigations of other of the inter-metallic compounds. Since the effect of pressure on the properties of the intermetallic compounds, and the correlation of these effects with similar measurements on the Group IV semiconductors, have been recently reviewed by one of the authors,[141] the discussion here will cover only the more important areas, and will not go into the intricacies of explanation of the individual properties of the different intermetallics. However, the similarity of the pressure effects on the Group IV and Group III–V semi-conductors clearly invites intensive investigation of the latter and of semiconductors forming similar families.

In the eighth section, the dependence on volume and on temperature of energy gaps, dielectric constants, and effective masses will be reported. Comparison of these variations clearly demonstrates the existence of explicit changes with temperature which are frequently an order of magnitude larger than the effects which would exist by reason of thermal expansion alone. The relative magnitudes of the implicit and explicit effects are significant even in approximate theories.

In the ninth section, the work carried out at Harvard on the variation of the ionization energy of certain impurities in germanium and silicon will be discussed.

In the final section, application of our knowledge of the changes in band structure and transport properties in the Group IV and Group III–V semiconductors to the study of the hot electron effect and of the tunnelling phenomenon will be very briefly discussed. Also, research projects

suggested by the previous work will be discussed and their potential usefulness evaluated. The extent to which parallel measurements on other
semiconductors are likely to provide information for the evaluation of their
band structure and for the separation of implicit and explicit effects of
temperature on the band structure and on the physical properties will be
considered.

The Appendix (page 236) lists the main symbols used in the text.

1.1. HISTORY OF PRESSURE MEASUREMENTS ON SEMICONDUCTORS, PARTICULARLY GERMANIUM AND SILICON

The early measurements of the effect of pressure on the properties of
semiconductors are reviewed in the paper by Paul and Brooks.[1] One of
the earliest determinations was that of Bridgman on tellurium,[2] which was
later interpreted by Bardeen.[3] The variation with pressure of the energy
gap in tellurium was deduced from the variation in the resistivity of a
nearly intrinsic sample. There has been more recent work on tellurium
and on selenium and related materials, principally by the group at the
University of Pennsylvania and by one or two groups in the U.S.S.R.[4]
However, this group of materials, which are of considerable practical and
theoretical importance and which show aspects of pressure behaviour not
found in the Group IV and III–V semiconductors, will not be discussed
in detail here. It is, however, felt by the authors that some of the phenomena examined in germanium can be similarly investigated with profit in
materials like tellurium. If we exclude occasional investigations of ionic
semiconductors and F-centre phenomena, the only other system extensively
investigated under pressure is that to be described here. The earliest work
on germanium was concerned mostly with the determination of the pressure
coefficient of the indirect energy gap; sometimes from measurement of
impure material, occasionally by the measurement of intrinsic material, and
in one instance by the measurement of the variation of the current through
a P–N junction having the ideal characteristic. These early measurements
gave values for the energy gap change with pressure for germanium that
were internally consistent within the experimental error of the measurements, and the more recent work in a number of laboratories has not upset
the initial findings. Apart from the work of Bridgman, however, the early
measurements were not made at pressures in excess of 10,000 kg cm^{-2}; it
so happens that the behaviour in germanium that is significant, and which
indicates the path that research should follow in order to gain information
about the conduction band structure occurs at pressures greater than 15,000
kg cm^{-2}. Bridgman[5] found a rapid increase in the resistivity of impure N-type
germanium between 15 and 30,000 kg cm^{-2}; when this determination was
extended to pressures of the order of 100,000 kg cm^{-2}—that were only partially hydrostatic—he found variations in the resistivity that showed extremely large effects of hysteresis, but nevertheless demonstrated the existence of a

maximum in the resistivity at about 50,000 kg cm^{-2}. The work of Bridgman to 30,000 kg cm^{-2} was repeated and extended by Paul and Brooks[1] on rather more pure material, and these authors deduced the change in an 'effective' energy gap with pressure, up to 30,000 kg cm^{-2}, as well as a change in the mobility of electrons to this pressure. Their interpretation required the existence in germanium of subsidiary minima in the conduction band structure that became important at pressures in excess of 15,000 kg cm^{-2}. The variation in mobility and in energy gap found experimentally was fitted in quite satisfactory fashion on the basis of a purely phenomenological treatment. The rationalization for the existence of other types of energy band minima in the conduction band structure of germanium came partly from experimental work on the germanium–silicon alloys done by Johnson and Christian[6] at R.C.A. and partly as a result of theoretical work on the germanium band structure carried out by Herman[7] and his collaborators. The most direct demonstration of the validity of the model of Paul and Brooks required the determination of the variation of mobility in N-type germanium with pressure, independent of any variations in the carrier densities. This demonstration was undertaken by Smith[30] in experiments on the variation of the drift mobilities of electrons and holes in germanium with pressure. Smith's measurements bore out exactly the mobility variation used by Paul and Brooks. Independently, similar measurements were made by Landwehr[8] at lower pressures. The model of Paul and Brooks could also be verified through a detailed consideration of the variation in mobility with pressure in a number of samples of germanium, where the measurements were done at several temperatures. These measurements have been carried out by Nathan and are reported elsewhere.[9] However, we shall establish the phenomenological theory and, within certain experimental errors, obtain an energy and a pressure coefficient for the higher energy minima in germanium. Confirmatory measurements require the variation of the Hall effect and galvanomagnetic coefficients in N-type samples of germanium to pressures up to 30,000 kg cm^{-2}. By this pressure enough electrons have changed over from one type of minimum to a second type of minimum in the conduction band so that the magnetoconductance or magnetoresistance measurements can be interpreted to give the symmetry of the second set of minima. This is rather a formidable problem from the experimental point of view. The first and easiest part of it was carried out by Benedek et al.[10] in measurements up to 10,000 kg cm^{-2}. These measurements were interpreted to give the variation with pressure of the curvature of the band edges in germanium but were insufficient to give information about the behaviour of electrons in conduction band minima other than the lowest (111) minima, because, by the maximum pressure reached, only a very small percentage of carriers had changed their position in the conduction band structure. Later measurements by Howard[11] extended the measurement of magnetoconductivity in N-type germanium samples to pressures of 20,000 $kg\,cm^{-2}$. Again, the limitation on the maximum pressure was an experimental one. Although these measurements have successfully verified many of the postulates of the two-band model first suggested by Paul and Brooks, they too are inadequate in establishing the symmetry type of the upper minima, and for the same reason as before. It happens that the symmetry of the states in the upper minima is probably quite well established already, through extrapolation from measurements on germanium–silicon alloys and from a reasonable interpretation of all of the theoretical work on the band structure of germanium. However, from the point of view of experimental tidiness, it is advisable that this symmetry be checked directly at very high pressures. The two-band theory of conduction at high pressures has been further tested in an exploratory experiment carried out by Bridgman and Paul[12] on an alloy of germanium and silicon. This will also be reported briefly in sub-section 3.6.

In parallel with these measurements of the conduction properties of germanium has been a programme of measurement on the indirect and direct optical energy gaps in this material. This has been carried out in a number of laboratories. The Harvard group measured both gaps at pressures up to 8,000 $kg\,cm^{-2}$. Measurements up to 1,000 $kg\,cm^{-2}$ have been carried out by Fan et al.[13] and by Neuringer,[14] while measurements in an extended pressure range, up to 200,000 $kg\,cm^{-2}$, have been reported by Drickamer and his collaborators.[15] Although the accuracy of these last measurements may be limited because of the non-hydrostatic nature of the applied pressure, they are nevertheless vital in mapping out the gross behaviour of the energy band minima. Drickamer's results will be discussed in Section 7.

The optical pressure measurements have confirmed, in general, the behaviour deduced from the electrical measurements. In addition the variation with pressure of the direct energy gap has been found; from the nature of the process it is not possible to find this variation from measurements of electrical conductivity. Measurements have also been made of the change in the infra-red refractive index in germanium and these results can be correlated with measurements on the r.f. dielectric constant.

The first pressure measurements on intrinsic silicon were carried out at Harvard by Paul and Pearson[16] and were reported in 1955. These results showed that the energy gap in silicon decreased with pressure, in contra-distinction to the behaviour in germanium. This variation was confirmed by optical measurements of Paul and Warschauer[17] and later by Neuringer,[14] although measurements at Purdue University[13] seemed to give a variation with the opposite sign. More careful determinations of the optical gap variation and an indirect determination by Nathan and Paul[18] on this material have confirmed the view that the variation in the energy gap of silicon, which is dependent on the behaviour of the (100) conduction band minima in this material, is a decrease at a small rate.

The earliest measurements on Group III–V intermetallics were carried out by Long[19] and by Keyes[19] and were reported in 1955. It soon appeared that the variation with pressure in the separation of the (000) conduction band minimum and the (000) valence band maximum in this material was almost identical with the variation of the separation of the same minima in germanium. Since then there have been many determinations of the effect of pressure on the optical and electrical energy gaps of indium antimonide and other intermetallic semiconductors. Most of these results suggest that the motion under pressure of a particular type of conduction band minimum relative to the valence band is almost independent of the material and depends only on the symmetry type of the minimum. The present experimental and theoretical situation in the intermetallic compounds has recently been reviewed by one of the authors, and the question of the correlation of pressure coefficients of the different minima critically examined. The main results of this criticism will be discussed in detail in Section 7.

Besides all this work, which has been directed mainly at the shifts with pressure in the conduction band levels relative to the valence band, there has been some effort to determine the changes in the ionization energy of different sorts of impurity inserted into the germanium and silicon lattices. Holland[20] determined the variation in the ionization energy of donor and acceptor impurities in the lattice of silicon, and has been able to correlate these variations, in qualitative fashion, with changes with pressure in the average effective mass and dielectric constant found from other experiments. He has, further, conducted an extensive investigation of the four impurity levels produced by substitution of gold in germanium and has found very striking changes in the ionization energy of most of these levels with pressure. Nathan[21] has also completed a study of the changes in the ionization energy of the gold-produced levels in silicon. At the present time, there is little theoretical understanding of the properties of these so-called deep-lying impurity levels, and there is in consequence only speculation regarding their pressure dependence.

1.2. Band Structures and Properties of Germanium and Silicon, and Their Pressure Dependence

In this section we shall review briefly the properties of the band structures of germanium, silicon, and the intermetallic compounds at atmospheric pressure. Current notions of the band structure of germanium and silicon are shown in Figures 1 and 2. There are several salient features of these band structures which also appear in the intermetallic compounds. The conduction band structure of germanium exhibits three types of minima: (1) Four minima in equivalent (111) directions, lying lowest of the three;

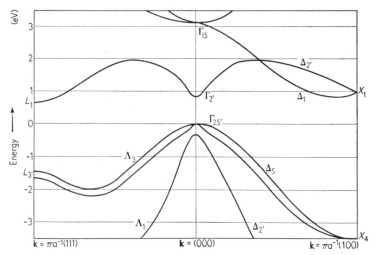

Figure 1. *Energy band structure of germanium. The abscissae are the wave vectors in the (111) and (100) directions. Energy is plotted as ordinate. The labelling of states follows the notation of Bouchaert, Smoluchowski, and Wigner. The zero of energy is chosen at the valence band maximum at $\Gamma_{25'}$. The approximate energy separations at $300°\ K$ are: $\Gamma_{25'} - L_1$: $0·65\ eV$; $\Gamma_{25'} - \Delta_1$ (min): $0·80 - 0·85\ eV$; $\Gamma_{25'} - \Gamma_{2'}$: $0·80\ eV$; $\Gamma_{25'} - \Gamma_{15}$: $3·1\ eV$; $L_1 - L_{3'}$: $2·1\ eV$; $X_1 - X_4$: $4·5\ eV$*

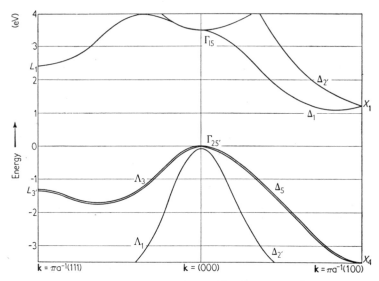

Figure 2. *Energy band structure of silicon. The abscissae are the wave vectors in the (111) and (100) directions. Energy is plotted as ordinate. The labelling of states follows the notation of Bouchaert, Smoluchowski, and Wigner. The zero of energy is chosen at the valence band maximum at $\Gamma_{25'}$. The approximate energy separations at $300°\ K$ are $\Gamma_{25'} - \Delta_1$ (min): $1·1\ eV$; $\Gamma_{25'} - \Gamma_{15}$: $3·5\ eV$; $L_1 - L_{3'}$: $3·7\ eV$; $X_1 - X_4$: $4·5\ eV$*

143

(2) Six minima in equivalent (100) directions, lying nearly $0\cdot2$ eV higher than the (111) minima;

(3) A minimum at the centre of the Brillouin zone lying about $0\cdot15$ eV above the (111) conduction band minimum at room temperature and atmospheric pressure.

These three minima have different symmetries, only the structure of the conduction band close to the minima is necessarily accurate, and the other bands that are exhibited in the Figure are estimated on the basis of an approximate theory and are not supposed to have much quantitative significance. It will be observed, however, that there exists at the centre of the Brillouin zone a second minimum of Γ_{15} symmetry lying quite a bit higher than the lowest band of $\Gamma_{2'}$ symmetry. The valence band of germanium is characterized by a partially degenerate structure. The two uppermost valence bands are degenerate at the origin of the Brillouin zone while the third band is split off by $0\cdot28$ eV through spin–orbit interaction. Again only the structure close to the centre of the Brillouin zone has been verified by experiments and the variation in the energy versus crystal momentum curves away from the origin is somewhat speculative. The valence band structure of silicon is similar to that of germanium except that the spin–orbit splitting is only about $0\cdot05$ eV. The conduction band structure is such that the lowest conduction band minimum is the one lying in the (100) direction, and the other minima in the (111) direction and at the centre of the Brillouin zone lie at very much higher energies. The valence band structures of the Group III–V compounds resemble those of germanium and silicon except that there may be some fine detail in the structure of the maximum close to $\mathbf{k} = 0$ brought about by removal of degeneracy due to the absence of inversion symmetry in the lattice. This fine structure is of no significance for most experiments, or for any of the phenomena discussed in the present review. Unlike the valence band, the conduction band structure in the intermetallic compounds shows more variation than in germanium and silicon, although it follows certain systematic trends with composition. Thus, for example, the (000) conduction band minimum appears to be lowest for the compounds with high average atomic number while the (100) minima appear to be lowest for compounds with lower average atomic number. Though these systematic trends cannot yet be predicted quantitatively with precision, the qualitative ideas are sufficient to guide pressure experiments when the constancy of the pressure behaviour of the minima of a given type for different compounds is taken into account.

For comprehensive reviews of the theoretical and experimental determination of semiconductor band structure, the reader is referred to the publications of Herman[7] and of Lax.[22] The most recent discussions of the theory are due to Herman[23] and to Phillips.[24] We shall discuss these results briefly to the extent that they have a bearing on the determination of the variations of band structure with pressure.

Actually there has been no published attempt at quantitative calculation of semiconductor band structure as a function of lattice constant, although an approximate theory has been given by Bassani.[25]

An approximate expression for the energy of a state at a symmetrical point in **k**-space is:

$$\langle E \rangle = E_k + V_{000} + \sum_n [E_k + V_{000} - E_n] |(\phi_\alpha, \phi_\alpha^n)|^2 \qquad \ldots (1)$$

Here ϕ_α represents a symmetry combination of plane waves with wave vectors of the reciprocal lattice. The ϕ_α^n represent core states. E_k is the kinetic energy corresponding to the reciprocal lattice vector in the plane wave combination, and V_{000} is the mean value of the potential energy of an electron in the crystal measured relative to an electron at infinity. The quantity $(\phi_\alpha, \phi_\alpha^n)$ is an orthogonality coefficient computed with ϕ_α normalized to the unit cell and ϕ_α^n is also normalized. E_n is the energy of a core state, and the summation is taken over all core states. The quantity in brackets is always positive and represents the effective repulsive energy between the core and a valence electron resulting from the requirement of orthogonality. Because of this orthogonality requirement, as discussed by Phillips and Kleinman,[26] the effective potential seen by a valence electron is very small. Thus the energy levels are not too far altered from the free electron values except that there is a constant shift due to the crystal potential, and free electron degeneracies are removed. Herman[23] has considered the effects of a constant shift in the quantity E_n on the energy levels in germanium. The resulting change in the quantity in brackets is referred to as the 'core shift'. Herman shows that the influence of the 'core shift' on the energies corresponding to symmetry points in the Brillouin zone depends on the symmetry of the corresponding wave function ϕ_α. States which are s-like show a much greater shift than states which are p-like about a given atom in the crystal. In consequence the $\Gamma_{2'}$ state changes much more rapidly with 'core shift' than does $\Gamma_{25'}$, and L_1 is intermediate. An estimate of the actual values of the shifts $\Delta E / |\Delta E_c|$ computed for germanium is as follows

$$
\begin{array}{llll}
\Gamma_{25'} & 0\cdot011 & L_1 & 0\cdot014 \\
\Gamma_{2'} & 0\cdot045 & \Delta_1 & 0\cdot0075
\end{array}
\qquad \ldots (2)
$$

If it were assumed that a negative shift ΔE_c corresponded to a decrease in lattice constant, then the differences between the four levels in formula (2) have a relative rate of shift in the same order as the pressure shifts of the corresponding differences. It would be tempting to relate the pressure shifts directly to the core shifts, but a closer examination shows that this is a gross oversimplification.

If we examine how the various terms in equation (1) change with lattice constant, we note that E_k, which is positive. varies as a^{-2}, and V_{000}, which is negative and larger in magnitude than E_k, varies as a^{-3}. Thus the first two terms of equation (1) become more negative with increasing pressure, and the quantity in brackets decreases. However, the coefficients $|(\phi_\alpha, \phi_\alpha^n)|^2$ are inherently positive and tend to increase in magnitude as the lattice constant decreases. For the s-like functions they increase as a^{-3}. Since the quantity in brackets which multiplies the orthogonality coefficient is large and positive, the net effect is an upward shift of the energy. Thus we have two main contributions to the energy shift with pressure. One is a negative contribution which is relatively insensitive to the symmetry of the level being considered, and the other is positive and relatively greater for s-like than for p-like levels. In fact, it is fairly easy to see that the positive contribution to the pressure shift will be qualitatively, though not quantitatively, like the 'core shifts' of Herman, since the orthogonality co-efficients are much larger for s-like than for p-like states. From this analysis we should expect to find that the relative shifts of pairs of levels with pressure would behave qualitatively like the core shifts, but that the absolute shifts would bear no relation to core shifts and could be of either sign. While equation (1) is based essentially on a single OPW approxi-mation, the matrix elements between different orthogonalized plane waves are relatively insensitive to core shift and to lattice constant, so that we should expect the qualitative relations deduced from equation (1) to hold even for diagonalization of the secular equation.

The changes of orthogonality coefficient with lattice constant occur because the core size is constant whereas the cell size decreases, so that the valence electron is forced by the exclusion principle to stay out of a larger fraction of the cell volume. To the extent that the contribution to the core shift comes predominantly from one core state, the repulsive part of the pressure shift will be in the same relative proportion for different states as the core shift. Thus, overall, the pressure shifts will tend to look like the core shifts but with a symmetry-independent negative contri-bution arising from the first terms of equation (1). When experimental absolute pressure shifts are computed with the aid of deformation poten-tials obtained from mobility measurements, this appears to be exactly what is observed.

The energy gap of semiconductors can be found experimentally from the variation of the intrinsic resistivity with temperature. If the variation of energy gap with temperature is assumed to be linear in the range of measurement, and the electron and hole masses and the temperature variation of the mobilities are known, the zero temperature gap and its temperature coefficient can be determined. The parallel experiment under pressure would be to redetermine the variation of the logarithm of the resistivity versus $1/T$ at an elevated pressure and to calculate from a change in slope of the resultant graph a change in the energy gap. How-ever, this is really unnecessary, and a determination of the variation with pressure of an intrinsic sample under carefully controlled temperature conditions, combined with a separate determination of the variation with pressure of the mobility of electrons and holes, can be simply interpreted to yield the pressure coefficient. It is necessary in this determination that the material be behaving entirely like an intrinsic semiconductor sample; however, if subsidiary measurements are made, it is easy to apply a correction for the residual density of impurity derived electrons. This sort of approach has been extensively used in the experiments to be described. Apart from the work of Hall, Bardeen, and Pearson,[27] it was the approach of all of the early work.

The second conventional method of determining the energy gap of semiconductor materials is to determine the variation with frequency of the optical absorption or the photoconductive response. The deduction of an energy gap from a photoconductive response spectrum, in principle, involves more parameters than a similar deduction from an absorption edge experiment. This is simply because both the effect of the absorption of radiation to produce primary carriers and the decay of the extra carriers in the sample have to be taken into account. Under appropriate conditions of low illumination and proper geometry, the experiments on photoconductive response can be interpreted confidently to give the same sort of information as the absorption spectrum. They are especially useful for measurements at small absorption coefficients as in this range they are much more sensitive than the direct measurement of absorption. The determination of the pressure variation of optical energy gaps through the measurement of the photoconductivity has not to our knowledge been made, although there is no experimental bar to the performance of such an experiment, and indeed in many ways it would be a much simpler experiment to perform than that of the absorption coefficient. It turned out in most of the experiments to be described that the performance of the absorption edge experiment was of no greater difficulty than that of the photoconductive response, and no additional measurement of the photoconductivity was felt to be necessary. The interpretation of an optical absorption spectrum to give an energy gap is a somewhat arbitrary procedure unless some analytical expression exists connecting the absorption coefficient with the valence and conduction band structure and the matrix elements for optical transitions. An approximate result can, however, be obtained by extrapolating experimental results to zero absorption coefficient, but this introduces inaccuracies due to the effects of phonon absorption and emission and exciton formation. Without detailed knowledge of the band structure and matrix elements, the *pressure coefficient* of the energy gap can still be found with considerable accuracy, since any error committed in the estimation of the absolute energy gap tends to be committed equally at all of the pressures of measurement. Nevertheless, it is quite clearly possible to make severe errors in the determination of

147

pressure coefficients of optical energy gaps where care is not taken to evaluate the effects of changes in matrix elements or phonon interactions on the functional dependence of the absorption coefficient on photon energy. The determination of the pressure coefficients of the elements of the band structure from optical experiments is a very strong tool and is bound to become stronger with increased knowledge of the theoretical dependence of the absorption coefficients on the band structures.

Very accurate determinations of optical energy gaps have also been made using a combination of high resolution optical spectroscopy and high magnetic fields. Such results have been reported by the groups at N.R.L. and Lincoln Laboratory under Dr. Burstein and Dr. Lax; they are described in considerable detail in the review by Lax. For our purposes, we note simply that it is, in principle, possible to extend these so-called magneto-band experiments to conditions of high pressures, and that under these conditions extremely accurate determinations of the variation of energy gaps and of effective masses with pressure could be found.

Reference should be made at this point to the ingenious method of determining the variation of the energy gap of semiconductors used by Hall, Bardeen, and Pearson. These authors measured the pressure variation of the slope of the current–voltage relation for a P–N junction near zero applied voltage. Since this slope depends in exponential fashion on the energy gap, it is in principle possible to find a very close approximation to its pressure dependence. Since the method also involves an estimation of the pressure coefficient of the mobility of the electrons and holes on either side of the P–N junction and also of the dependence on pressure of the lifetimes, the final result is somewhat uncertain. However, these variations are often small compared with the effect of the change in energy gap; Hall, Bardeen, and Pearson made no corrections of this kind, yet their pressure coefficient is very close to the accepted value.

The variation of the mobility could be estimated from independent experiments on samples of impure N- and P-type materials, and some idea of the variation in lifetime could be obtained from pressure experiments specifically designed to measure this quantity. If the variation in the lifetime in such experiments is found to be small, then it might be a reasonable extrapolation to suppose that it is also small in the P–N junction experiment. Alternatively the variation with pressure of the lifetime in the actual P–N junction used could be found and the energy gap determined. If such variations of lifetime are found to be large, this would seriously prejudice the extraction of the pressure coefficient of the energy gap from the variation of the P–N junction current with voltage as a function of pressure.

The method would seem, in principle, to be particularly appropriate for materials that are sufficiently impure so that pressure experiments in the intrinsic range of their behaviour are difficult. In practice, another difficulty appears. In the Harvard Laboratory this seemed at one time to be the best method to try to extend the determination of the pressure dependence of the energy gap in silicon to pressures as high as 30,000 kg cm^{-2}.† Investigations by Smith and others on the possibility of the use of measurements on P–N junctions showed that, for many of the P–N junctions normally available, not only is the pressure coefficient quite different from that found from direct determinations of the energy gap as a function of pressure, but also the absolute magnitude of the energy gap determined from the $\mathcal{J}$–V characteristic of the junction can be quite different from the absolute value of the energy gap determined otherwise. It may be that these discrepancies result from the existence in the P–N junction layer of impurities yielding deep lying energy levels. Whether or not this is so, it would appear to be a prerequisite for determination of the variation of the energy gap of any semiconductor by the P–N junction method that the theoretical $\mathcal{J}$–V characteristic be followed. If this condition is not met, we feel that it is extremely dangerous to try to interpret a pressure experiment to give the pressure dependence of the energy gap. Hall, Bardeen, and Pearson appeared to go to some trouble in their original determination to find a P–N junction that showed the theoretical current–voltage characteristic.

So far we have confined ourselves to the discussion of the determination of the thermal and optical energy gaps in semiconductors. It is also of interest to know the curvature of the energy versus crystal momentum curves at the extrema of the conduction and valence bands. The average effective mass that occurs in different experiments can be redetermined as a function of pressure. For example, the ratio of the principal effective masses for the (111) and (100) minima in germanium and silicon, respectively, can be found from magnetoresistance or magnetoconductivity experiments. The variation in this ratio with pressure can be just as simply determined from the appropriate galvanomagnetic experiment under high pressure conditions.

The most accurate method of finding the effective mass tensor in semiconductor materials employs cyclotron resonance. Unfortunately, the number of materials in which cyclotron resonance can be observed, and the temperature range over which such experiments are feasible, is very limited. It has not been possible—nor indeed, has it been felt to be necessary —to try to repeat the classical cyclotron resonance measurements as a function of pressure. The effect of pressure on the curvature of the energy bands is quite small and is almost within the error of the determination of the effective mass from cyclotron resonance experiments. Expressions containing different combinations of the elements of the effective mass tensor enter into the mobility, free carrier absorption coefficient, dia-

† The recent availability of very pure silicon single crystals implies that this determination can now be made straightforwardly from a resistivity experiment versus pressure at an accessible temperature.

magnetic susceptibility, band-to-band absorption coefficient, and so on. In principle, the variation with pressure of the effective mass components can be found from a repetition of these experiments as a function of pressure. In practice, it is nearly always difficult to find the variation of effective mass with pressure in a situation where the carrier scattering time can also vary with the pressure. Only in a few experiments, such as the determination of the absorption coefficient due to free carriers and in the diamagnetic susceptibility, does the effective mass occur independent of the scattering time tensor. The variation of the electrical susceptibility of the free carriers, as determined from the reflectivity of polished samples, is probably one of the more precise methods of obtaining the effective mass variation. To date, however, the determination as a function of pressure has not been reported, although a number of experimenters have performed this experiment as a function of temperature.

2. APPARATUS AND TECHNIQUES

Since much of the apparatus used in the high pressure experiments has already been described in the literature, it will be discussed only briefly here. Special features of the apparatus used by other institutions will be mentioned later where necessary.

Two different designs of pressure-producing apparatus were used. Both were developed by Bridgman.[28] The first (see Figure 3) is capable of reaching hydrostatic pressures of 30,000 kgcm^{-2} in an enclosure of some $0\cdot5$ in. diameter and 3 in. length. The temperature can be varied and controlled to less than $0\cdot1°$C variation by immersing the entire apparatus in an oil bath;[1] in practice the temperature range was restricted to between room temperature and 100°C. Seven electrical terminals can be inserted into the pressure vessel.[28] The pressure is measured using a manganin wire gauge calibrated against the freezing point of mercury and a phase transition in bismuth.† This apparatus has been described by Bridgman in the supplement to his book, as well as in a special paper;[29] its use in semiconductor work has been referred to by Paul and Brooks,[1] and further described by Smith.[30] The calibration and use of manganin wire gauges have also been adequately described before.[29-31] In our work this apparatus has been used for the measurement of the variation of resistivity[1] and drift mobility,[30] and for the investigation of hot-electron tunnelling phenomena.

Briefly, the operation of this apparatus is as follows. The high pressure is developed in the vessel A, which has a $0\cdot5$ in. diameter central hole, and is coned at a small angle on its outside. Fitting over this vessel is a set of

† In all of the Harvard work, which is the majority of that to be reported, it has been assumed that the freezing pressure of mercury at 0°C is 7,640 kgcm^{-2} and the transition pressure from bismuth-I to bismuth-II at 30°C is 25,420 kgcm^{-2}. These are Bridgman's determinations, and are probably correct to 1 per cent.

3 rings B, coned to match the outside of the vessel A. As a $0 \cdot 5$ in. diameter carboloy piston C is forced into the $0 \cdot 5$ in. hole by the $3 \cdot 5$ in. diameter piston assembly D, the vessel A is itself forced into the rings B by the 6 in. diameter piston assembly E. The forces are balanced so that the $0 \cdot 5$ in. diameter hole remains at a constant diameter under the opposing tendencies of the two piston assemblies. The manganin gauge and sample are mounted on the plug which has suitably insulated electrical terminals in it.

The second type of apparatus has also been described by Bridgman.[28] Modifications of it that allow fluid under high pressure to be conducted via

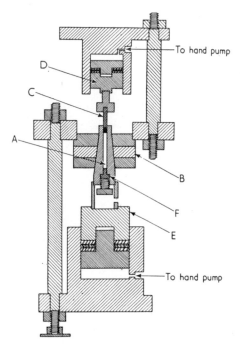

Figure 4. *High pressure apparatus for obtaining*
30,000 kg cm^{-2}

flexible stainless steel tubing to a final vessel containing the experimental samples have been described recently;[31] a schematic drawing of a typical installation is shown in Figure 4. For semiconductor work this modification is important in that it is often imperative that the temperature be very closely controlled; it is much easier to control the temperature of the final pressure vessel, which is isolated except for the slim stainless steel tubing, than the entire pressure assembly. The use of this tubing also permits the location of the pressure vessel in any special relation to subsidiary apparatus such as magnets, cryostats, spectrometers, and the like.

Such apparatus has been used, with liquid and gaseous pressure transmitters, at temperatures between 45° and 600° K. There is no low temperature limit, except that set by the freezing of the transmitting fluid. The limitations at high temperature are the weakening of the pressure cylinder, and the difficulty of finding easily manageable liquids for the temperature bath.

The pressure is again measured using a manganin wire gauge.

The second type of apparatus has been used with a gas as transmitting fluid, to pressures of the order of 10,000 kg cm^{-2} at temperatures down to 45° K;[20] with a liquid pressure transmitter, to pressures of 8,000 kg cm^{-2} at room temperature where the final pressure vessel had sapphire windows and was used in measurements of optical absorption coefficient;[32] with a liquid pressure transmitter, to pressures of 20,000 kg cm^{-2} at temperatures

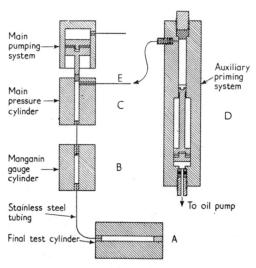

Figure 4. *High pressure apparatus for obtaining 20,000 kg cm^{-2}*

up to 100° C; and with a liquid pressure transmitter, to pressures of 20,000 kg cm^{-2} at temperatures close to room temperature, where the final pressure vessel was made of hardened beryllium copper, and was used in measurements of the galvanomagnetic properties[33].

In this apparatus the general procedure is as follows. The final pressure vessel A is designed to suit the particular experiment being performed. If it is one that measures electrical resistivity or galvanomagnetic properties, then sealing plugs with electrical terminals are required. If it is one that measures optical properties, special window arrangements are necessary. The particular techniques associated with specific measurements in various designs of final vessel have been described fully,[20, 21, 30, 33] and need not be elaborated on again here. The final pressure vessel may be connected by an intermediate cylinder B, containing a manganin gauge, to the pressure producing cylinder C. On occasion, B can be omitted and the gauge inserted elsewhere. Its presence is a convenience in that it separates the delicate gauge from other parts of the apparatus that have to be dismantled frequently, but it can also be a nuisance in that two additional pressure seals are required. The high pressure in cylinder C is developed by the super-structure which contains a $3 \cdot 5$ in. diameter piston assembly, narrowing down to a $0 \cdot 5$ in. diameter piston entering C. Usually a priming pressure of 2,000 kg cm^{-2} is developed in A, B, and C by subsidiary intensifiers D which pump fluid through a by-pass hole E into cylinder C. If liquid pressure transmitters are being used, one stage of intensification is adequate, while if gases are being employed, a rather greater volume in the subsidiary cylinders is necessary. Again, the important details of the seals for piston assemblies and plugs have been described elsewhere.[20, 21, 30, 33, 34]

3. CONDUCTION MEASUREMENTS ON GERMANIUM

3.1. INTRODUCTION

Historically, the relative energy and the pressure coefficients of the energy of the states corresponding to the (111) and (100) minima in germanium were extracted from data on the changes of resistivity and mobility, together with a variety of other data on effective masses, impurity ionization energies, and parameters of silicon–germanium alloys. Instead of trying to recon-struct the laborious process of induction used in the years since the beginning of the experiments, we shall instead start by assigning *approximately* correct energies and pressure coefficients to the different conduction band minima, deduce the general form of the electrical, optical, and other properties to be expected, and then compare these expectations with experimental results. The overall agreement of prediction and experiment will corroborate our tentative assignments of band structure and pressure coefficients and allow us to obtain from experiment fairly exact values of many of the parameters.

The location on an energy–momentum diagram of the three types of conduction band minima in germanium has been discussed in Section 1 and is indicated in Figure 1. The change in position of these three minima with pressure is shown in Figure 5. Relative to the valence band maximum, the (111) minima move up at a rate of 5×10^{-6} eV cm^2 kg^{-1}. The (000) minimum moves up faster, at a rate of $1 \cdot 3 \times 10^{-5}$ eV cm^2 kg^{-1}. The (100) minima remain relatively static or move down at a rate less than 2×10^{-6} eV cm^2 kg^{-1}.

The absolute changes in energy of conduction and valence band states, i.e. the deformation potentials, are not found from hydrostatic pressure experiments alone and will not be further considered in this review. (These can, however, be separated out. See, for example, Brooks,[35] Herring and

Vogt,[35] and the review by Keyes[36].) Changes in the spin–orbit splitting of the valence bands are taken to be negligible.[37]

The ionization energies of the Group V donor and Group III acceptor impurities change very slowly with pressure, at approximately 10^{-8} eV cm^2 kg^{-1}.[20] Changes in the ionization energies of any impurities other than the hydrogenic kind, which can be large,[20] do not affect conduction properties of the samples discussed in this section.

The fractional changes in the effective masses,[20, 38] dielectric constants,[39] elastic coefficients,[40] and the density[41] are all of the order of 10^{-6} cm^2 kg^{-1}. The pressure coefficients required are listed in Table 1.

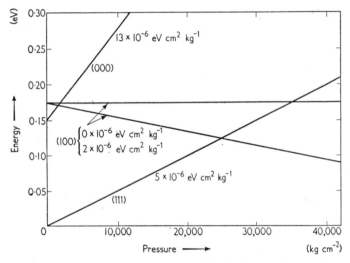

Figure 5. *Displacement with pressure of the three conduction band minima in germanium, relative to an (assumed) fixed valence band*

There are very few carriers in the (000) conduction band minimum at atmospheric pressure, and still fewer at any higher pressure. There are similarly few in the (100) minima, but this number increases with increasing pressure. Indeed, at about 35,000 kg cm^{-2} the (111) and (100) minima have the same energy. The significance of these movements for the electrical conductivity will now be discussed.

At pressures less than 10,000 kg cm^{-2}, the (000) and (100) minima can be ignored, and any conductivity changes must come from a change either in the density or mobility of the carriers in the (111) minima. Density changes can be ruled out because the $0 \cdot 01$ eV hydrogenic donor ionization energy characteristic of germanium will be at most doubled by pressure even to 100,000 kg cm^{-2}, and the donors will remain fully ionized under all conditions of the experiment.

Thus the change in resistivity below 10,000 kg cm^{-2} must be caused entirely by a change in mobility, and this in turn must arise from changes in the carrier effective mass, in the deformation potential, and in the elastic constants. If the ionized impurities contribute to the scattering mechanism, changes in the dielectric constant will also affect the mobility. Since the pressure coefficients of these parameters amount to a few per cent in 10,000 $kg\,cm^{-2}$, we expect and find changes in the mobility and the resistivity of this order.

For pressures above 10,000 $kg\,cm^{-2}$ the argument already given for the constancy of the impurity derived electron density remains valid, but two additional causes for changes in carrier mobility appear which can give much greater pressure effects.

TABLE 1. PRESSURE COEFFICIENTS OF PARAMETERS FOR GERMANIUM

Quantity	Pressure coefficient	Source	Section
Energy gap, valence band– (111) minima	$+5 \times 10^{-6}$ eV cm²kg⁻¹	Paul and Brooks[1]	3
Energy gap, valence band– (100) minima	-2×10^{-6} eV cm²kg⁻¹	Brooks and Paul[46]	3
Energy gap, valence band– (000) minima	$+1\cdot3 \times 10^{-5}$ eV cm²kg⁻¹	Cardona and Paul[66]	4
Spin–orbit splitting in valence band	0	Warschauer and Paul[37]	4
Group V donor and Group III acceptor ionization energies	10^{-8} eV cm²kg⁻¹	This review. Also Holland[20]	9
Effective mass of electrons and holes (fractional change)	$\sim 10^{-6}$ cm²kg⁻¹	Nathan[21]	3
Dielectric constant (fractional change)	$\sim 10^{-6}$ cm²kg⁻¹	Cardona et al[39]	5
Elastic coefficients (fractional change)	$\sim 10^{-6}$ cm²kg⁻¹	Koppelmann, Landwehr, Bailyn[40]	3
Density (fractional change)	$\sim 10^{-6}$ cm²kg⁻¹	Bridgman[41]	3

The first is that, as the (111) and (100) minima come closer in energy, the fixed number of conduction electrons will be shared between the two sets of minima, and the effective mobility will be a weighted average of the two mobilities characteristic of each type. The second is that a new scattering process will appear corresponding to interchange of electrons between the two types of minima and generated by relatively short wavelength lattice vibrations. This process, which we call 'interband' scattering, is to be distinguished from scattering between different minima of the same set, termed by Herring, 'intervalley scattering'. The interband scattering will therefore be maximum in the vicinity of the cross-over point in energy of the two types of minima, and will be low at low pressures when the (111) minima are lower in energy, and at very high pressures, when the (100) minima are the lower. The maximum in the interband scattering near the cross-over point of the two minima should cause a maximum in the resistivity at about this pressure. The variation of the conductivity with pressure, shown in Figure 6, clearly displays the qualitative characteristics described. A relatively flat variation of the resistivity at low pressures is followed by a very sharp increase to pressures of about 30,000 kg cm^{-2}. The predicted maximum in the resistivity was observed in partially non-hydrostatic experiments carried out by Bridgman. The hysteresis in his measurements makes it difficult to interpret them quantitatively. Nevertheless, the fact that the maximum is to be found in samples of germanium from different sources at different times, and is also to be found in silicon–germanium

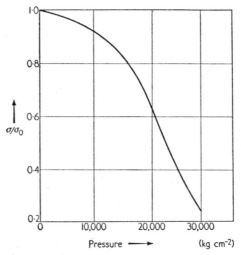

Figure 6. *Normalized conductivity of N-type germanium versus pressure at 295° K*

alloys measured under completely hydrostatic pressure conditions (see below) establishes beyond doubt that the maximum in the resistivity is genuine.

Next let us suppose that the sample is at least partially intrinsic at the temperatures and pressures of measurement. Below 10,000 kg cm^{-2} the energy gap between the (111) minima and the valence band maximum will increase and the density of intrinsic electrons and holes will decrease. The resistivity will increase rapidly, with the carrier density change swamping the small effects on the mobilities. As the pressure is further increased, the (100) minima approach the (111) set and the apparent rate of increase of the forbidden gap slows down. Eventually, above the energy cross-over point of the (111) and the (100) minima, the gap will decrease with pressure. In the pressure region above 15,000 kg cm^{-2}, large changes in the electron mobility as discussed above, superimposed on the alteration in carrier density caused by the combination of an increase of the valence band–(111) minima separation and a decrease in the separation between valence band and (100) minima, will produce a complicated resistivity-pressure relation.

3.2. Impurity Deionization

It will be evident that it is important for the interpretation of the resistivity data on non-intrinsic samples that it be established that the changes are due to changes in the carrier mobility and not to changes in carrier density. There are two separate arguments employed in this proof. The first is based on experiments carried out by Holland[20] on the pressure coefficients of the ionization energies of arsenic and aluminium-doped silicon at $50°$ K. Holland found that these ionization energies changed of the order of 5×10^{-4} eV in 10,000 kgcm^{-2} and argued that the change was consistent with independent estimates of the pressure coefficients of the effective mass and dielectric constant, the two parameters entering the theoretical expression for the ionization energy. It seems plausible that the order of magnitude of the change in the ionization energy should be the same in germanium, and that there should be a similar correlation with the changes in effective mass and dielectric constant. On this basis the change in the ionization energy is negligible and no impurity deionization will occur to the highest pressure of measurement.

The second, and conclusive, argument cites the measurement of the drift mobility of carriers injected into bars of the semiconductor. This measurement has been carried out to 30,000 kgcm^{-2} in a very complete and thorough fashion by Smith,[30] and will now be briefly described. The reader will find that, if he pleases, he can omit sub-section 3.3 without losing the thread of the argument.

3.3. Drift Mobilities under Pressure

The basic experiment to measure the average velocity acquired by a group of minority carriers under the action of an electric field was performed by Haynes and Shockley,[42] and several[43] modifications and improvements have been suggested since then. In general, one uses a crystal geometry of the type illustrated in Figure 7, such that the equations describing the motion of carriers reduce to those for a one-dimensional model. Minority carriers are injected at one point in a crystal bar, swept down the bar to a collector contact by an applied electric field, and detected at the collector. Measurement of the transit time, separation between emitter and collector, and electric field suffice to yield the average mobility.

The electric field, applied across the ends of the crystal through broad area contacts, is preferably pulsed at a low repetition rate. A high field, applied for a time just long enough to 'flow' the injected carriers between emitter and collector, and repeated at, say, 30 c/s, does not heat the sample. The field is measured using two ohmic probes set opposite emitter and collector as in Figure 7. This method eliminates errors due to the contact resistance at the end of the crystal and to the effects of crystal inhomogeneity outside the region of interest.

A point-contact emitter injecting minority carriers continuously was adopted by Smith. The reasons for preferring this method[44] are discussed in his thesis; it is, however, possible that a pulsed field–pulsed emitter arrangement, not required by Smith and, in fact, rejected by him for experimental reasons, would be adaptable for the high pressure experiment and might yield higher sensitivity in crystals more difficult to measure than germanium.† When the sweep field is off, a distribution of carriers

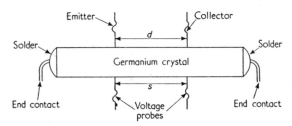

Figure 7. *Arrangement for drift mobility experiments*

builds up underneath the emitter point. The spatial distribution of excess carriers, determined by diffusion and recombination alone, is sharply peaked immediately underneath the point. When the field is turned on, this distribution migrates and spreads, and is detected as a pulse by the collector.

The collector used was a single back-biased rectifying contact. Emitter, collector, and potential contacts were made of $0 \cdot 002$ in. gold wire suitably doped with acceptor or donor impurity and welded on to the crystal. Pressed contacts give, in general, better rectifying, emitting, and collecting characteristics, but are unpredictable and unreliable in high pressure experiments.

In his thesis, Smith discusses the mathematical solution to the drift and diffusion problem in considerable detail, adapting work previously published by Brooks[45] and others to the particular configuration. He made the following assumptions, and justified their correctness or lack of effect on the final solution: (1) Charge neutrality at each point in the crystal; (2) Low excess carrier density, a condition in the hands of the experimenter; (3) Correctness of a one-dimensional approximation; (4) Constancy in space and time, and at different pressures, of the number of ionized impurities; (5) Smallness of the excess conductivity compared with the equilibrium conductivity. Under the further assumption that the emitter

† We are indebted to Dr. A. C. Smith for private discussion of this point.

can be approximated by a point source at $x = 0$ of constant strength S_0, the solution of the steady state equation and the boundary conditions

$$D' \frac{\partial^2 p_1}{\partial x^2} - \frac{p_1}{\tau} = S_0 \delta(x); \quad \lim_{x \to \infty} p_1(x) = 0; \quad \lim_{x \to -\infty} p_1(x) = 0 \quad \dots (3)$$

$$p_1 \text{ continuous at } x = 0$$

is found to be
$$p_1(x) = \frac{S_0 L}{2D'} \exp(-|x|/L); \quad L^2 = D'\tau \quad \dots (4)$$

where
$$D' = \frac{(n_0 + p_0)}{(n_0/D_p) + (p_0/D_n)}, \quad \frac{1}{\tau} = r(n_0 + p_0)$$

and n_0 is the equilibrium electron density, p_0 the equilibrium hole density, D_n and D_p the diffusion coefficients for electrons and holes, $r(n_0 + p_0)$ the rate of thermal generation of electron–hole pairs, and p_1 the excess hole density.

When the sweep field is turned on, it is assumed (and later justified) that the emitter does not inject. Then the equation governing carrier motion is

$$-D' \frac{\partial^2 p_1}{\partial x^2} + \mu' E_0 \frac{\partial p_1}{\partial x} + \frac{\partial p_1}{\partial t} + \frac{p_1}{\tau} = 0 \quad \dots (5)$$

$$p_1(x, 0) = (S_0 L/2D') \exp(-|x|/L) \quad \dots (6)$$

$$\lim_{x \to \pm \infty} p_1 = 0; \quad \lim_{t \to \infty} p_1 = 0$$

The solution is

$$p_1(x, t) = \frac{S_0 L}{4D'} \left\{ \exp\left(\frac{x - \mu' E_0 t}{L}\right) \mathrm{erfc}\left[\sqrt{\left(\frac{t}{\tau}\right)} + \frac{x - \mu' E_0 t}{2\sqrt{(D' t)}}\right] + \right.$$
$$\left. + \exp\left(\frac{-x - \mu' E_0 t}{L}\right) \mathrm{erfc}\left[\sqrt{\left(\frac{t}{\tau}\right)} + \frac{x - \mu' E_0 t}{2\sqrt{(D' t)}}\right] \right\} \quad \dots (7)$$

In the above relations

$$\mu' = \frac{n_0 - p_0}{(n_0/\mu_p) + (p_0/\mu_n)}; \quad E_0 = \frac{j}{q(\mu_n n_0 + \mu_p p_0)}$$

and μ_n and μ_p are the electron and hole mobilities, j the total current density in the sample, and q the electronic charge.

If the collector is at $x = d$, the time t_m at which the pulse maximum reaches it is given by differentiation of equation (7)

$$\left(\frac{\partial p_1}{\partial t}\right)(\text{at } x = d, t = t_m) = 0$$

$$= \frac{S_0 L}{4D'} \left\{ \frac{-\mu' E_0}{L} \exp\left(\frac{d - \mu' E_0 t_m}{L}\right) \mathrm{erfc}\left[\sqrt{\left(\frac{t_m}{\tau}\right)} + \frac{d - \mu' E_0 t_m}{2\sqrt{(D' t_m)}}\right] + \right.$$
$$+ \frac{\mu' E_0}{L} \exp\left(-\frac{d - \mu' E_0 t_m}{L}\right) \mathrm{erfc}\left[\sqrt{\left(\frac{t_m}{\tau}\right)} - \frac{d - \mu' E_0 t_m}{2\sqrt{(D' t_m)}}\right] -$$
$$\left. - \frac{2}{\sqrt{(\pi t_m \tau)}} \exp\left[-\frac{t_m}{\tau} - \frac{(d - \mu E_0 t_m)^2}{4D' t_m}\right] \right\} \quad \dots (8)$$

The first approximation to t_m is $t_0 = d/(\mu' E_0)$. If equation (8) is expanded in terms of t_1 where $t_m = t_0 + t_1$, it can be shown that t_1/t_0 is less than experimental errors for the samples and conditions of the measurement. Furthermore, by choosing $n_0 \gg p_0$, or $p_0 \gg n_0$, μ' can be made equal to μ_p or μ_n without the necessity for awkward ambipolar corrections. Smith estimates that the assumption of zero emitter width gives a solution within 1 per cent of the true solution when the effective emitter width is no greater than the diameter of the wire used; that the effect of finite length to the crystal is unimportant as long as both emitter and collector are several diffusion lengths (L) away from the ends; that the effect of the emitter field in producing an asymmetrical carrier distribution about $x = 0$ at $t = 0$ has a negligible effect on t_m for the samples and emitter currents used; that the effect of continued injection from the emitter after the sweep field is turned on is similarly unimportant; and that the assumption that steady state conditions are reached at the emitter before the sweep field is turned on is amply satisfied. He shows that the extension of the theory to three dimensions changes the expression for the pulse maximum arrival time by an increment smaller than the experimental error.

Smith also considers the shape of the received pulse in the case where there are two types of minority carrier of different mobilities, e.g. the two types of hole in the germanium valence bands, or the two types of electron in the (111) and (100) conduction bands. Clearly, an average mobility will be measured in every case where the relaxation time for scattering between bands is much less than the transit time of the drift experiment. This condition is nearly always met by a large margin, except perhaps at quite low temperatures.

The details of Smith's experimental arrangements and of his careful reduction of his data will not be reproduced here. Figure 8 shows a comparison of conductivity mobility variation with pressure—deduced from the variation with pressure of the resistivity of a sample chosen so that the carrier density would be constant with pressure (i.e. except for changes in density of the sample)—and experimental data on the drift mobility of electrons in a P-type crystal, where the mobility is normalized to give the best fit to the line. The r.m.s. deviation of the points from the line is less than the probable error associated with each point. The conclusion is that the drift mobility and the resistivity have the same pressure dependence within an experimental error of 2 per cent. It is still possible that the large changes with pressure found are caused by a change in temporary trapping of the carriers. Smith adduces convincing experimental observations concerning carrier lifetime variation with pressure and plausible arguments concerning the occurrence of high densities of traps to refute this possibility.

We therefore exclude hydrogenic impurity deionization under pressure as an element affecting resistivity data, and proceed to a quantitative discussion of the problem.

3.4. INTERBAND SCATTERING THEORY

The theory of the total conductivity of electrons in the two distinguishable sets of conduction band minima has been briefly reported by Brooks and Paul,[46] and discussed in detail by Nathan,[21] and by Nathan, Paul, and Brooks.[9]

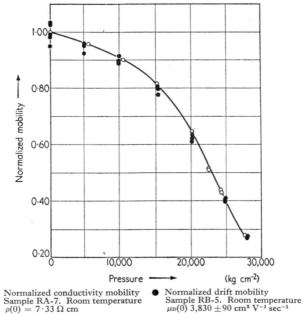

O Normalized conductivity mobility
Sample RA-7. Room temperature
$\rho(0) = 7\cdot33\ \Omega$ cm

● Normalized drift mobility
Sample RB-5. Room temperature
$\mu_D(0)\ 3,830 \pm 90$ cm^2 V^{-1} sec^{-1}

Figure 8. *Comparison of pressure dependence of conductivity and drift mobilities of electrons in germanium*

We designate quantities referring to the properties of the (111) minima by a subscript 'g' and those which refer to the properties of the (100) minima by a subscript 's'. The electrical conductivity σ is then given by

$$\sigma = q(n_g\mu_g + n_s\mu_s + p\mu_p) \qquad \cdots (9)$$

where n_x is the density of electrons in the x conduction band,† x is 'g' or 's', p is the density of holes in the valence band, and μ_x is the mobility of the carriers in the x-band.

Under the assumption of the validity of Boltzmann statistics, i.e. $|(E_x - E_f)/kT| \gg 1$ where E_f is the Fermi energy and E_x the energy of a band edge, we have

$$\left.\begin{aligned}
n_g &= C_0 C_g \exp(E_f - E_g)/kT \\
n_s &= C_0 C_s \exp(E_f - E_g - \Delta E)/kT \\
p &= C_0 C_v \exp(E_v - E_f)/kT
\end{aligned}\right\} \cdots (10)$$

† The subscript x will be used as a general subscript when quantities referring to more than one band are meant.

where E_g, E_v are the energies of the conduction and valence band edges, ΔE is the energy separation of the two conduction band sets of minima, C_0 is equal to $2(2\pi kT/h^2)^{3/2}$, C_x is equal to $m_{dx}^{3/2}v_x$, m_{dx} is the density of states effective mass for the x-band, and v_x = the number of minima in the x-band.

The existence of more than one type of hole is taken into account by lumping them into the factor C_v. It is easily shown that the presence of the extra conduction band does not affect the complete ionization of hydrogenic impurities in germanium down to 20° K. Hence, measurement of the conductivity of an N-type sample as a function of pressure yields the pressure variation of an effective mobility

$$\mu_{eff} = (\mu_g n_g + \mu_s n_s)/n_0 \qquad \ldots (11)$$

with

$$n_g = \frac{n_0}{1 + (C_s/C_g)\exp(-\Delta E/kT)} \qquad \ldots (12)$$

$$n_s = \frac{n_0}{1 + (C_g/C_s)\exp(\Delta E/kT)} \qquad \ldots (13)$$

and
$$n_0 = N_d - N_a$$

From equation (10) we have

$$n_i^2 = np = C_0^2 C_v C_g \left[\exp(E_v - E_g)/kT\right]\left[1 + \frac{C_s}{C_g}\exp\left(-\frac{\Delta E}{kT}\right)\right] \qquad \ldots (14)$$

Let us consider first a crystal with a large number of intrinsic carriers, and assume that n_0 is determined initially by a measurement of the resistivity at low temperature and atmospheric pressure. Then

$$n = \frac{n_0}{2} + \left[\left(\frac{n_0}{2}\right)^2 + n_i^2\right]^{1/2}$$

$$p = -\frac{n_0}{2} + \left[\left(\frac{n_0}{2}\right)^2 + n_i^2\right]^{1/2}$$

n_g, n_s are given by equations (12) and (13) with n substituted for n_0. Without further theoretical consideration of the mobility variation with pressure, we can discuss the motion of the band edges.

The conductivity of N- and P-type samples chosen to give negligible variation of carrier density with pressure at a given temperature will yield the mobility variation with pressure through equation (9). If, furthermore, the impure samples are chosen so that lattice scattering predominates, the conductivity variation of the impure samples will provide the variation of μ_{eff} and μ_p for the intrinsic one. The requirements of dominant impurity derived electron or hole densities, and no contribution of ionized impurity scattering, are in opposition, but simultaneous satisfaction of these conditions is achievable; hence, μ_{eff} versus P and μ_p versus P can be found.

Since the variation of the band edges with pressure is assumed, we can find σ versus P if the mass variation with pressure of C_v, C_g, and C_s is neglected. We shall see later that this is legitimate. The fit of the experimental and calculated σ versus P curves is then very satisfactory. The statement of this fit is, however, a trivial one, since the pressure coefficients of the energy minima we have given as postulates were originally derived from these data. Nevertheless, it is possible, albeit with inferior accuracy, to obtain the energy variation of the minima from optical experiments[15, 32] or an extrapolation of these, when the coefficients we assumed earlier are again found. The fit of calculated and experimental σ versus P is then genuine and unforced.

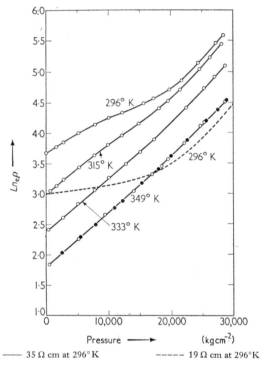

—— 35 Ω cm at 296° K   ----- 19 Ω cm at 296°K

Figure 9. *Resistivity versus pressure at several temperatures for an N-type sample of germanium*

The inverse procedure for the derivation of $[(\partial/\partial P)(E_g - E_v)]_T$, ΔE, and $[(\partial/\partial P)(E_s - E_v)]_T$ from the experimental data is worth mention. From the experimental σ versus P curve, n_i versus P is derived, using the experimental μ_{eff} versus P and μ_p versus P for the impure samples at the same temperature and the equation

$$\left[\left(\frac{n_0}{2}\right)^2 + n_i^2\right]^{1/2} = \left[\frac{\sigma}{q} - \frac{(\mu_{\mathrm{eff}} - \mu_p)n_0}{2}\right]\frac{1}{(\mu_{\mathrm{eff}} + \mu_p)} \qquad \ldots (15)$$

163

From equation (14) and an equation

$$n_i^2 = np = C_0^2 C_v C_g \exp(-E_{G,\text{eff}}/kT) \qquad \ldots (16)$$

defining the effective gap $E_{G,\text{eff}}$, we obtain

$$E_{G,\text{eff}} = E_{Gg} - kT \ln(1 + \mathscr{C}) \qquad \ldots (17)$$

where

$$\mathscr{C} \equiv \frac{C_s}{C_g} \exp(-\Delta E/kT)$$

The pressure variation of E_{Gg} is found from the low pressure variation of $E_{G,\text{eff}}$, when the logarithmic term is negligible. Also, if the pressure variation of E_{Gg} is assumed linear to the top pressures, $\mathscr{C}$ may be obtained

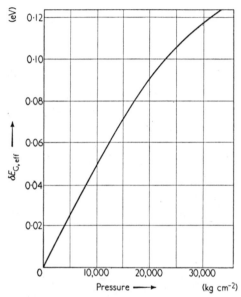

Figure 10. *Change of effective energy gap of germanium at 349° K*

from the higher pressure data. Figure 9 shows the resistivity as a function of pressure for a 35 Ωcm sample[1] at several temperatures; Figure 10 gives the deduced pressure variation of $E_{G,\text{eff}}$, showing the curvature at high pressures caused by the growing influence of the (100) minima; and Figure 11 gives the pressure variation of $\mathscr{C}$, as deduced from the same experimental data. No experimental points are shown on Figure 11 below 15,000 kg cm^{-2} because $\mathscr{C}$ is too small to produce a measurable deviation in $E_{G,\text{eff}}$ from the initial straight line of Figure 10. From Figure 11, if we can assume that the C are independent of pressure, which is fairly accurate, we can deduce

$$\left(\frac{\partial}{\partial P}(\Delta E)\right)_T \quad \text{and} \quad \frac{C_s}{C_g}\exp(-\Delta E_0/kT)$$

where ΔE_0 is the value of ΔE at zero pressure. Nathan found

$$\left(\frac{\partial}{\partial P}(\Delta E)\right)_T = -5 \times 10^{-6}\,\mathrm{eV\,cm^2\,kg^{-1}}$$

by this procedure; this implies that

$$\frac{\partial}{\partial P}(E_s - E_v) = 0$$

since

$$\left[\frac{\partial}{\partial P}(E_g - E_v)\right]_T = +5 \times 10^{-6}\,\mathrm{eV\,cm^2\,kg^{-1}}$$

He also found

$$\frac{C_s}{C_g}\exp\left(\Delta E_0/kT\right) = 0{\cdot}014$$

justifying neglect of the logarithm in equation (17) at low pressures.

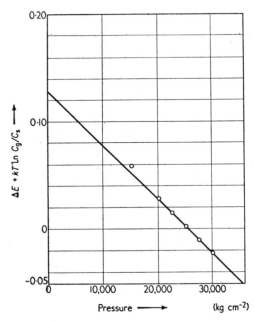

Figure 11. *Change of energy separation of germanium (111) and (100) minima with pressure*

The evaluation of C_s/C_g and ΔE_0 is not straightforward from these data alone. We can choose to draw on other reasoning or experiment to give us either of these, or we can make our best estimate from these data, and then compare this with other experiments and ideas; we follow the latter track.

Nathan noted, from his data on impure N-type samples at different temperatures, that the normalized effective electron mobilities approached each other but did not quite coincide at pressures up to 30,000 kg cm^{-2}. He reasoned that the normalized mobility was temperature-independent at $\Delta E = 0$; there are several independent requirements for this to be correct, not all of them directly verifiable, but most of them entirely plausible. Assuming their correctness, we deduce that 30,000 kg cm^{-2} is slightly below the pressure for which $\Delta E = 0$; from the pressure coefficient of ΔE we can then deduce $\Delta E_0 > 0 \cdot 15$ eV and $C_s/C_g > 2 \cdot 6$. We postpone discussion of the reasonableness of these estimates until after we have discussed the mobilities.

The calculation of the mobilities[21, 46] involves a number of assumptions of varying credibility.

(1) A scattering time $\tau(E)$, independent of direction, is assumed to exist. Certainly this assumption is normally made, although it is not strictly justified for all configurations of constant energy surface and types of scattering. For spheroidal energy surfaces away from the centre of the Brillouin zone, Herring and Vogt have shown that $\tau(E)$ should be replaced by $\alpha(E)\boldsymbol{\tau}$ where $\boldsymbol{\tau}$ is a tensor diagonal with respect to the axes of the spheroid. If the spheroid is quite eccentric, as in the germanium (111) minima and possibly the silicon (100) minima, τ is nearly isotropic for lattice scattering. Herring's arguments for an isotropic τ are borne out, at least approximately, by experimental measurements of the magnetoconductivity.[47] When the scattering event is between states in different sets of minima, a $\tau(E)$ almost certainly exists.[35] The range of values of the electron wave vector $\mathbf{k}$ over an ellipsoid of constant energy, to or from which there is scattering, is required to be much smaller than the $\mathbf{k}$ vector between the centres of the two minima. Clearly, with this condition, the scattering probability is independent of the initial and final states involved, as nearly the same wavelength phonon is used. A relaxation time therefore exists for inter-valley scattering, and for interband scattering also, provided that $\Delta E/kT$ is not too large. If $\Delta E/kT$ is large, one of the constant energy ellipsoids, whose states can participate in the scattering event, may extend so far over the Brillouin zone that the above reasoning breaks down. Given an idea of the approximate location of the (100) as well as the (111) minima in the Brillouin zone, and, assured that ΔE is not much greater than $0 \cdot 15$ eV, it can be shown that the range of $\mathbf{k}$ values in one constant energy ellipsoid is only a fraction of the $\mathbf{k}$ vector joining the closest pair of (111) and (100) minima.

(2) We also assume that the only important types of scattering are intravalley and interband scattering that use acoustical lattice vibrations. We neglect ionized impurity scattering, since we choose our samples initially so that lattice scattering is predominant. We can check this by calculation, or by verifying the temperature dependence of the mobility.

166

We neglect also optical mode scattering and intervalley scattering. The contribution of both of these must be small, since they would produce a deviation of the temperature dependence of the mobility from a $T^{-1 \cdot 5}$ law. Such deviation as exists ($T^{-1 \cdot 7}$) can be wholly explained by the dependence of the effective mass on temperature. (We hasten to add that the error in the effective mass dependence on temperature is sufficient to allow a little intervalley or optical mode contribution.)

The neglect of intervalley scattering when interband scattering is allowed is not really inconsistent if we remember that group theoretical arguments[35] on selection rules indicate that scattering between (111) minima on the zone boundary will be small, while the interband scattering event is not forbidden.

(3) We further assume that the bands are parabolic in energy from their minimum energy up to an energy greater than ΔE. It is doubtful if this assumption is justified at high energies. The non-parabolicity could probably be taken into account by assigning a small dependence of C_g and C_s on the temperature and of C_s on ΔE but this refinement has not been carried out.

(4) We further assume that only the (111) and (100) minima possess electrons. This is probably a very good approximation as the (000) minimum, with a low effective mass, is $0 \cdot 15$ eV above the (111) set at atmospheric pressure, and moves away as pressure is applied.

(5) We neglect the energy of the interacting phonon, both in intravalley and interband transitions. This assumption is not well justified, and will be discussed later.

(6) We assume, finally, that the effective masses in both bands are almost independent of pressure and completely independent whenever the mass enters into expressions about state densities. There is no *a priori* reason for the more stringent assumption. We might expect the mass changes to be of the order of $\delta E/E$ where δE is the change in the energy separation E of the states considered and the states of the nearest interacting band, and therefore, of the order of magnitude $0 \cdot 05$ in $10{,}000$ $\mathrm{kg\,cm^{-2}}$ ($\delta E = 10^4 \times 5 \times 10^{-6}\,\mathrm{eV}$; $E \sim 1$ eV). While these changes are important enough for the mobility in one set of minima when interband scattering is not present, they have much less effect than changes in the energy level positions when carrier density changes are involved.

Using these assumptions, we can write

$$\frac{1}{\tau(E)} = \frac{1}{\tau_v(E)} + \frac{1}{\tau_b(E)} \qquad \ldots (18)$$

where $\tau_v(E)$ is the scattering time for intravalley transitions and $\tau_b(E)$ is the scattering time for interband transitions.

For each type of scattering the reciprocal of the relaxation time will be proportional to the transition probability multiplied by the density of final states. Hence, for $\Delta E > 0$,

$$\frac{1}{\tau_g(E)} = A_g C_g' E^{1/2} + B_{g1} C_s'(E - \Delta E)^{1/2} \nu_{s1} + B_{g2} C_s'(E - \Delta E)^{1/2} \nu_{s2} +$$

$$+ B_{g3} C_s'(E - \Delta E)^{1/2} \nu_{s3} + \ldots \qquad E \geqslant \Delta E$$

$$= A_g C_g' E^{1/2} \qquad E \leqslant \Delta E \qquad \ldots (19)$$

$$\frac{1}{\tau_s(E)} = A_s C_s'(E - \Delta E)^{1/2} + B_{s1} C_g' E^{1/2} \nu_{g1} + B_{s2} C_g' E^{1/2} \nu_{g2} + \ldots$$

If $\Delta E < 0$, we interchange subscripts 'g' and 's' throughout. In equation (19) E_g is taken as the zero of energy, and A_x is the intravalley transition probability, B_{xi} the interband scattering probability, C_x' the density of states factor $= (m_{lx}^{1/2} m_{tx}) (4\sqrt{(2)}\pi)/h^3$, m_{lx} the longitudinal mass component in band x and m_{tx} the transverse component. $B_{s1}, B_{s2}, \ldots, B_{g1}, B_{g2}, \ldots$, and $\nu_{s1}, \nu_{s2}, \nu_{g1}, \nu_{g2}, \ldots$ label the different minima, since the transition probabilities to them are not necessarily the same. We shall, however, immediately re-define

$$\sum_j B_{gj} \nu_{sj} = B_g \nu_s$$

and

$$\sum_j B_{sj} \nu_{gj} = B_s \nu_g$$

We can show that $B_g = B_s = B$ from detailed balance considerations. Then the conductivity mobilities μ_g and μ_s are given by

$$\mu_g = q\langle \tau_g(E) \rangle (1/3) (1/m_{lg} + 2/m_{tg})$$

$$\mu_s = q\langle \tau_s(E) \rangle (1/3) (1/m_{ls} + 2/m_{ts}) \qquad \ldots (20)$$

where

$$\langle \tau_y^n(E) \rangle = \frac{4}{3\sqrt{(\pi)}} \int_0^\infty \tau^n(y) \, y^{3/2} \exp(-y) \, dy \qquad \ldots (21)$$

and $y = E/kT$.

What difficulty there is lies in the evaluation of the integrals. It can be shown, however, that certain analytic expressions are approximately correct in limiting cases

$$\langle \tau_g^n(E) \rangle = \frac{4}{3\sqrt{(\pi)} [A_g C_g'(kT)^{1/2}]^n}$$

$$\left[\int_0^\Delta y^{3/2 - n/2} \exp(-y) \, dy + \int_\Delta^\infty \frac{y^{3/2 - n/2} \exp(-y) \, dy}{\{1 + S[1 - (\Delta/y)]^{-1/2}\}^n} \right]$$

$$= D_g^n (I_{1n} + I_{2n}) \qquad \ldots (22)$$

where $\Delta = (\Delta E/kT)$

$$D_g = [A_g C_g'(kT)^{1/2}]^{-1}$$

$$S = \frac{BC_s' \nu_s}{A_g C_g'} = \text{interband scattering parameter.}$$

I_{1n} can be evaluated in terms of tabulated functions for $n < 4$. I_{2n} can be evaluated analytically for $\Delta = 0$ or ∞. Otherwise, it can be found approximately by expanding the integrand in a Taylor series about $\Delta = 0$, and integrating term by term between Δ and ∞. Difficulties in the convergence of the resulting sum are discussed by Nathan, who concludes that the approximations shown in Table 2 are close to the exact values. Inadequacies in the approximations could be overcome by numerical integration but this has not been done, nor indeed considered necessary as yet. The quantities shown in Table 2 are $\langle \tau(\Delta) \rangle_N = \langle \tau(\Delta) \rangle / \langle \tau(\infty) \rangle$ for $\Delta > 0$. The integrals for $\Delta < 0$ are found from the relation

$$\langle \tau_g^n(-\Delta, S) \rangle = \langle \tau_s^n(\Delta, S') \rangle \text{ where } S' = \frac{BC_g' \nu_g}{A_s C_s'}$$

TABLE 2. SCATTERING INTEGRALS

n	$\langle \tau_g^n(\Delta) \rangle_N \equiv \langle \tau_g^n(\Delta) \rangle / \langle \tau_g^n(\infty) \rangle$	$\langle \tau_s^n(\Delta) \rangle_N \equiv \langle \tau_s^n(\Delta) \rangle / \langle \tau_s^n(\infty) \rangle$
1	$1 - \left[\dfrac{S(\Delta+1)}{1+S} - \dfrac{S\Delta}{2(1+S)^2} \right] \exp(-\Delta)$	$\dfrac{1}{1+S'} - \dfrac{S'\Delta}{2(1+S')^2}$
2	$\text{erf}(\Delta^{1/2}) - \dfrac{2}{\sqrt{(\pi)}} \Delta^{1/2} \exp(-\Delta) +$ $+ \dfrac{1}{(1+S)^2} \left[1 - \text{erf}(\Delta^{1/2}) + \dfrac{2}{\sqrt{(\pi)}} \Delta^{1/2} \exp(-\Delta) \right] -$ $- \dfrac{2\Delta}{(1+S)^3} [1 - \text{erf}(\Delta^{1/2})]$	$\dfrac{1}{(1+S')^2}$
3	$1 - \exp(-\Delta) \left[1 - \dfrac{1}{(1+S)^3} \right]$	$\dfrac{1}{(1+S')^3}$

$\text{erf } x \equiv \dfrac{2}{\sqrt{(\pi)}} \int_0^x \exp(-u^2) \, du$

All values for $\Delta > 0$

3.5. COMPARISON OF EXPERIMENTAL AND THEORETICAL MOBILITIES

The conductivity of an N-type sample as a function of pressure can be written

$$\frac{\sigma}{\sigma_0} = \left(\frac{n_g}{n_{g0}} \right) \left(\frac{\mu_g}{\mu_{g0}} \right) + \left(\frac{n_s}{n_{g0}} \right) \left(\frac{\mu_s}{\mu_s^*} \right) \left(\frac{\mu_s^*}{\mu_{g0}^*} \right) \left(\frac{\mu_{g0}^*}{\mu_{g0}} \right) \quad \dots (23)$$

where the subscript '0' refers to zero pressure, and the asterisk refers to the mobilities if there were no interband scattering. It is assumed that there is no contribution to the conductivity by intrinsic carriers at any pressure or temperature where data are to be fitted; that there is no contribution from the s band at zero pressure, and that lattice scattering alone determines the mobility. The experimental samples are carefully chosen and examined[21] to ensure that these conditions are approximated within errors of the order of 1 per cent.

As discussed earlier, n_s, n_g, and $\mathscr{C}$ can be determined simply. In Nathan's experiments they were calculated at 76° C, and there is no bar to their similar determination at other temperatures. In equation (23), the unknowns are μ_g^*, μ_{g0}^*, S, Δ_0, μ_s^*, S'. S and S' involve combinations of unknowns. Nathan has been able to limit the reasonable values of Δ_0, S, and S', and of the parameters entering S and S', by a complex combination of analysis and physical reasoning summarized below. First he assumes that at low pressures there is no contribution from the s band; this is later validated by the agreement of the theory and experiment. Then,

$$\frac{\sigma}{\sigma_0} = \frac{n_g\,\mu_g}{n_{g0}\,\mu_{g0}} \qquad \ldots (24)$$

Since n_g/n_{g0} is known at 76° C, μ_g/μ_{g0} can be computed at this temperature. Also, at low pressures,

$$\frac{\mu_g}{\mu_{g0}} = \frac{\mu_g^*\left[1 - \dfrac{S(1+\Delta)}{1+S}\exp(-\Delta) + \dfrac{S\Delta}{2(1+S)^2}\exp(-\Delta)\right]}{\mu_{g0}^*\left[1 - \dfrac{S(1+\Delta_0)}{1+S}\exp(-\Delta_0) + \dfrac{S\Delta_0}{2(1+S)^2}\exp(-\Delta_0)\right]} \qquad \ldots (25)$$

If μ_s^* is assumed pressure independent, μ_g/μ_{g0} can be plotted versus Δ_0, with S as a parameter, for a fixed, chosen value of $\Delta - \Delta_0$. Such curves are shown in Figure 12, and the experimental curve in Figure 13. Comparison shows that if we keep $\Delta E_0 > 0 \cdot 15$ eV, the ratio of the probability of interband scattering to intravalley, B/A_g, is greater than unity. This is to be excluded on physical grounds, if only because the interacting phonons for interband scattering are undoubtedly larger than those for intravalley scattering. A clue to the solution of this difficulty is provided by Figure 14 which shows $\mu_{eff}(2,500\,\text{kg cm}^{-2})/\mu_{eff,0}$ plotted versus T. For $T < 200°$ K, the ratio is temperature independent and equal to $0 \cdot 99$. The ratio must tend to 1 as the temperature is lowered if the pressure is affecting only the interband scattering. The residual coefficient is therefore attributable to a temperature-independent pressure coefficient of μ_g^*

$$\mu_g^* = \mu_{g0}^*(1 - 4 \times 10^{-6} P); \qquad P \text{ in kg cm}^{-2}$$

When this explicit variation of mobility with pressure is used to correct Figure 13 to give μ_g/μ_{g0} (interband effects only) comparison of this Figure with Figure 12 can be used to provide the functional relationships between S and Δ_0 shown in Figure 15, and between B/A_g and S shown in Figure 16. None of the values shown in these Figures seem physically unreasonable, and consistently chosen values would give a fit to the low pressure data. Addition of the experimental data to 30,000 kg cm^{-2} allows further reduction of the range of the parameters allowed.

We redirect attention to equation (23). For any chosen value of S, the contribution of the first term is fixed, since Δ_0, C_g/C_s, and μ_g^*/μ_{g0}^* are then known. The contribution of the second term can then be found at, say,

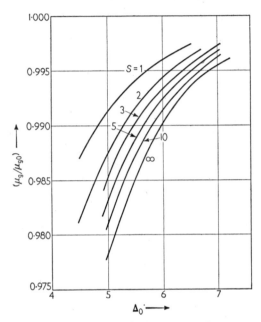

Figure 12. *Calculated* (μ_g/μ_{g0}) *versus* Δ_0 *with* S
as a parameter, for $\Delta - \Delta_0 = 0 \cdot 5$

30,000 kg cm^{-2} (where it is high), and the parameters entering the second term scrutinized. For this scrutiny we note that n_s/n_{g0} is known, and that μ_s^* and S' are the only other undetermined parameters. However,

$$\frac{\mu_s^*}{\mu_{g0}^*} = \frac{m_{lg}}{m_{ls}}\left(\frac{2K_s+1}{2K_g+1}\right)\frac{A_g C_g'}{A_s C_s'}; \qquad \frac{S'}{S} = \left(\frac{C_g'}{C_g}\right)^2 \frac{v_g A_g}{v_s A_s} \quad \ldots (26)$$

and

$$\frac{\mu_s^*}{\mu_{g0}^*} = \frac{m_{lg}}{m_{ls}}\left(\frac{2K_s+1}{2K_g+1}\right)\frac{S' v_s C_s'}{S v_g C_g'} \quad \ldots (27)$$

so that μ_s^* is known as a function of S' for each S, provided m_{lg}, m_{ls}, K_s, K_g, v_s, v_g, C_s', C_g' can be estimated. Experimental evidence is conclusive that $v_g = 4$, and general group theoretical arguments, as well as experiment, give $v_s = 6$. The m_{lg}, K_g, C_g' are well verified for the lowest (111) minima from magnetoresistance and cyclotron resonance data. The best argument for the m_{ls}, K_s, C_s' of the (100) minima is given by the magnetoresistance measurements of Glicksman and Christian[48] in silicon–germanium alloys, when K_s is found to be almost independent of composition in all alloys where the (100) minima are the lowest. Since K_s does not alter with composition, we estimate that to a first approximation the longitudinal and transverse masses do not alter either. The pressure dependences of the K and m are

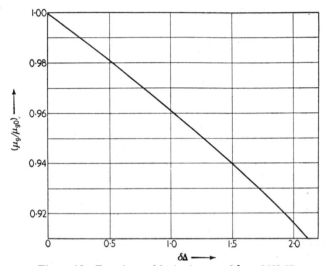

Figure 13. *Experimental* (μ_g/μ_{g0}) *versus* $\delta\Delta$ *at 349° K*

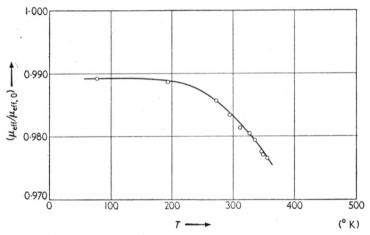

Figure 14. *Initial pressure coefficient of electron mobility as a function of temperature*

small enough (see below) that we can afford to avoid this requirement here, especially in view of the other assumptions.

We therefore calculate S' and μ_s^*/μ_{g0}^* for each S and plot this in Figure 17. This is useful, in that we can set a limit on μ_s^*/μ_g^*; Bridgman's measurements to 100,000 kg cm^{-2} give μ_s^* at the top pressure; despite the hysteresis and lack of returnability in his measurements, we can deduce $\mu_s^*/\mu_{g0}^* < 1$. Then

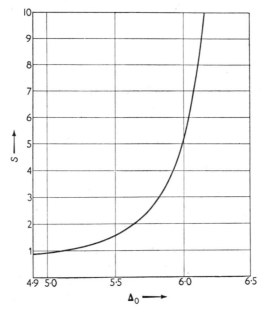

Figure 15. *S versus* Δ_0 *for* $(\mu_g/\mu_{g0})i_b = 0\cdot9927$

$S < 6$, $S' < 1$. Also shown in Figure 16 is B/A_s, calculated as a function of S. Since we expect this ratio to be less than 1, S is reduced below 5. We should remember that a different relation between S and S' and μ_s^*/μ_{g0}^* will be found if our estimate of the parameters describing the s band has to be changed. This will be kept in mind in setting limits on S and Δ_0. The fit to the experimental data is unaffected, provided all the parameters are consistently adjusted.

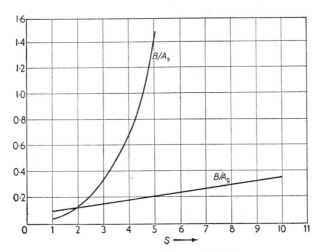

Figure 16. *Ratio of transition probabilities versus S*

Since S is now connected parametrically with all the other variables, we can settle on the best S by fitting the experimental data with curves calculated using different S. The sort of fit to experiment obtained for $S = 1$ and $S = 5$ is shown in Figure 18. Clearly the fit for both is adequate, and further reduction in choice of S is unlikely.

In his thesis, Nathan discusses in detail the combinations of Δ_0, S, S', etc., all of which give a good fit to the experimental data on the conductivity,

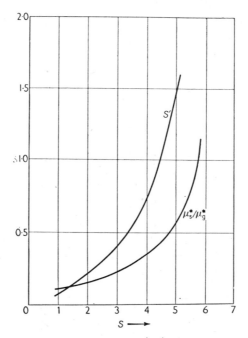

Figure 17. *S' and (μ_s^*/μ_g^*) versus S*

but which correspond to slightly different assumptions about the parameters of the upper s band whose values are admitted to be slightly uncertain. The ranges of the parameters, consistent choice of which yield excellent agreement with the experiment, are

$$
\begin{aligned}
0 \cdot 15 \text{ eV} &\leqslant \Delta E_0 \leqslant 0 \cdot 18 \text{ eV (provided phonon energies are neglected)}\dagger \\
1 &\leqslant S \leqslant 3 \\
0 &\leqslant S' \leqslant 0 \cdot 4 \\
0 \cdot 1 &\leqslant B/A_g \leqslant 0 \cdot 2 \\
0 &\leqslant B/A_s \leqslant 0 \cdot 4 \\
0 \cdot 1 &\leqslant \mu_s^*/\mu_g^* \leqslant 0 \cdot 2 \\
2 \cdot 6 &\leqslant C_s/C_g \leqslant 7 \cdot 2
\end{aligned}
$$

† This range of values is found from the fit of theory to experiment, assuming we know n_0 accurately. Uncertainties in n_0 are important, and it is estimated that, at the outside, they could change ΔE_0 by $\pm 0 \cdot 03$ eV.

Finally, Nathan has estimated that the use of better approximations to the scattering time integrals would affect the demonstrated fit of theory and experiment very little, and would leave the ranges of the parameters essentially unaltered.

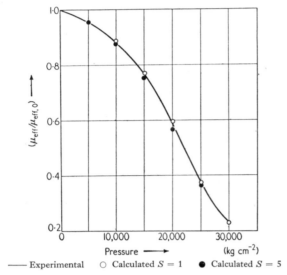

Figure 18. *Normalized effective mobility in N-type germanium versus pressure at 349° K*

3.6. DISCUSSION OF RESULTS OF INTERBAND SCATTERING THEORY

From the overall fit of the experimental and calculated curves, it is apparent that the interband scattering theory presented is adequate to explain the present data. We believe that alternative explanations have been eliminated by experiments such as those of Smith. To recapitulate, the (000) and (111) minima in the conduction band of germanium move away from a (relatively) fixed valence band maximum, while the (100) set remain static relative to the same maximum. At elevated pressures, the (111) and (100) sets share the conduction band electrons, with the (100) set getting increasingly the larger share. Scattering between the (111) and (100) states reduces the mobility of electrons in both bands. The pressure coefficient of the energy of the (111) band is deducible with considerable accuracy, as is a quantity $\mathscr{C}$ and its pressure dependence. The parameters of the (100) set of minima and of the interband scattering can be deduced within fairly narrow limits, using general physical assumptions.

Crucial to this theory is the existence of a minimum conductivity, roughly at the pressure where the minima are equal in energy. This minimum has been found in partially hydrostatic experiments of Bridgman and is almost certainly genuine. Also crucial is a changeover of the pressure coefficient of the total energy gap from a positive quantity to a zero or negative quantity.

175

Nathan's results indicate a zero coefficient, while earlier deductions of Paul and Brooks (using inferior data) gave a negative coefficient. A reversal in sign of the coefficient has been found at about the expected pressure in partially hydrostatic optical experiments of Drickamer.[15] (See below.) The disagreement of Nathan's and Drickamer's coefficients is numerically small, and although troublesome for a neatly finished picture, does not upset the general theory.

Optical and galvanomagnetic experiments on silicon–germanium alloys[6] have shown that, as silicon is added to germanium the valence band–(111) minima energy gap increases much faster than the gap between the valence band and the (100) minima. When the (100) minima in silicon are tracked in energy through alloys of increasing germanium content, the extrapolated position in pure germanium is some $0 \cdot 2$ eV above the (111) set, in fair agreement with the position assigned to the extra set of minima required in our theory and so far referred to as the (100) set. The similarity of the germanium and silicon lattices, the existence of similar sets of conduction band minima, the coincidence in energy of the extrapolated (100) minima (from silicon–germanium alloys) with our (100) set all point to an identification of the (100) minima with the (100) minima in germanium that exist and correspond to the lowest set in silicon. This identification is substantiated by magnetoresistivity measurements of Glicksman that identify the lowest set of conduction band minima in high silicon content silicon–germanium alloys as being of the (100) type; and in which is found a mass ratio in the principal directions of the constant energy ellipsoids equal to that found in pure silicon. Anticipating a little, we note also that the pressure coefficient of the energy gap in pure silicon[16] is a *decrease* of about $-1 \cdot 5 \times 10^{-6}$ eV cm^2 kg^{-1}. All of this information emboldens us to guess that the properties measured for the (100) set of silicon minima may, with small error, be assigned to the (100) germanium set. Let us add, immediately, that this sort of extrapolation must be carried out with caution. In the case of germanium and silicon, the separation of the (100) minima from interacting states in the valence bands is about the same; and this helps our thesis. We are, however, encouraged to expect similar extrapolations for other sets of minima, and perhaps to other, similar, substances, such as grey tin. This topic will be pursued further in later sections.

Since the addition of silicon to the germanium lattice moves the (100) minima relatively closer to the valence band than the (111) set, we expect that the behaviour of the resistivity of germanium under pressure may be found at much lower pressures in the alloys. This apparently fruitful field of study has not been extensively cultivated for two reasons: (1) Good single crystals of silicon–germanium alloys of known uniform composition are not easy to produce, and have not been available to us in adequate supply; (2) The addition of disorder scattering to the lattice scattering may make quantitative fits of theory and experiment difficult. Nevertheless, experiments on alloys very readily show the sorts of effects that our theory predicts. As an example, Bridgman and Paul[12] found a maximum in the resistivity of an 8 per cent silicon–germanium alloy at a pressure of about 20,000 kg cm^{-2}. There does not seem to be much doubt that, if good alloy samples were available, a whole range of experiments could be done at low pressures on the interband scattering mechanism. We have, for the most part, confined ourselves thus far to germanium; in any case, it is for this element that the necessary quantitative fits will be established most easily.

3.7. THE EXPLICIT EFFECT ON THE ELECTRON MOBILITY

Figure 14 demonstrates that, quite apart from interband scattering effects, there is an explicit effect of pressure on the mobility in the (111) minima. There is, of course, also an explicit effect for the (100) minima. We have no way of obtaining it directly, although an analysis of the effects on the silicon mobility would probably suffice. We recall that

$$\mu_n \propto \frac{C_p K_g (2K_g+1)}{E_{lg}^2 \; m_{lg}^{5/2}} \qquad \ldots (28)$$

in the (111) set of minima. C_p is some average of the elastic constants, and E_{lg} is the deformation potential for the conduction band edge. (The relative contributions of transverse and longitudinal mode lattice vibrations to the scattering are not pertinent to our argument here; we shall talk in terms of dilatational effects on occasion.)

The deformation potential is the rate of change of the energy of the conduction band edge with strain, whether dilatational or shear. Since it appears that the change of $E_g - E_v$ is linear to 10,000 kg cm^{-2}, the change with pressure of the deformation potential is probably less than 5 per cent, unless there is accidental cancellation by changes in the valence band deformation potential. In principle, we might estimate $\delta E_{lg}/E_{lg}$ by solving the wave equation in a strained crystal by a perturbation method. Then

$$E_g = E_{g0} + d(0|V|0) + d^2 \sum_i \frac{|(0|V|i)|^2}{E_g - E_i} \qquad \ldots (29)$$

where $(0|V|0) = E_{lg}$; E_{g0} is the energy of the conduction band edge in an unstrained crystal; d is the dilatation; V is the interaction potential; $(0|V|i)$ are matrix elements between the conduction band edge state, labelled '0', and states i of the same k vector, having energy eigenvalues E_i.

Approximately, using the completeness theorem,

$$\frac{\delta E_{lg}}{E_{lg}} \simeq \frac{dE_{lg}}{(E_g - E_i)_{av}} \qquad \ldots (30)$$

10,000 kg cm^{-2} corresponds to a dilatation of 0·01. The deformation potential may be of the order of 10 eV, while the average energy denominator may be of the order of 1 eV. This implies that changes of the order of

10 per cent in 10,000 kgcm^{-2} cannot be excluded. It is to be noted that Drickamer finds an (approximately) linear change of gap in silicon to pressures of 100,000 kgcm^{-2}. On the other hand, changes in compressibility with pressure have to be taken into account, and it may well be that decreasing compressibility and increasing E_{lg} produce compensatory effects. The argument is tenuous; in the absence of better information we have to assume E_{lg} constant to pressures of 10,000 kgcm^{-2}, bearing in mind that the information we can now derive about the other parameters can only limit their variation, not define it. Bridgman's determinations of the volume compressibility give

$$V = V_0(1 - aP + bP^2)$$

with
$$a = 12 \cdot 69 \times 10^{-7} \text{ cm}^2 \text{kg}^{-1}$$
$$b = 3 \cdot 56 \times 10^{-12} \text{ cm}^4 \text{kg}^{-2}$$

Since the compressibility $\qquad \beta = \dfrac{3}{C_{11} + 2C_{12}}$

then $(C_{11} + 2C_{12})_N = 1 \cdot 056$, where $(y)_N$ denotes the ratio of the value of a quantity at 10,000 kgcm^{-2} to its value at zero pressure.

Nathan[21] deduced, from an analysis of measurements of Bailyn,[49] that all of the elastic constants changed similarly with pressure, and that $(C_p)_N \simeq 1 \cdot 06$. Koppelmann and Landwehr[50] found coefficients for all of the constants of the same order of magnitude. McSkimmin's[51] results also give $(C_p)_N \simeq 1 \cdot 05$. We shall assume therefore a 5 per cent increase in 10,000 kgcm^{-2}.

Recent precise measurements by Howard[11] have shown that K_g decreases by about 1 per cent in 10,000 kgcm^{-2}, which is much less than the change found earlier by Benedek, Paul, and Brooks;[10] however, the latter acknowledged that their estimate was very uncertain, and we shall therefore adopt Howard's result. Thus, assuming E_{lg} independent of pressure, $(C_p)_N \simeq 1 \cdot 05$, $(K_g)_N \simeq 0 \cdot 99$, we find

$$(m_{lg})_N \simeq 0 \cdot 97$$
$$(m_{tg})_N \simeq 0 \cdot 98$$

i.e. that the mass changes in 10,000 kgcm^{-2} are only 2 or 3 per cent. The assumptions in our analysis are such that the exact numbers should not be taken seriously, but the order of magnitude of the changes should.

In principle, the magnitude of these changes may be compared with those expected from a perturbation theory treatment[52] giving

$$\left.\begin{array}{l} \dfrac{m}{m_{tg}} - 1 = \dfrac{2}{3m} \sum_{i=L_3'} \dfrac{|(0|\,p_x + \omega p_y + \omega^2 p_z|i)|^2}{E_g - E_i} \\[3em] \dfrac{m}{m_{lg}} - 1 = \dfrac{2}{3m} \sum_{i=L_2'} \dfrac{|(0|\,p_x + p_y + p_z|i)|^2}{E_g - E_i} \end{array}\right\} \quad \dots (31)$$

178

where $\omega^3 = 1$, m is the free electron mass, and p the momentum operator. In practice, the changes in the energy denominators are unknown. We can say that the changes are of the right order of magnitude, and find some indications of discrepancies, e.g. we would expect m_{lg} to vary much less than m_{tg}, which is not found. However, we are again on unsure ground, and can draw no quantitative conclusions inside our order of magnitude, already stated. We can say, however, that the mass changes will alter the density of states factor C_g so little that the parameters of the interband scattering theory will be almost unaffected. The volume dependence of the mass allows us to estimate its implicit and explicit temperature dependence; since this is a complex subject of some importance, we postpone it until Section 8.

3.8. Weaknesses in the Present Position

It is trite to remark that there are many places where those who require rigorous agreement between theory and experiment will find room to cavil. Among these there are at least three areas where it is clear that more work is necessary for a fully satisfactory picture.

(1) Bridgman's minimum in the conductivity was found in irreversible non-hydrostatic pressure experiments. His measurements, and those of Bridgman and Paul[12] establish the rough pressure dependence adequately; however, it would be advantageous if the hydrostatic measurements could be pushed at least high enough in pressure so that the conductivity minimum is included, and the scattering parameters and energy level shifts re-established.

(2) The changeover of carriers to the (100) minima is inferred from evidence converging on this solution. The direct demonstration of this can be afforded by galvanomagnetic experiments defining the tensor effective mass of the conduction band electrons at the higher pressures. Such experiments require a phenomenological theory that includes the inter-band scattering mechanism. The Hall effect and the magnetoresistance coefficients[11, 21, 48] have been calculated in terms of averages of the scattering time for the two sets of minima in the conduction band, for the case of low electric and magnetic fields. The treatment is a generalization of the standard one to be found, for example, in articles by Abeles and Meiboom[53] and Shibuya.[54] To date the galvanomagnetic experiments have been carried out up to 20,000 $\mathrm{kg\,cm^{-2}}$;[10, 11] while this has established, *inter alia*, the rate of transfer of carriers out of the (111) minima, the pressure is not high enough to permit a study of the carriers in the (100) minima. New techniques will have to be developed to complete this phase of the experiment. Alternatively, the symmetry of the upper (100) minima could be established by piezoresistance experiments under pressure,[36] as it is likely

that this technique will lend itself better to experimentation in the higher pressure range.

We shall not, in this review, consider the galvanomagnetic experiments that have been completed in the detail we have thought appropriate for the conductivity measurements. Howard's thesis[11] and technical report should be consulted for such detail, and we shall confine ourselves to an outline of the procedure and results.

If $\Delta\sigma_l$ is a longitudinal magnetoconductance, i.e. the increment in conductance for electric and magnetic fields both in a (100) direction, and $\Delta\sigma_t$ is a transverse magnetoconductance, i.e. the increment in conductance for electric field in the (100) and magnetic field in the (010) direction, then for the lowest (111) ellipsoids in germanium Howard[11] finds

$$\frac{\Delta\sigma_l}{\Delta\sigma_t} = \frac{2(K_g-1)^2}{(2K_g+1)(K_g+2)}$$

provided we can assume τ_l/τ_t independent of energy. K_g has a somewhat different meaning than in the early part of this section. Instead of $K_g = m_{lg}/m_{tg}$, the ratio of the longitudinal to the transverse components of the effective mass tensor, we have

$$K_g = (m_{lg}/m_{tg})(\tau_{tg}/\tau_{lg})$$

τ_{lg}, τ_{tg}, and τ_{tg} are the three diagonal components of a relaxation time tensor which is diagonal in the same axes as the effective mass tensor. At low fields the magnetoconductances for constant energy surfaces in the (111) directions are

$$\left.\begin{aligned}
\frac{\Delta\sigma_l}{H^2} &= -\frac{nq^4}{c^2}\frac{2}{9}K(K-1)^2\frac{\langle\tau_l^3\rangle}{m_l^3} \\[2ex]
\frac{\Delta\sigma_t}{H^2} &= \frac{nq^4}{c^2}\frac{K}{9}(2K+1)(K+2)\frac{\langle\tau_l^3\rangle}{m_l^3}
\end{aligned}\right\} \quad \dots (32)$$

If the ellipsoids lie in the (100) directions, the corresponding expressions, for the same field directions, are

$$\left.\begin{aligned}
\frac{\Delta\sigma_l}{H^2} &= 0 \\[2ex]
\frac{\Delta\sigma_t}{H^2} &= -\frac{nq^4}{c^2}K(K^2+K+1)\frac{\langle\tau_l^3\rangle}{m_l^3}
\end{aligned}\right\} \quad \dots (33)$$

where $\quad \langle\tau_l^3\rangle = \dfrac{4}{3\sqrt{(\pi)}}\displaystyle\int_0^\infty \tau_l^3(y)y^{3/2}\exp(-y)\,dy; \quad y = \dfrac{E}{kT}$

Combining these results in the two-band case, where the conductances are additive, and confining ourselves to low fields, we find

$$
\left.
\begin{aligned}
\frac{\Delta\sigma_l}{H^2} &= -\frac{2n_g q^4}{9c^2} K_g(K_g-1)^2 \frac{\langle\tau_{lg}^3\rangle}{m_{lg}^3} \\[2ex]
\frac{\Delta\sigma_t}{H^2} &= -\frac{n_g q^4}{9c^2} K_g(2K_g+1)(K_g+2)\frac{\langle\tau_{lg}^3\rangle}{m_{lg}^3} - \\[2ex]
&\quad -\frac{n_s q^4}{c^2} K_s(K_s^2+K_s+1)\frac{\langle\tau_{ls}^3\rangle}{m_{ls}^3}
\end{aligned}
\right\} \quad \dots (34)
$$

As before the letters 'g' and 's' refer to the two different bands. We see that $\Delta\sigma_l/\Delta\sigma_t$ gives the pressure dependence of K_g at low pressures, where the contribution of the s band to $\Delta\sigma_t$ can be neglected. Then $\Delta\sigma$ gives the pressure dependence of

$$
n_g \frac{\langle\tau_{lg}^3\rangle}{m_{lg}^3}
$$

Under certain conditions the pressure dependences of n_g and $\langle\tau_{lg}^3\rangle/m_{lg}^3$ can be separated out. $n_g(P, T)$ leads to $\Delta E(P)$, and $\langle\tau_{lg}^3\rangle/m_{lg}^3$ (P) can be interpreted to give information about the amount of scattering between the (111) and (100) bands, since

$$
\frac{\dfrac{\langle\tau_{lg}^3\rangle^{1/3}}{m_{lg}}(P)}{\dfrac{\langle\tau_{lg}^3\rangle^{1/3}}{m_{lg}}(0)} = \frac{\dfrac{\langle\tau_{lg}\rangle}{m_{lg}}(P)}{\dfrac{\langle\tau_{lg}\rangle}{m_{lg}}(0)}
$$

in the absence of interband scattering.

By analysis of this sort, the details of which can be found in reference 11, Howard finds that

$$
\Delta E(P)(\text{eV}) = 0\cdot21 \pm 0\cdot03 + (6\cdot5 \pm 1)\times10^{-6} P \ (P \text{ in kg cm}^{-2})
$$

Thus his $\Delta E(0)$ is within the range of variation found by Nathan, but its most probable value is higher. The pressure dependence is exactly what we expect if we assign to the second set of minima the pressure coefficient appropriate for the (100) minima in silicon, and is thus somewhat different from Nathan's coefficient. We are unable to judge whether Howard's or Nathan's coefficients are the more reliable from the measurements themselves, but the former perhaps fit better with the energy level variations in silicon–germanium alloys and with the idea of similar pressure coefficients for minima of the same symmetry. The quantitative differences do not affect the overall agreement in the deductions from the different experiments.

Howard also finds that he must introduce interband scattering to explain his results, which is predicted from the simple resistivity analysis. He is able to deduce from his determination of $\Delta\sigma_l/\Delta\sigma_t$ versus pressure the pressure dependence of K_g. This variation is small, of the order of 1 per cent in 10,000 kg cm^{-2}, and was used earlier in our analysis of the explicit effect on the mobility. The variation is, however, non-linear to 20,000 kg cm^{-2} and this is not presently understood.

(3) We have so far neglected the energy of the interband scattering phonons. This is unlikely to be negligible in comparison with the energy level differences with which we are concerned, and it was omitted in the original treatment simply to make the problem more tractable mathematically. With the presently accepted knowledge of the germanium band structure and scattering mechanism it is doubtful if we can improve our theory much. The lattice vibration spectrum of silicon has been established by neutron scattering measurements of Brockhouse.[55] The position of the (100) minima in silicon has been determined[56] (85 per cent of the distance to the zone boundary). If we make the reasonable assumption that the position of this minimum changes very little between germanium and silicon, then we find that the energy of the transverse acoustic phonon linking the (111) and (100) extrema is 0·009 eV. However, the relative contributions of transverse and longitudinal acoustical modes, and of the optical modes, are not established. It is appropriate here to remember that the temperature dependence of the lattice scattering mobility changes from $T^{-1\cdot7}$ to $T^{-2\cdot6}$ as we pass from germanium to silicon.

If it is hard to include the effect of phonon energies in our attempted correlation of theory and experiment, we must at least try to justify the proposition that only small errors are committed by their neglect.

In one limiting case, we find

$$\langle\tau_g(\Delta)\rangle_N = \frac{\langle\tau_g(\Delta)\rangle}{\langle\tau_g(\infty)\rangle}$$

$$= \int_0^{\Delta-\Delta_p} y\exp(-y)\,dy + \int_{\Delta-\Delta_p}^{\Delta+\Delta_p} \frac{y\exp(-y)\,dy}{\{1+S_a[1-(\Delta-\Delta_p)/y]^{1/2}\}} +$$

$$+ \int_{\Delta+\Delta_p}^{\infty} \frac{y\exp(-y)\,dy}{\{1+S_a[1-(\Delta-\Delta_p)/y]^{1/2}+S_e[1-(\Delta+\Delta_p)/x]^{1/2}\}} \quad \cdots (35)$$

In this equation $\Delta_p = \hbar\omega/kT$ where $\hbar\omega$ is the phonon energy (if there is more than one phonon, additional triplets of integrals are required); S_a and S_e are interband scattering parameters similar to S, for phonon absorption and emission processes, respectively.

The full effect of these additions is hard to see from inspection of equation

(35). However, we can obtain some idea from approximation: suppose Δ_p is large enough, and Δ small enough, that the major contributions to equation (35) come from the first two terms, and that the third is relatively much smaller. We can then extend the upper limit of the integration of the second term to infinity without much error, and obtain, instead of equation (36), equation (37)

$$\langle \tau_g(\Delta) \rangle_{N1} = 1 - \left[\frac{S(1+\Delta)}{1+S} - \frac{S\Delta}{2(1+S)^2} \exp(-\Delta) \right] \qquad \ldots (36)$$

$$\langle \tau_g(\Delta) \rangle_{N2} = 1 - \left[\frac{S_a(1+\Delta-\Delta_p)}{1+S} - \frac{S_a(\Delta-\Delta_p)}{2(1+S)^2} \right] \exp(\Delta_p - \Delta) \quad \ldots (37)$$

Taking $S_a = S = 1$, and $\Delta = \Delta_p = 1$

$$\langle \tau_g(\Delta) \rangle_{N1} \simeq 17/24; \quad \langle \tau_g(\Delta) \rangle_{N2} = 1/2$$

This indicates that the relaxation time is 40 per cent longer when the effect of the phonon energy is neglected. We deliberately chose a case where the extra scattering possible by phonon energy absorption would be appreciable. Whether the situation is as bad as this makes it look is hard to say without a more searching examination and evaluation of the integrals. We are inclined to think it is not too bad, because of the good fit obtained by Nathan to his experimental results. However, this example is sufficient to advise us not to dismiss the effects of phonon energies in more sophisticated treatments based on more information about the energy bands and vibration spectra.

Note added in proof. Recently Mr. S. C. Yu has re-examined the theory, evaluating the integrals numerically and taking into account the phonon energy approximately. The more careful calculation does not significantly modify the conclusions derived from the simpler theory discussed here.

4. OPTICAL ABSORPTION MEASUREMENTS ON GERMANIUM

4.1. INTRODUCTION

For semiconductors whose band structures are of the general form of Figures 1 and 2, there are six main types of optical absorption often investigated, whose pressure dependence may yield useful information.

(1) The first involves absorption of a photon in order to transfer an electron from a valence band state to a conduction band state of the same crystal momentum. In germanium the minimum energy for such a transition occurs for crystal momentum zero. The resultant electron and hole may be bound in exciton states, or may be free in true conduction and valence band states. This type of absorption, with or without exciton formation, may also occur with the absorption or emission of an optical

phonon of zero momentum, giving the possibility of transitions at photon energies lower than the energy gap. The energy dependence of the absorption coefficient will depend on whether the transition is parity-allowed or not. There have been numerous publications on this subject, particularly in connection with the spectra obtainable when the sample is in a magnetic field; the reader is referred to two recent review papers for further details and references to earlier work on the subject.[57, 58]

(2) The absorption under (1) is referred to as direct absorption, to distinguish it from the so-called indirect absorption, which involves the transfer of an electron from the valence band maximum to the state lowest in energy in the conduction band. Selection rules then demand the interaction through emission or absorption of a phonon, with momentum equal to the difference in momentum between the initial and final electronic states. Again excitons may be formed, in their different excited states. The reader is again referred to the recent reviews for particular discussion, and references to the earlier work on the subject.

(3) At wavelengths longer than those corresponding to the absorption edge, radiation is absorbed to cause transitions between states in the conduction band or in the valence band. This absorption is the same as (2) except that both initial and final states are in the same band. Classical treatments of this effect have been in existence for many years, so that the absorption is called free carrier absorption or Drude–Zener absorption. The process is discussed in many standard texts and has received attention more recently in quantum theoretical treatments by Meyer[59] and by Rosenberg and Lax.[60] We are not aware, however, of any pressure measurements specifically on this type of absorption, so that we shall not have occasion to discuss it here. We shall, however, estimate the usefulness of pressure measurements in this connection in sub-section 4.3.

(4) Direct transitions similar to those of (1) are possible between the sub-bands of the degenerate valence band structure. Experimental results such as those discussed by Kahn[61] and the detailed analysis of Kane[62] are well known, and have been instrumental in establishing the spin–orbit splitting in germanium. Parallel investigations in some of the inter-metallics have also been carried out.[63]

(5) Optical absorption can also occur through the excitation or ionization of impurities. Absorption measurements have been mostly confined to the hydrogenic impurities, while the deeper lying impurities have been extensively investigated through the measurement of photoconductive spectra. More recently, Zeeman effects on the spectra of the hydrogenic impurities have been measured and analysed.[64] No measurements under pressure have been carried out. Such experiments on the hydrogenic impurities would have to be carried out at helium temperatures, where the experimental difficulties are very acute.

(6) Finally, it is possible for radiation to be absorbed by the lattice

vibrations, without any alteration in electronic energies.[65] No measurements of pressure variations of this absorption have been reported.

4.2. Pressure Measurements

(1) Pressure investigations of the absorption caused by direct transitions have been reported by Fan et al.,[13] Neuringer,[14] and Cardona and Paul.[66] The pressure coefficient of the energy gap corresponding to these transitions has also been measured indirectly by Paul and Warschauer.[32] All of the investigations have been carried out without magnetic field, and have been of low spectral resolution, so that details of exciton effects were not observed. The spectra have not been analysed for the dependence of the absorption coefficient on energy, nor for changes of the shape of the absorption coefficient versus energy curves with pressure. All of the investigators have confined themselves to the displacement of the energy corresponding to a fixed absorption coefficient with pressure and have estimated this to give the coefficient of the direct transition optical absorption edge. The investigations of Fan et al., of Neuringer, and of Paul and Warschauer, all gave coefficients of this edge of the order of $1 \cdot 2 \times 10^{-5}$ eV cm² kg⁻¹. However, measurements of such absorption spectra with magnetic field (but no pressure) have established that the early investigations which purported to measure the direct transition, were in fact carried out to maximum energies barely as high as the direct optical energy gap. Later work by Cardona and Paul[66] is not open to this objection: curves obtained by them are shown in Figure 19, and isoabsorption lines in Figure 20. We conclude that the average rate of increase of this energy gap is $1 \cdot 3 \times 10^{-5}$ eV cm² kg⁻¹, and that the rate is decreasing slowly with increasing absorption coefficient, i.e. increasing energy distance from the minimum transition energy possible.

This coefficient is in agreement with the earlier investigations, although the reason is not quite clear. It may be[67] that transitions of this type are occurring at energies lower than the gap energy with the interaction of optical phonons, or it may be that the spectral resolution that had to be employed by Fan et al. and by Neuringer was wide enough to permit transitions for spectrometer wavelength settings nominally short of the direct transition absorption edge.

The slow decrease with increasing absorption coefficient is in qualitative agreement with the supposition that the (000) conduction band minimum is non-parabolic for part of the energy range of the measurement. It would, however, be hazardous to attempt a correlation of the change in the coefficient with changes in the shape of the energy versus crystal momentum relation, without a more sophisticated examination of the functional dependence of the absorption coefficient on energy and effective mass.

(2) The indirect transition absorption has been more widely investigated, particularly by Paul and Warschauer[32] and by Slykhouse and Drickamer.[15] Again, magnetic fields have not been applied, and exciton effects have been

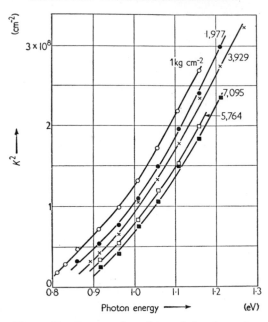

Figure 19. *Pressure dependence of the absorption due to direct transitions in germanium*

neglected. Fine structure on the absorption edge caused by the different interacting phonons has been smeared out in the spectra of all of the investigations. Discussions of the form of the absorption edge dependence

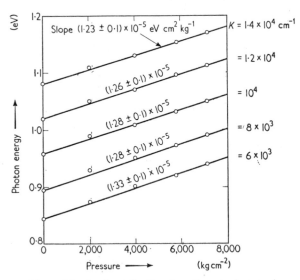

Figure 20. *Isoabsorption lines from the experiments of Figure 19*

186

on energy and on other parameters is largely unnecessary as a result, except for one aspect of major importance. While the inexactness of the absorption curves (inexactness in the light of the present day highly quantitative measurements on semiconductors, not in comparison with earlier investigations of absorption edges) relieves us of the necessity for a discussion of pressure changes of effective masses, matrix elements, oscillator strengths, refractive indices, and phonon distributions, we cannot ignore the dependence of the absorption coefficient on the square of an energy denominator $(E_{g0} - E_g)$ where E_{g0} is the (000) conduction band energy and E_g the (111) edge. The zero pressure value of this difference is about $0 \cdot 15$ eV, and the

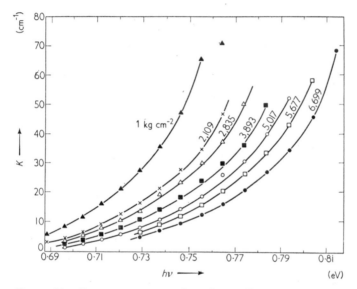

Figure 21. *Room temperature absorption coefficient of germanium versus photon energy at several pressures*

value at 10,000 atm about $0 \cdot 23$ eV, causing a change in the square of a factor of $2 \cdot 3$. The consequent change in shape of the band edge with pressure very easily introduces errors in deduction from isoabsorption plots.

All of the investigations give about the same coefficient, $\sim 8 \times 10^{-6}$ eV cm^2 kg^{-1} from isoabsorption plots at high values of the absorption coefficient, or from displacement of the curves of absorption coefficient versus energy with pressure. A typical set of such curves, from Paul and Warschauer, is shown in Figure 21. Isoabsorption plots from these data are shown in Figure 22 and the variation of the slope of such lines displayed in Figure 23. It is quite clear that the shape change is important, and that the correct coefficient of the energy gap is less than 6×10^{-6} eV cm^2 kg^{-1}. There seems to be disagreement on this point; however, since the measurements of MacFarlane et al.[68] show that the most important intermediate

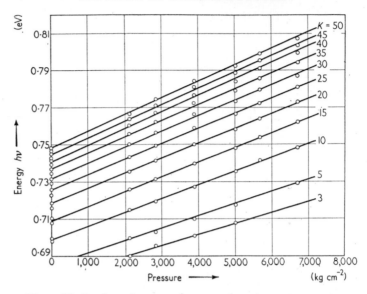

Figure 22. *Isoabsorption curves for germanium at room temperature*

state for indirect transitions in germanium is the (000) state at about 0·80 eV above the valence band, and not any higher (000) states, it would seem to be inevitable that absorption edge shape changes would occur, and must be taken account of in even an approximate treatment.

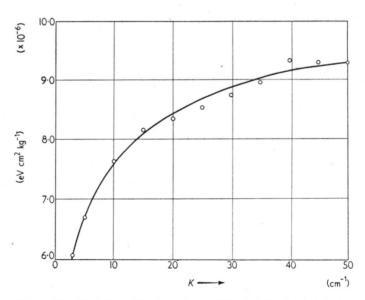

Figure 23. *Variation with absorption coefficient of the slope of the iso-absorption lines shown in Figure 22*

Paul and Warschauer analysed their data with very approximate relations between the absorption coefficient and the photon energy of the form

$$K = a(h\nu - E_G)^2 \quad \text{and} \quad K = b(h\nu - E_G)^3 \qquad \ldots (38)$$

where a and b depend, *inter alia*, on $(E_{g0} - E_g)^{-2}$. By plotting $K^{1/2}$ versus $h\nu$, and $K^{1/3}$ versus $h\nu$, these authors found the energy gap as a function of pressure by extrapolation to $K = 0$. Their gap coefficients lay between $3 \cdot 9$ and $4 \cdot 7 \times 10^{-6}$ eV cm^2 kg^{-1}. No significance is to be attached to these numbers other than that they are close to the coefficient for the thermal gap reported in Section 3, i.e. 5×10^{-6} eV cm^2 kg^{-1}. The optical measurements are not therefore in disagreement with the electrical ones, but are much less exact in the coefficients they provide. Since the change of shape of the absorption edge is caused by changes in $E_{g0} - E_g$, the changes of $a^{1/2}$ and $b^{1/3}$ of the equations above can be interpreted to give the coefficient of $E_{g0} - E_g$, and thus of $E_{g0} - E_v$. Within a moderate error, the latter coefficient found by Paul and Warschauer, 1×10^{-5} eV cm^2 kg^{-1}, is in agreement with the coefficient determined from measurements on the direct transition absorption edge reported under sub-section 4.2(1).

The Slykhouse and Drickamer measurements of the edge have been reported essentially as the displacement with pressure of the energy corresponding to a chosen absorption coefficient. This energy increases to a maximum and then decreases at a rate of -2×10^{-6} eV cm^2 kg^{-1}. The method of analysis is open to the same criticism as mentioned above, namely the neglect of shape changes. However, it is clear that the results are in general agreement with the picture of the displacement of the (111) and (100) minima we have drawn in Section 3. It is to be noticed, particularly, that Slykhouse and Drickamer are able to extrapolate their data to find a zero pressure separation of the (111) and (100) minima of $0 \cdot 2$ eV, in agreement with the earlier result.

(3) As stated above, there are no published measurements of the pressure dependence of the free carrier absorption known to us.

(4) Unpublished measurements by Paul and Warschauer on highly doped P-type samples of germanium, that showed the characteristic features of the absorption caused by intervalence band transitions, revealed no detectable change in the absorption spectra to pressures of 7,000 kg cm^{-2}.

(5) and (6) No measurements are known to us.

4.3. Discussion

It is clear that measurements of the shift of the absorption edge with pressure provide unambiguous quantitative evidence for changes in the energy gap; it is equally clear that caution about possible edge shape changes is necessary if quantitative correlations are to be made with other experiments. We believe that measurements to date have been correlated successfully with more exact measurements and estimates from resistivity data. The question arises whether better optical experiments are worth-while. The experimental difficulties are considerable, and resolution of the sort needed for interpretations such as those of the R.R.E. group[57, 68] would be hard to attain under high pressure conditions. Even if the experiments were possible, it is doubtful if they are necessary. As far as the indirect transitions are concerned, the exact energy level shifts can be obtained from resistivity data, and a check for consistency is adequate. It would be impracticable to try to fit the absorption curves under pressure to disentangle changes in the refractive index (easily found otherwise—see Section 5) matrix elements, phonon spectra, and the like. If these parameters could be found otherwise, it might be worthwhile to use changes in shape of the absorption curves as an overall check. On the other hand, the optical absorption measurements are helpful in some materials where the resistivity measurements under pressure are difficult (e.g. for low purity high gap semiconductors, only intrinsic at high temperatures).

Measurements of the direct transition energy gap, where it is greater than the indirect gap, are quite a different matter. Here the optical measurements are the most direct for the determination of the pressure coefficient of the gap.

Other optical experiments which could usefully be repeated at high pressures include: (1) Magnetoabsorption experiments, which should give a very accurate value for the pressure coefficients of the energy gap and also possibly of the effective mass in the (000) minimum; (2) Radiative recombination experiments, with or without magnetic fields, which should give accurately the pressure dependences of energy gaps and possibly of some of the phonon energies; (3) Photoconductivity measurements on deep-lying impurities, with or without magnetic fields, which may give the pressure dependence of impurity ionization energies; (4) Reflection measurements in the visible and ultra-violet regions, which should give the shifts of the prominent peaks of reflection found there that seem to be correlated with identifiable valence–conduction band transitions.

Little would probably be learnt from the following pressure experiments: (1) On exciton spectra, since the resolution required is high and the change in the exciton binding energy is probably small; (2) On lattice vibration spectra, since the effect is expected to be very small; (3) On free carrier absorption, since the effect of changing mass is also expected to be small.

Our final remarks in this section concern the sort of measurement made by Drickamer and his collaborators to pressures of the order of 100,000 kg cm^{-2}. Drickamer's pressures are approximately hydrostatic, but, in any case, the effect of finite non-diagonal components of the strain is of less importance than in measurements of, for example, transport properties. It seems to us that, given the apparatus, this method represents one of the most fruitful approaches in mapping out the gross pressure behaviour of the band structure. Thus the changeover from (111) to (100) type minima in the conduction band of germanium is graphically illustrated by a maximum in Drickamer's results for optical energy gap versus pressure. The *actual* pressure coefficients from such measurements are, however, no more accurate than from experiments at lower pressures. Moreover, it does not seem to be possible to follow gradual changes in the shape of the edge, which, as we have indicated, can very easily affect the deduced coefficients. This applies, in Drickamer's germanium data, both to the (111) and (100) edge determinations. Drickamer has not yet measured the (000) edge displacement to high pressures. Such results might be interesting. We compute that by 100,000 kg cm^{-2} the (000) minimum will be some 2·1 eV above the valence band (if it moves linearly with pressure). It is to be noted, however, that the lowest state in the silicon conduction band at $\mathbf{k} = 0$ corresponds to a Γ_{15} state; is it possible that the effect of decreasing lattice constant in germanium will be to lower the energy for this state relative to the $\Gamma_{2'}$ state and that there will be a maximum in the direct energy gap as well?

5. ELECTRIC SUSCEPTIBILITY OF GERMANIUM AND SILICON

5.1. INTRODUCTION

Extensive measurements of the pressure and temperature dependence of the dielectric constants of germanium and silicon have been reported by Cardona, Paul, and Brooks,[39, 69] and of the temperature dependence by Lukes[70] and Briggs and Konkel.[71]

If $\epsilon - i\epsilon'$ is the complex dielectric constant of a solid, then $\epsilon = 1 + 4\pi\chi$, and $\epsilon' = 4\pi\sigma/\omega$, where χ and σ are the electric susceptibility and conductivity at the angular frequency ω.

The complex refractive index $n - i\nu$ is defined by $(n - i\nu)^2 = \epsilon - i\epsilon'$ so that $n^2 - \nu^2 = \epsilon^2$ and $2n\nu = \epsilon'$. ν is the extinction index. The real and imaginary parts of the dielectric constant are related through the Kramers–Kronig relations. Estimates of the spectrum of ϵ' from optical transmission and reflection data have given the directly measured value of ϵ, within small experimental error. The intrinsic electric susceptibility χ_0 per unit volume is given by

$$\chi_0 = \frac{2q^2 \hbar^4}{3m^2} \sum_{k,n,m} \frac{|\int \psi_{nk}^* \nabla \psi_{mk} \, d\Omega|^2}{(E_{nk} - E_{mk})^2} \qquad \dots (39)$$

where m is the electron mass, $\mathbf{k}$ a wave vector, and ψ_{nk} the wave function in band n, with eigenvalue E_{nk}. The summation is over occupied bands n and unoccupied bands m. The experimental determination of χ from the Kramers–Kronig relations and the frequency spectrum of σ, or K the absorption coefficient, shows that the virtual transitions contributing most to χ are separated in energy by 2–6 eV. The pressure and temperature dependence of the intrinsic dielectric constant therefore reflects the motion of the whole band structure with strain, and not any small part of it. In this sense the coefficients are quite different from those so far discussed. The measurements have value in that they serve as a check for the general order of magnitude of the effects on the whole band structure that we expect; if there are changes with pressure of the band structure very different from those of its energy extrema, the dielectric constant may demonstrate them. As we shall see, this is just what does happen in the case of silicon. In addition, the pressure coefficient of the dielectric constant is required for the proper interpretation of measurements on impurity ionization energies, impurity scattering, and optical absorption. The establishment of explicit temperature coefficients considerably larger than those caused by thermal expansion is a significant, but not unexpected, result of the measurements.

Equation (39) describes only the intrinsic part of the susceptibility. At finite temperatures lattice vibration absorption occurs in both germanium and silicon.[65] Calculation of the corresponding contribution to the static dielectric constant shows this to be only about 0·02 per cent of the whole.[39] There is, therefore, no difference between the square of the refractive index and the dielectric constant in pure germanium or silicon; this is not so in the intermetallic compounds, due to the polar nature of the bond. Neither is it true in impure semiconductors at finite temperatures, when the free carriers contribute to the susceptibility. As in the case of the absorption, this contribution is adequately described by the classical theory when the product of angular frequency and carrier relaxation time, $\omega\tau$, $\gg 1$. Hence,

$$\chi_c = -\frac{Nq^2}{m^* \omega^2} \qquad \ldots (40)$$

if the energy versus crystal momentum relation is parabolic, and N, m^* are the carrier density and the appropriate average effective mass, respectively. The formula has to be modified, and especially the definition of the mass revised, when $\omega\tau > 1$, or when the bands are non-parabolic. Additional contributions to the susceptibility are to be expected when the free carriers can make virtual transitions among the different branches of a degenerate band structure such as the valence band of germanium.

The measurements to be discussed were directed at the determination of the pressure and temperature dependences of the intrinsic dielectric constant (or refractive index or electric susceptibility) and of the conduction band electron effective masses. The experiments chosen were designed partly for their feasibility and partly for the ease of extraction of reliable data from the measurements. Thus the determination of the dielectric constant at microwave frequencies[72] was excluded because of experimental difficulties. Even were it experimentally a tractable problem, it is not evident what information would be obtained that has not been found already by other, simpler experiments. The radiofrequency measurements of Dunlap and Watters[73] have been repeated. These authors employed capacitors of germanium and silicon in conventional r.f. impedance bridge measurements. The technique required the use of high resistivity samples, which were obtained by doping the element with an impurity yielding levels lying deep in the energy gap, and performing the measurement at low temperatures.

We shall omit a description of the methods for the microwave determination of dielectric constant and free carrier susceptibility, as no additional measurements as a function of pressure have, to our knowledge, been reported. Several techniques have been used to determine the refractive index, reflectivity in the infra-red,[74] interference fringes in thin films of crystals,[75] the deviation of prisms,[76] and ellipticity measurements of reflected polarized light.[77] The second method was used by Cardona et al. to obtain the pressure dependence of the intrinsic refractive index, while the first three methods have been used by them and by the other authors to find the temperature dependence of this index and of the free carrier susceptibility.

5.2. EXPERIMENTAL RESULTS

We shall omit a description of the experimental methods and the reduction of data as these can be found in the original papers, and shall discuss, first, briefly, the adaptations for pressure and temperature variations, and second, the experimental results.

For the r.f. determinations, capacitors of silicon doped with gold and germanium doped with manganese were used. They had conductivities low enough for the measurements to be accurate, at temperatures at or below $77°$ K in the case of germanium, and below about $263°$ K in the case of silicon. The capacitance bridge was a twin T-type 821A General Radio bridge; the overall accuracy of the capacitance determination was $\pm 0 \cdot 1$ pF at 10 Mc/s. Careful correction procedures are required for the effects of pressure and temperature on stray capacitance, which are described in much detail in Cardona's thesis. The final results are summarized in Table 3. Irreproducibility of the temperature coefficients of different silicon samples above $180°$ K and germanium ones near $77°$ K was attributed by Cardona et al.[39] to volume fluctuations in the impurity concentration of the samples. Dunlap and Watters had previously attributed an apparent frequency variation of the dielectric constant found in germanium to similar fluctuations. No temperature coefficient of ϵ determined in this way is given in Table 3, but the low temperature linear part of the variation checks adequately with the better established change, over a wider temperature range, found for the refractive index.

The refractive index variation with pressure and temperature, using the interference patterns produced in thin crystals, requires no special techniques in addition to those already referred to. The wavelengths of the maxima and minima are found directly from a recording of the energy transmitted from a Perkin–Elmer monochromator through the sample to a thermocouple detector. Since

$$\frac{1}{n}\left(\frac{dn}{dP}\right)_T = \frac{1}{\lambda}\left(\frac{d\lambda}{dP}\right)_T - \frac{1}{t}\left(\frac{dt}{dP}\right)_T \qquad \ldots (41)$$

where t is the sample thickness, n its refractive index, and λ the wavelength of a particular maximum or minimum, and since the compressibility correction is easily made, the refractive index change is unambiguously determined. The results are listed in Table 3.

TABLE 3. CHANGES OF THE DIELECTRIC CONSTANT OF GERMANIUM
AND SILICON WITH PRESSURE AND TEMPERATURE

Material	Pressure coefficient $\frac{1}{\epsilon}\left(\frac{d\epsilon}{dP}\right)_T$ (cm²kg⁻¹)	Pressure coefficient $\frac{2}{n}\left(\frac{dn}{dP}\right)_T$ (cm²kg⁻¹)	Calculated temperature coefficient $\frac{1}{\epsilon}\left(\frac{d\epsilon}{dT}\right)_P$ (deg.K⁻¹)	Observed temperature coefficient $\frac{2}{n}\left(\frac{dn}{dT}\right)_P$ (deg.K⁻¹)
Germanium	$-1 \cdot 2 \pm 0 \cdot 3 \times 10^{-6}$	$-1 \cdot 4 \pm 0 \cdot 4 \times 10^{-6}$	$1 \cdot 7 \times 10^{-5}$	$13 \cdot 8 \pm 0 \cdot 8 \times 10^{-5}$
Silicon	$-0 \cdot 4 \pm 0 \cdot 1 \times 10^{-6}$	$-0 \cdot 6 \pm 0 \cdot 4 \times 10^{-6}$	$0 \cdot 6 \times 10^{-5}$	$7 \cdot 8 \pm 0 \cdot 8 \times 10^{-5}$

Similarly from

$$\frac{1}{n}\left(\frac{dn}{dT}\right)_P = \frac{1}{\lambda}\left(\frac{d\lambda}{dT}\right)_P - \frac{1}{t}\left(\frac{dt}{dT}\right)_P \qquad \ldots (42)$$

and parallel measurements we can find the temperature coefficients of refractive index listed in Table 3. The refractive index variation with temperature can be found more easily from the rotation of the ray refracted at minimum deviation through a prism of the material. Distortion of the windows of the pressure apparatus, and the non-axial beam requirements, would make this a difficult measurement at high pressures. Several auto-collimating arrangements were tried by Cardona for his temperature measurements; all gave the same results within experimental error. The temperature coefficient of the long wavelength index is equal to that given by the film measurement, and is used in Table 3. The variation of the increment with wavelength is exhibited in Figure 24 which shows a tendency for the increment to increase at wavelengths near the intrinsic absorption edge. In Figure 25 the variation with temperature of the long wavelength index is shown; here there is a tendency to non-linearity at the lower temperatures.

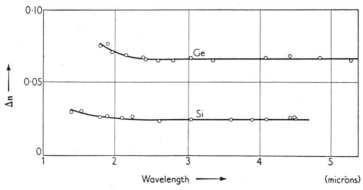

Figure 24. *Increase in refractive index of germanium and silicon between 87° K and 297° K as a function of wavelength*

The contribution of the free carriers to the electric susceptibility is usually found from reflectivity measurements. The reflectivity in air is given by

$$R = \frac{(n-1)^2 + \nu^2}{(n+1)^2 + \nu^2}; \quad n^2 - \nu^2 = \epsilon_0 - 4\pi\chi_c \qquad \ldots (43)$$

and will pass through a minimum roughly at the wavelength where ν_2 becomes comparable with $(n-1)^2$. Typical reflection curves are shown in Figure 26. At wavelengths shorter than those corresponding to minimum R, $\nu^2 \ll (n-1)^2$ and the equation reduces to

$$R = \frac{(n-1)^2}{(n+1)^2} \qquad \ldots (44)$$

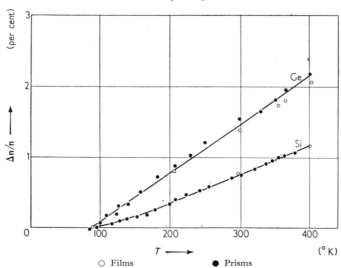

O Films   ● Prisms

Figure 25. *Variation of refractive index of germanium and silicon with temperature*

195

Since $n^2 = \epsilon_0 - 4\pi\chi_c$, χ_c is determined. Alternatively, equation (43) may be used, where $\nu = \lambda K/4\pi$ must be determined. In practice one uses the simpler formula if it is valid over a wide enough wavelength range for accurate determinations.

Cardona et al.[69] measured the reflectivity of N- and P-type germanium and silicon samples at room temperature and nitrogen temperature, in order to find the temperature coefficient of the free carrier electric susceptibility,

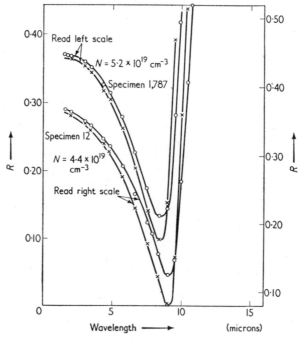

Figure 26. *Wavelength dependence of the reflectivity of heavily doped N-type germanium*

and thus of the carrier mass. Previous measurements by Spitzer and Fan[78] at room temperature had established the general form of the reflection spectra.

The experimental determination of R is relatively routine. Curves such as those of Figure 26 were analysed, mostly in the wavelength region below the minimum in R, in order to obtain the change in n with temperature. This change is due in part to changes in the intrinsic refractive index—which is known, if only from the change in reflectivity at the shortest wavelengths of measurement, where χ_c is negligible—and due for the other part to changes in χ_c. Equation (40) shows that the latter changes must be due solely to changes in m^*, since changes in the carrier density are not possible for the heavily doped samples used. Besides giving the mass change with temperature, the magnitude of χ_c can be used to give m^* if N is known.

Determination of N proceeds from measurements of the Hall constant; this is not a trivial deduction, and an error of 10 per cent has to be allowed for uncertainties in the relation between carrier density and Hall constant in a heavily doped semiconductor. For detailed consideration of this point, the reader is referred, for example, to Cardona's discussion.[39, 69] Table 4 gives a resumé of the results of this work, where it is seen that the mass changes are of the order of 7 per cent between 90 and 300° K, and that there is a dependence of the average mass on the doping level.

TABLE 4. DEPENDENCE OF CARRIER EFFECTIVE MASS ON
TEMPERATURE AND DOPING

Material	Origin	Source identification mark	Carriers/cm³	$\dfrac{m^*(297° \text{K}) - m^*(90° \text{K})}{m^*(297° \text{K})} \times 100$	$\dfrac{m^*}{m}$
Ge, N-type	R.C.A.	1787	$5 \cdot 2 \times 10^{19}$	6	0·26
	Westinghouse	12	$4 \cdot 4 \times 10^{19}$	6	0·24
	Bell	1136	$1 \cdot 1 \times 10^{19}$	5	0·21
	Raytheon	322	$3 \cdot 7 \times 10^{18}$	9	0·14
	Raytheon	Pa	$2 \cdot 0 \times 10^{18}$	7	0·14
	Westinghouse	PK	?	10	?
	Westinghouse	5	?	8	?
	Lincoln	985	?	6	?
	G.E.	112	?	9	?
Ge, P-type	R.C.A.	1781	6×10^{19}	25	0·5
	I.B.M.	44	$2 \cdot 5 \times 10^{19}$	28	0·3
	Lincoln	1017	$2 \cdot 4 \times 10^{19}$	30	0·5
	Westinghouse	59	8×10^{18}	35	0·4
Si, N-type	Bell	445	$1 \cdot 1 \times 10^{20}$	10	0·44
	Bell	427 I	$6 \cdot 5 \times 10^{19}$	9	0·44
	Bell	427 II	$6 \cdot 4 \times 10^{19}$	9	0·43
	Bell	427 III	$6 \cdot 4 \times 10^{19}$	9	0·43
Si, P-type	Sylvania	Sy	?	12	?

No systematic series of measurements of the change in the reflectivity with pressure has been carried out, as it is estimated that distortion of the pressure windows would introduce errors, and therefore alternative methods of finding changes in n and m^* are to be preferred.

5.3. DISCUSSION

The pressure coefficients of the dielectric constant cannot be correlated directly with changes in energy gaps corresponding to particular regions of the band structure. An approximate correlation may be attempted after noting that the major contribution to the dielectric constant of germanium and silicon comes from transitions between 2 and 6 eV, and that a very strong peak at 4 eV dominates these transitions. The pressure and temperature coefficients of the dielectric constant may be compared with those of this dominating peak.

The temperature coefficient of the peak in germanium has been determined by Cardona and Sommers,[79] who found a coefficient of $-1 \cdot 8 \times 10^{-4}$ eV deg.K^{-1} whereas the data of Table 3 would require a temperature coefficient of $-2 \cdot 7 \times 10^{-4}$ eV deg.K^{-1}. In view of the crudeness of the model, the agreement is not bad.

The pressure coefficient of the germanium peak has not yet been determined. From the data of Table 3, we estimate it as $+2 \cdot 4 \times 10^{-6}$ eV $kg^{-1} cm^2$.

Anticipating a little, we notice that the pressure coefficient of ϵ_0 for silicon has the same sign as for germanium, and that this is opposite to that expected from the pressure coefficient of the minimum energy gap. This in itself shows the limited applicability of formulae which attempt to relate the measured smallest energy gap to the dielectric constant.[80]

The smallness of the dielectric constant change reassures us that our assumption of constancy of refractive index in the analyses of optical absorption experiments[32] creats negligible errors. As we shall see, the measurement allows us to correlate changes of average effective mass, and dielectric constant, with the measured changes in the ionization energy of 'hydrogenic' impurities (Holland: see Section 9).

The results of similar radiofrequency measurements on polar compounds (lithium fluoride, magnesium oxide, sodium chloride, potassium bromide) by Mayburg should not be directly compared to the germanium and silicon ones, since the changes in lattice polarizability are important in the case of the alkali halides.[39]

Similar considerations apply to the determination of the pressure coefficient of the refractive index, by a method similar to that described above, of magnesium oxide by West and Makas.[81] However, a coefficient of

$$\frac{1}{n}\left(\frac{dn}{dP}\right)_T = 0 \cdot 2 \times 10^{-6} \, cm^2 \, kg^{-1}$$

was found for diamond by Burstein and Smith[82]—that is, of the opposite sign to the effect in germanium and silicon, from measurements of the photoelastic constants under uniaxial strain. The difference in sign can be explained[83] on the basis of a simple classical model. Suppose

$$\epsilon_0 = 1 + \frac{bN_0}{\omega_0^2}$$

where N_0 is an oscillator density, ω_0 the oscillator frequency, and b a constant. Then

$$\frac{1}{\epsilon_0}\left(\frac{d\epsilon_0}{dP}\right)_T = \left(1-\frac{1}{\epsilon_0}\right)\left(\frac{1}{N}\frac{dN}{dP}\right)_T - \left(1-\frac{1}{\epsilon_0}\right)\frac{2}{\omega_0}\left(\frac{d\omega_0}{dP}\right)_T \quad \ldots (45)$$

In general, N_0 and ω_0 increase with pressure and the two terms compensate. Although

$$\frac{1}{\omega_0}\left(\frac{d\omega_0}{dP}\right)$$

will vary from material to material, it is clearly possible for it to be small for a material of high ω_0, or low ϵ_0 (i.e. diamond) and larger for a material of low ω_0, or high ϵ_0 (germanium). The change in sign in the case of diamond does not then seem to be unreasonable. When the change in ϵ_0 is thus separated into changes in oscillator density and electronic polarizability, it seems plausible that the explanation on the basis of a classical model is also valid for a quantum mechanical treatment.

Several comments can be made on the temperature coefficients of ϵ_0 or n. In the first place, the changes observed are much larger than expected from changes in the volume alone, as deduced from the pressure coefficients and listed in the third column of Table 3.

The increase in the increment of the refractive index at wavelengths close to the absorption edge may be explained as due to the displacement of the energy gap towards longer wavelengths when the temperature is increased. Experimentally this shift is known, for example, from the results of Dash and Newman.[84] Also, from the Kramers–Kronig relation, the change Δn_1 in n_1, at wavelength λ_1, is

$$\Delta n_1^2 = \Delta \nu_1^2 + \frac{2}{\pi^2}\int_0^\infty \frac{\Delta(nK)}{1-\lambda^2/\lambda_1^2}d\lambda \quad \ldots (46)$$

where K is the absorption coefficient and ν_1 the extinction index, negligible at $1\cdot8$ microns (in the germanium case).

As $\lambda_1 \to \infty$,

$$\Delta n_{rf}^2 = \frac{2}{\pi^2}\int_0^\infty \Delta(nK)d\lambda \quad \ldots (47)$$

From equations (46) and (47), and the results of Dash and Newman, Cardona finds:

for germanium, $\dfrac{\Delta n_1 - \Delta n}{n} = 0\cdot0039$ at $\lambda_1 = 1\cdot8$ microns

for silicon, $\dfrac{\Delta n_1 - \Delta n}{n} = 0\cdot001$ at $\lambda_1 = 1\cdot3$ microns

199

to be compared with experimental values of 0·0025 and 0·0014. The agreement is not particularly good, but is just within the experimental error of the measurements.

The low temperature curvature of the variation of the refractive index of silicon with temperature is similar to a quadratic variation found for diamond between 120° K and 700° K by Ramachandran.[85] Similar non-linear effects are found in the temperature variation of the energy gap. Theories of Antoncik[86] and Fan[87] concerning the energy gap predict a quadratic variation below the Debye temperature, and close to a linear variation near this temperature. Experimental determination of the variation of the gap with temperature (for recent data, for example, see Haynes, Lax, and Flood[88]) is in qualitative agreement with the theory. If the effect of temperature on the whole band structure is similar to that on its extrema—which is not unreasonable—then the non-linear variation of the refractive index in silicon ($\theta_D = 636°$ K) is also not unreasonable. It would be idle to pretend any quantitative fit, however. Indeed, the theories of Lukes[89] and Antoncik[90] for the temperature coefficient of the refractive index, which assume a single type of classical oscillator with temperature independent oscillator strength, and a temperature dependence of the oscillator frequency equal to that for the *minimum* energy gap, are of only qualitative value. This is most clearly demonstrated by the experiments of Archer[91] and of Philipp and Taft,[92] which show that the major contribution to the refractive index comes from vertical interband transitions of energy separation between 2 and 6 eV.

The temperature coefficient of the refractive index of germanium has also been reported by Lukes,[70] and of germanium and silicon by Briggs and Konkel.[71] The Lukes result for silicon is about 25 per cent higher than that of Cardona, outside of experimental error. However, since the implicit (volume) effect of temperature predicted from the pressure coefficient is an order of magnitude smaller than the observed coefficient, this discrepancy, so far unexplained, does not affect our qualitative observations on the relative sizes of the pressure and temperature variations of refractive index. There is a similar unexplained discrepancy in the germanium results, of about the same size. The results of Briggs and Konkel also differ in detail from those of both Cardona and Lukes, but are of the same order. The fact that Cardona's results were obtained from two sets of measurements on prisms and films makes us slightly favour his conclusions, although the matter is by no means settled.

Several general comments can be made about the experiments on free carrier susceptibility and effective mass. Although the pressure coefficients of the tensor compounds of the effective mass are defined only to order of magnitude, they are very much smaller than the explicit temperature coefficient deduced from Cardona's results. This will be discussed in Section 8.

Cardona's results in Table 4 are not confirmed by all other investigators. One or two sets of results (giving changes of factors of 2 or 3) can probably safely be discarded. Others, notably those of Bowers,[93] on the magnetic susceptibility, find smaller temperature coefficients of the mass. We shall, until more evidence—which is needed—is at hand, assume that Cardona's rather extensive investigation has given definitive results. The variation with temperature is for the most part established within a few per cent, although one places little reliance on the determination for P-type germanium. It is interesting to note that, if the mobility of the electrons in germanium is assumed proportional to $m^{*-5/2}$, then the mass dependence on temperature adequately explains the discrepancy between the theoretical $T^{-1.5}$ law and the experimentally observed $T^{-1.7}$ one. We noted this in Section 3, and were careful there to avoid drawing any hard and fast conclusions concerning the absence of intervalley or optical mode scattering.

The second observation we can make is that there appears to be a distinct dependence of the measured mass on impurity density, that is outside any error in the deduction of this density from Hall constant measurements. The effective mass for low densities has been established by cyclotron resonance measurements of Lax et al.,[94] and of Dresselhaus et al.[95] Experiments on infra-red reflectivity carried out by Spitzer and Fan,[78] on specific heat by Keesom and Seidel[96] and diamagnetic susceptibility by Bowers[93] and Stevens et al.[97] can also be interpreted to give the effective masses pertinent for different densities of impurities. The conclusion of these various investigations is that the mass changes with doping are significantly less than are indicated by Cardona's measurements. The reader is referred to the original papers for the detailed discussion; in summary, while this question is not settled, the weight of the present evidence favours mass changes smaller than those of Table 4.

Some variation of effective mass with temperature and with doping would be expected on the basis of theoretical consideration of the band structure of germanium and silicon. One would expect appreciable non-parabolicity in the conduction band in the direction of maximum curvature of the band edge. The contribution of electrons in these higher energy regions at high temperatures (effect of Boltzmann distribution) or high doping (effect of degeneracy) will increase the average mass. A quantitative estimate of this effect can be made for germanium if a value of the $L_{3'}-L_1$ gap is assumed from reflectivity data.[69] The mass variation between 90° K and 297° K is estimated at a little over 3·5 per cent, about half the value observed by Cardona. The variation due to doping is less than 10 per cent, appreciably smaller than the experimental results of Table 4, but in line with the experimental results of other investigators.

These theoretical estimates do not yet count any explicit dependence of the $L_{3'}-L_1$ separation on either doping or temperature. Cardona and Sommers[79] have recently measured the temperature dependence of this separation, finding a coefficient of $-4\cdot2\times10^{-4}$ eV deg.K^{-1}. The $(L_{3'}, L_1)$ interaction is the main one determining the transverse electron mass, at the bottom of the L_1 band, so that its temperature dependence will amount to a decrease of 4 per cent between 90° K and 297° K. The longitudinal mass in the L_1 band depends on energy separations whose values are not yet known. If we assume their temperature dependence to be the same as for the transverse mass, we should obtain a negative contribution to the temperature coefficient of the L_1 effective mass of 4 per cent between 90° K and 297° K. We note that this increases the discrepancy between theory and the experimental results of Table 4.

Special comment is appropriate for the results on P-type germanium of Cardona and of Geist.[98] The temperature coefficient of the masses found is large; however, vertical intervalence band transitions make a large contribution to the refractive index. Cardona et al.[69] conclude that these prohibit accurate estimations of masses and mass changes, from reflectivity experiments.

Although these measurements on highly doped samples establish a dependence of an average mass coefficient on temperature and possibly on doping level, this must not be interpreted immediately as an alteration in the curvature of the energy–momentum relation. For one thing, the impurity density is so large that impurity band effects must be considered, as well as any effect of the impurities on the position of the conduction band edge. The carrier density is probably high enough so that if the band edge is non-parabolic near its origin, redistribution of the carriers with temperature, or increased doping, will change the average mass.

6. PROPERTIES OF SILICON AT HIGH PRESSURES

6.1. INTRODUCTION

We recall that there is only one type of low lying conduction band energy minimum in silicon, in the (100) direction, and that the valence band structure is similar to that of germanium but with a smaller spin–orbit splitting. The pressure coefficient of the minimum energy gap, quoted in Section 3 as $-1\cdot5\times10^{-6}$ eV cm^2 kg^{-1}, is established by experiments on optical absorption and electrical resistivity. The energy gap corresponding to the direct optical transition has not yet been established. The spin–orbit splitting is harder to investigate; as a result, although the pressure measurements cover the same range of experiments, fewer phenomena are exhibited, and the data appear to be reasonably straightforward to interpret.

6.2. ELECTRICAL CONDUCTIVITY

Bridgman[2] measured the resistivity of silicon under hydrostatic pressure conditions to 30,000 kg cm^{-2} and also to 100,000 kg cm^{-2} in a soft matrix of silver chloride. His results could not be interpreted even qualitatively because of hysteresis; it appears now that long term trapping effects may have caused this trouble. Paul and Pearson[16] then reported measurements on much purer crystals, which still showed slight hysteresis but which were adequate to provide the pressure coefficients of the electron mobility and the energy gap. The best reported measurements of the pressure coefficients of the electron and hole mobilities are those of Smith[30] which showed smaller hysteresis effects on removal of the pressure. These measurements established that the fractional increases of the electron and hole mobilities were $3 \cdot 1 \times 10^{-6}$ cm^2 kg^{-1} and $3 \cdot 8 \times 10^{-6}$ cm^2 kg^{-1}, respectively, to a maximum pressure of 30,000 kg cm^{-2}. These explicit effects are comparable in magnitude to the same effects in germanium, and are caused by changes in the masses, elastic constants, and deformation potentials. Again, it is difficult to separate out the contributions, and we can only say that, unless there are (unlikely) large cancelling effects, the change with volume of these parameters is established within limits.

The measurements by Paul and Pearson on pure material were carried out at temperatures high enough so that the material was intrinsic to the highest pressure of 7,000 kg cm^{-2}. The energy gap coefficient of $-1 \cdot 5 \times 10^{-6}$ eV cm^2 kg^{-1} was deduced, without correction for mobility changes; these, however, are so small as to have no effect on the coefficient.

This coefficient was later confirmed in a novel fashion by Nathan and Paul.[18] These authors noted that the silicon energy gap had been determined from measurements on crystals doped with gold. Gold in silicon produces an acceptor level, $0 \cdot 54$ eV below the conduction band edge, and a donor level $0 \cdot 35$ eV above the top of the valence band. If crystals are counter-doped with hydrogenic donor impurity so that all acceptor levels below the gold level are filled, and the hydrogenic donors are emptied, then the Fermi level will lie somewhat below the $0 \cdot 54$ eV gold level. The crystal can be P-type, and show an ionization energy equal to the energy separation between the gold acceptor level and the valence band. If a second crystal is doped with more hydrogenic donor impurities, then the gold acceptor level may be made to act like a source for conduction band electrons; the Fermi level will be closer to the gold acceptor level, the crystal will be N-type, and the observed ionization energy will be the energy separation of the conduction band minimum and the gold acceptor level. The sum of these two energies, determined in two separate experiments, was shown by Carlson et al.[99] to add to the accepted total gap energy of silicon at $0°$ K. Nathan and Paul repeated the experiments on two such crystals at temperatures such that the impurity level was deionizing, to a maximum pressure of 30,000 kg cm^{-2}. At low pressures they found the pressure coefficients shown in Table 5, namely $-1 \cdot 2 \times 10^{-6}$ eV cm^2 kg^{-1} and $-0 \cdot 3 \times 10^{-6}$ eV cm^2 kg^{-1}, which sum to the accepted coefficient for the total gap. At higher pressures the coefficients increased. It is felt that this probably represents a failure of the analytic formula used to represent the carrier density, rather than a true increase of the pressure coefficients. When the statistics for these levels are worked out, it becomes clear that there are only limited ranges where analytic formulae are strictly applicable, and that outside of these ranges, when the coefficients are small (as they are in this case), a lack of knowledge of the *compensating* impurities, as well as those providing the ionizing energy levels, effectively prevents deduction of the correct coefficient for the ionization energy.

TABLE 5. PRESSURE COEFFICIENTS OF ENERGY LEVELS IN SILICON

Quantity	Pressure coefficient $(eV\,cm^2kg^{-1})$	Source
Energy gap, valence band–(100) minima, $1 \cdot 16$ eV	$-1 \cdot 5 \times 10^{-6}$ 0 to -2×10^{-6} -2×10^{-6} < 0 $-1 \cdot 5 \times 10^{-6}$	Paul and Pearson[16] Paul and Warschauer[17] Slykhouse and Drickamer[15] Neuringer[14] Nathan and Paul[18]
Ionization energy, gold donor level, $0 \cdot 35$ eV above valence band	$\leqslant 5 \times 10^{-8}$	Nathan and Paul[18, 100]
Ionization energy, gold acceptor level, $0 \cdot 54$ eV below conduction band (w.r.t. conduction band)	$-1 \cdot 2 \times 10^{-6}$	Nathan and Paul[18, 100]
Ionization energy, gold acceptor level, $0 \cdot 62$ eV above valence band (w.r.t. valence band)	$-0 \cdot 3 \times 10^{-6}$	Nathan and Paul[18, 100]
Ionization energy, arsenic donor level, $0 \cdot 049$ eV below conduction band	-5×10^{-8}	Holland[20, 101]
Ionization energy, aluminium acceptor level, $0 \cdot 057$ eV above valence band	0 to $+2 \times 10^{-8}$	Holland[20, 101]
Ionization energy, indium acceptor level, $0 \cdot 16$ eV above valence band	$+4$ to $+6 \times 10^{-8}$	Holland[20, 101]

Although our knowledge of the silicon band structure would seem to exclude the possibility of non-linear band gap coefficients at such low pressures, it is still necessary to check the non-linear effect found by Nathan and Paul. The pressure results themselves hardly exclude the possible existence of a second set of conduction band minima approaching the valence band at a rate not much greater than that of the lowest set. The results of Paul and Pearson on intrinsic samples do not reach high enough pressures. Neither do the optical measurements to be described below, except for those of Drickamer. On the other hand, (100) symmetry is found for the minima in silicon from magnetoresistivity measurements, electron nuclear double resonance experiments establish accurately the position in **k**-space of the lowest (100) minima, and there seems to be no interband scattering effect similar to that in germanium in the N-type silicon pressure experiments. We conclude, nevertheless, that the anomalous increase found by Nathan and Paul needs to be checked. In our laboratory these experiments would be most simply performed on the present day pure samples of silicon, if one could be found with a substantial density of intrinsic carriers at temperatures below $100°$ K, or on P–N junctions that show the ideal characteristic.

6.3. Optical Absorption

Measurements of the change in the energy of the optical absorption edge were reported at the Atlantic City Conference on Photoconductivity by Fan et al.[13] and by Paul and Warschauer, and were in considerable disagreement. Fan et al., in measurements to 1,000 atm, found a pressure coefficient of $+5 \times 10^{-6}$ eV cm^2 kg^{-1} while that of Paul and Warschauer, determined to pressures of 8,000 kg cm^{-2}, was -2×10^{-6} eV cm^2 kg^{-1}. Later measurements to the same pressure by Paul and Warschauer[17] using a high dispersion grating monochromator, and by Neuringer to 1,000 kg cm^{-2}, again yielded the latter coefficient. It seems likely that this is the correct one, since it has been determined in several independent ways; however, the cause of the opposite result of Fan and his colleagues is not explained.

Perhaps the clearest evidence comes from the experiments of Slykhouse and Drickamer[15] at pressures up to 140,000 kg cm^{-2} which also give a coefficient of $-2 \cdot 0 \times 10^{-6}$ eV cm^2 kg^{-1}. The energy gap apparently varies linearly up to the maximum pressure, which is itself of interest. The compressibility of silicon is certainly non-linear to this pressure. If one expects the displacement in energy to be more nearly proportional to dilatation than to pressure, then only a compensatory increase in deformation potential can achieve this linearity. At this stage, however, this possibility is only a speculation.

6.4. Electric Susceptibility

The results of Cardona et al. for the pressure and temperature dependence of the dielectric constant and refractive index were shown in Table 3. Since the dielectric constant is nearly equal to the square of the refractive index, we expect agreement of the coefficients, and this is confirmed, albeit with considerable imprecision. The pressure coefficients are unconfirmed by other experiments, and, as discussed in Section 5, temperature coefficients different from these have been given by Lukes[70] and by Briggs and Konkel.[71] However, since the results of these experiments disagree among themselves, and the results quoted in Table 3 are found from separate sets of experiments on the interference spectra of thin single-crystal films and the rotation of the minimum deviated ray in prisms, we are inclined to accept the latter tentatively. Undoubtedly, additional experiments on both silicon and germanium at another laboratory are advisable and would help to resolve this confusion.

All of the temperature coefficients, however, agree in establishing an explicit temperature coefficient of the dielectric constant much larger than the one derived from thermal expansion.

Measurements of the reflectivity of heavily doped N- and P-type samples can be interpreted to give a dependence of some average effective mass on impurity density and temperature. The results are indicated in Table 4. The same general comments apply here that were made for germanium in Section 5.

6.5. SUMMARY

The interpretation of the silicon measurements is uncomplicated compared with germanium, since there appear to be no conduction band minima close to the lowest (100) set. This is not to say that the measurements are all correlated and interpreted, only that a set of concepts and a theory describing germanium will probably encompass silicon also. Other data on silicon will be reviewed in Sections 8 and 9.

7. INTERMETALLIC COMPOUNDS

7.1. INTRODUCTION

The results of pressure measurements on the Group III–V compounds, such as indium antimonide, have been recently reviewed by Paul[102] in a volume dealing exclusively with these materials.[103] This work, which is based to some extent on the work on germanium and silicon, is rapidly expanding, and it seems appropriate to give here only a condensed version of the earlier review.[102]

TABLE 6. SECTION OF THE PERIODIC TABLE

		B	C	N	O	F
		Al	Si	P	S	Cl
Cu	Zn	Ga	Ge	As	Se	Br
Ag	Cd	In	Sn	Sb	Te	I
I	II	III	IV	V	VI	VII

A section of the Periodic Table is shown in Table 6, and the properties of the Group IV and Group III–V materials in Table 7.[102] We have noted some systematic trends in these compounds already in Section 1.2. The minimum energy gap decreases as the average atomic number increases, while the gap is greater in a compound than in its isoelectronic Group IV element. The valence band structure is similar in all of the compounds. On the other hand, the lowest identified states in the conduction bands are of three types: (1) at the (000) position in the Brillouin zone ($\Gamma_{2'}$ or Γ_1); (2) along the (100) directions (Δ_1); (3) along the (111) directions (L_1). There appears to be some systematic trend of the relative energies of these three minima with average atomic number. Thus the Δ_1 states are lowest in silicon, are probably lowest in gallium phosphide, and perhaps also in diamond. The L_1 states are lowest in germanium, where the atomic number is higher, and they appear to be close to the extreme position in gallium antimonide and in grey tin. The Γ_1 minimum is lowest in indium antimonide and tends to be low for compounds of high average atomic number.

Where such examination is possible, alloys of group members show intermediate properties. However, strikingly non-linear effects occur when the changeover in properties involves a change in conduction band extrema. An early example of this arose from the study of the optical energy gap in silicon–germanium alloys.[104] From 0 per cent to about 15 per cent silicon the lowest conduction band minimum is of the L_1 type, while from 15 per cent to 100 per cent silicon the Δ_1 states form the extrema. Measurements of magnetoresistance[104] have confirmed this interpretation, and have also shown that the mass ratio (and quite probably the masses) in the L_1 and Δ_1 minima in the alloys are very close to their values in the pure substances. Although changes in lattice constant accompany changes in alloy composition, this is not the main cause of the change in energy gap: thus, for example, the energy gap changes by about $0 \cdot 15$ eV between 0 and 10 per cent silicon content whereas the gap change that would result from the change in lattice constant by this composition is only $0 \cdot 05$ eV. For the (100) minima, a decrease in the lattice constant through alloying increases the appropriate energy gap, whereas a decrease caused by pressure decreases it. Extrapolation from its variation in energy in silicon rich alloys is clearly useful in fixing the energy of the Δ_1 minima in pure germanium. A thorough study of the effects of alloying on all possible alloy systems of the group might establish a systematic behaviour of the different minima with lattice constant and ionicity, and in fact this seems a logical consequence of any systematic variation among the compounds themselves.

Many of the properties of the $\Gamma_{2'}$, Γ_1, Δ_1, and L_1 extrema are similar in the different materials. The similarity in properties that depend only on the symmetry of the states is trivial. Less obvious are similarities in effective mass, yet the Δ_1 states seem to maintain the same mass ratio (and thus probably mass) between 100 per cent and 15 per cent silicon in silicon–germanium alloys, and the analysis of pressure results in germanium involving higher minima, which are most probably of a Δ_1 type, require an effective mass very similar to that of silicon. The masses in all $\Gamma_{2'}$ or Γ_1

TABLE 7. PROPERTIES OF THE GROUP IV ELEMENTS AND GROUP III–V COMPOUNDS

Compounds containing boron, nitrogen, thallium, and bismuth are not included in the Table. Conduction band minima are labelled 'speculative' ('spec.') if the type is a systematic extrapolation or based on a pressure coefficient, and are unlabelled if the type is considered assured through measurement of cyclotron resonance, optical absorption, effective mass, etc. The $\Gamma_{2'}$ minima in the diamond lattice become Γ_1 in the zinc blende. The Δ_1 minima in the diamond lattice may shift to the Brillouin zone edge point X_1 in the zinc blende, but we have continued to refer to the Δ_1 states only. Temperatures of energy gaps are mixed; the room temperature gaps more easily allow comparisons where higher minima are present. Little attempt has been made to obtain the very latest values of the parameters in columns 1–3. On the other hand, columns 4 and 5 represent our best present assessment of the pressure coefficients.

Compound	1 Lattice constant (25° C) (Å)	2 Energy gap (eV)	3 Conduction band minima	4 $\left(\dfrac{dE_g}{dP}\right)_T$ (eV cm² kg⁻¹)	5 $\left(\dfrac{dE_g}{d\ln V}\right)_T$ (eV)
C	3·567	5·3 (300° K)	Δ_1 (spec.)	$<10^{-6}$ (a)	—
Si	5·43	1·21 (0° K)	Δ_1	$-1\cdot5\times10^{-6}$ (b)	$+1\cdot5$
Ge	5·66	0·66 (300° K) 0·803 (300° K) 0·85 (300° K)	L_1 $\Gamma_{2'}$ Δ_1	5×10^{-6} (c) 12×10^{-6} (d) 0 to -2×10^{-6} (e)	$-3\cdot8$ -9 0 to $+1\cdot5$
Sn	6·489	0·08 (0° K)	L_1 (spec.)	5×10^{-6} (f)	—
AlP	5·47	3·1 (300° K)	Δ_1 (spec.)	—	—
AlAs	5·66	2·16 (300° K)	Δ_1 (spec.)	—	—
AlSb	6·10	1·6 (300° K)	Δ_1 (spec.)	$-1\cdot6\times10^{-6}$ (g)	—
GaP	5·47	2·2 (300° K) 2·6 (300° K)	Δ_1 (spec.) Γ (spec.)	$-1\cdot7\times10^{-6}$ (h) $-1\cdot8\times10^{-6}$ (i)	— —

GaAs	5.66	1.53 (0°K)	Γ_1	9.4×10^{-6} (j)	-7
				12×10^{-6} (k)	-9
		1.89 (0°K)	Δ_1 (spec.)	Negative	
GaSb	6.10	0.81 (0°K)	Γ_1	16×10^{-6} (l)	-9
				12×10^{-6} (g)	-6.75
			L_1	-5×10^{-6} (m)	-2.8
			Δ_1	Negative (g)	—
InP	5.9	1.34 (0°K)	Γ_1	4.6×10^{-6} (g)	-6.15
			Δ_1 (spec.)	-10×10^{-6} (g)	$+7.45$
InAs	6.07	0.36 (300°K)	Γ_1	5.5×10^{-6} (n)	-3.3
				8.5×10^{-6} (l)	-5.1
				4.8×10^{-6} (g)	-2.9
InSb	6.49	0.27 (0°K)	Γ_1	15.5×10^{-6} (o)	-6.7
				14.2×10^{-6}	-6.1

REFERENCES

(a) CHAMPION, F. C., and PRIOR, J. R. Nature, Lond. 182, 1079 (1958)

(b) PAUL, W., and PEARSON, G. L. Phys. Rev. 98, 1755 (1955); NATHAN, M. I., and PAUL, W. Bull. Amer. phys. Soc. 2, 134 (1957); PAUL, W., and WARSCHAUER, D. M. J. Phys. Chem. Solids 5, 102 (1958); FAN, H. Y., SHEPHERD, M. L., and SPITZER, W. G. Photoconductivity Conference at Atlantic City (Eds. Breckenridge, Russell, and Hahn) (Wiley, New York, 1956); NEURINGER, L. J. Phys. Rev. 113, 1495 (1959); SLYKHOUSE, T. E., and DRICKAMER, H. G. J. Phys. Chem. Solids 7, 210 (1958)

(c) BRIDGMAN, P. W. Proc. Amer. Acad. Arts Sci. 79, 129 (1951); MILLER, P. H., and TAYLOR, J. H. Phys. Rev. 76, 179 (1949); TAYLOR, J. H. Phys. Rev. 80, 919 (1950); HALL, H. H., BARDEEN, J., and PEARSON, G. L. Phys. Rev. 84, 129 (1951); WARSCHAUER, D. M., PAUL, W., and BROOKS, H. Phys. Rev. 98, 1193 (1955); FAN, H. Y., SHEPHERD, M. L., and SPITZER, W. G. Photoconductivity Conference at Atlantic City (Eds. Breckenridge, Russell, and Hahn) (Wiley, New York, 1956); PAUL, W., and WARSCHAUER, D. M. J. Phys. Chem. Solids 5, 89 (1958); MICHELS, A., van ECK, J., MACHLUP, S., and TEN SELDAM, C. A. J. Phys. Chem. Solids 10, 12 (1959); PAUL, W. Phys. Rev. 90, 336 (1953); PAUL, W., and BROOKS, H. Phys. Rev. 94, 1128 (1954)

(d) NEURINGER, L. J. Phys. Rev. 113, 1495 (1959); PAUL, W., and WARSCHAUER, D. M. J. Phys. Chem. Solids 5, 89 (1958); CARDONA, M., and PAUL, W. J. Phys. Chem. Solids 17, 138 (1960)

(e) BROOKS, H., and PAUL, W. Bull. Amer. phys. Soc. 1, 48 (1956); HOWARD, W. E. Thesis (Harvard University, 1961) (Available as Report HP-7, Division of Engineering and Applied Physics, Harvard University); SLYKHOUSE, T. E., and DRICKAMER, H. G. J. Phys. Chem. Solids 7, 210 (1958)

(f) GROVES, S. H., and PAUL, W. Bull. Amer. phys. Soc. 7, 184 (1962)

(g) EDWARDS, A. L., and DRICKAMER, H. G. Phys. Rev. 122, 1149 (1961)

(h) EDWARDS, A. L., SLYKHOUSE, T. E., and DRICKAMER, H. G. J. Phys. Chem. Solids 11, 140 (1959)

(i) ZALLEN, R., and PAUL, W. Unpublished measurements

(j) EDWARDS, A. L., SLYKHOUSE, T. E., and DRICKAMER, H. G. J. Phys. Chem. Solids 11, 140 (1959); See reference (g) above

(k) PAUL, W., and WARSCHAUER, D. M. Unpublished measurements

(l) TAYLOR, J. H. Bull. Amer. phys. Soc. 3, 121 (1958)

(m) SAGAR, A. Phys. Rev. 117, 93 (1960); KEYES, R. W., and POLLAK, M. Phys. Rev. 110, 1001 (1960)

(n) TAYLOR, J. H. Phys. Rev. 100, 1593 (1958)

(o) LONG, D. Phys. Rev. 99, 388 (1955); KEYES, R. W. Phys. Rev. 99, 490 (1955)

states are small, and the matrix element between the light hole states and the $\Gamma_{2'}$ or Γ_1 states appears to be constant for all members of the group,[105] so that—neglecting spin–orbit interaction—the mass varies almost directly with the energy gap at $\mathbf{k} = 0$.

Various authors have discussed the systematic variations of energy gap, carrier mobility, melting point, and hardness with lattice constant, average atomic number, and degree of ionicity.[106] The basis for these discussions has been the connection between bond strengths, bond lengths, and atomic constitution. Extrapolations from such systematic variations have been rather successful, especially in predicting new semiconductors, but the theory used does not give the details of band structure and band interaction, and fails to explain the changes in effective mass and carrier mobility associated with changes in the extrema of the conduction band.

Early theoretical work of Herman[107] and of Callaway[108] attempted to establish the main features of the conduction and valence band structures by applying perturbation theory to the solutions for the band structures of germanium and silicon. It was not pretended that this calculation constituted more than a qualitative guide; however, trends in the band structure as the degree of ionicity or the atomic number of the metallic constituents were changed were predicted with fair success. The displacement in energy of the three types of conduction band minima was expected to be different in the different substances. Since the separation in germanium of all three minima is less than $0 \cdot 2$ eV at atmospheric pressure, it is clear that the lowest minimum might be of different symmetry in the different compounds. Also since the differences in the energy of the minima are small enough so that calculation *ab initio* cannot accurately distinguish the order of occurrence in germanium or silicon, it is not to be expected that such information will be available in the intermetallics either; however, the number of possibilities may be reduced by the use of some guiding experimental information and judicious extrapolation.

In this section we hope to demonstrate that pressure measurements provide a valuable tool in explaining the conduction band structure of some of the intermetallics, by helping to establish the energies of the three types of conduction band minima relative to one another at atmospheric pressure. They also involve the identification of a single pressure coefficient with a particular type of conduction band extremum as was discussed in Section 1.

7.2. Pressure Measurements

Changes in the band structure under pressure have been measured in aluminium antimonide, gallium phosphide, gallium arsenide, gallium antimonide, indium phosphide, indium arsenide, and indium antimonide. The results are shown in Table 7. We note, first of all, that the coefficients found for the energy gap in indium antimonide, $1 \cdot 4 \times 10^{-5}$ eV cm^2 kg^{-1}

and $1 \cdot 55 \times 10^{-5}$ eV cm^2 kg^{-1} are very close to that for the direct gap in germanium. We noted earlier the equality of the pressure coefficients of the (100) gaps in germanium and silicon. The approximate equality in the pressure coefficients of these two types of minima naturally leads us to speculate on a unique association of pressure coefficient and type of band edge in the Group IV and Group III–V materials. The test of this speculation is contained in Table 7.

It would take us too long to discuss in detail the position regarding each of the intermetallics. However, we note that in several of them, there occurs more than one type of conduction band minimum within a few kT of the absolute minimum energy of the conduction band. Different types of experiments are used to determine the pressure coefficients of these minima. In nearly every case, the pressure coefficient is characteristic only of the type of minima involved. The glaring exceptions are the Γ_1 minima in indium arsenide and indium phosphide. Recent investigation of indium arsenide by Zallen at Harvard gives a coefficient of about 1×10^{-5} eV cm^2 kg^{-1}, and there are indications that the coefficient for indium phosphide quoted in Table 7 is similarly low. Thus we conclude that there is a surprising correlation of the pressure coefficients; this result has already been discussed in Section 1.2.

This correlation allows us to plan experiments to investigate the higher minima in a way not possible at the lower pressures. This procedure is identical in principle to that adopted in Section 3. However, when the minima start close enough in energy at atmospheric pressure that they contribute to transport phenomena, the identification of their contribution is very much helped by the addition of the pressure data; the pressure, by separating the minima, can force some minima into greater prominence and some into less, and permit, for example, an estimation of the energy separation at atmospheric pressure. The results of this type of analysis are included in Table 7.

We shall illustrate these general statements with a discussion of gallium arsenide, referring the reader to Paul's review for a critique of the other compounds.

The band structure of gallium arsenide was discussed from a theoretical standpoint by Callaway[108] who suggested that the conduction band minimum might lie at the centre of the Brillouin zone. This was experimentally verified by, for example, Glicksman,[109] Spitzer and Fan,[110] and Barcus, Perlmutter, and Callaway.[111] Evidence for higher minima was presented by Gray and Ehrenreich[112] from the occurrence of a maximum in the Hall coefficient of highly doped material at elevated temperatures. Further evidence was forthcoming from measurements of Spitzer and Whelan[113] on the optical absorption spectrum of N-type crystals; these showed long wavelength absorption which might be caused by phonon assisted transitions from the (000) minimum to higher minima. Gray and Ehrenreich estimated that a second set of minima $0 \cdot 2$–$0 \cdot 4$ eV above the (000) minima would explain their result; Spitzer and Whelan estimated a separation of $0 \cdot 25$ eV. In reviewing the situation, and using later data on the Hall coefficient at high temperatures, data on the energy gap variation in gallium arsenide–gallium phosphide alloys, and data from the pressure measurements of Howard, Ehrenreich[114] concluded that the higher minima lay in the (100) direction in **k**-space and were $0 \cdot 35$ eV higher in energy than the (000) minimum. This, however, takes us a little ahead of the historical development of the pressure measurements.

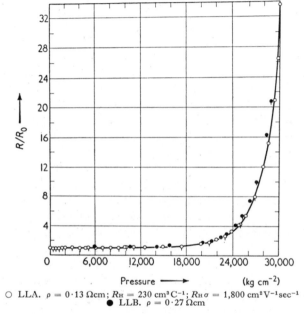

Pressure ⟶ (kg cm^{-2})

○ LLA. $\rho = 0 \cdot 13$ Ωcm; $R_H = 230$ cm^{3}C^{-1}; $R_H \sigma = 1,800$ cm^{2}V^{-1}sec^{-1}
● LLB. $\rho = 0 \cdot 27$ Ωcm

Figure 27. *Pressure dependence of the resistivity of N-type gallium arsenide*

From Table 7 it is clear that, if the pressure coefficients of the different minima in gallium arsenide are the same as those in germanium, silicon, and indium antimonide, the higher minima—which must be (111) or (100) —will become the lower set at moderate pressures. For example, if the higher set at $0 \cdot 35$ eV away is a (100) set, a pressure of 25,000 kg cm^{-2} will bring the minima to approximately equal energies; if a (111) set, nearly twice the pressure will be required. In electrical experiments, the effect of a pressure increase should be especially dramatic, since sets of multiple minima of high effective mass and state density are forced into competition with a single (000) minimum of low state density. Howard[115] has measured the change with pressure of the electrical resistivity of an impure N-type sample to pressures of 30,000 kg cm^{-2}; his result is shown in Figure 27, a relatively flat curve to 20,000 kg cm^{-2}, followed by an increase of a factor of 35 at 30,000 kg cm^{-2}. This is reminiscent of Figure 6 for germanium, and the sharpening and heightening of the curve are consistent with (000)–(111) or (000)–(100) combinations rather than competition between sets of minima of nearly equal state density such as the (111) and (100). Ehrenreich used this curve of Howard's in his summary analysis and succeeded in fitting theory and experiment well using a few plausible assumptions.

At the moment of writing, the higher reaches of the band structure of gallium arsenide seem to be established, yet there are disquieting features about the situation. Ehrenreich used in his analysis a coefficient for the (000) minimum found by Edwards, Slykhouse, and Drickamer[116]— $9\cdot4\times10^{-6}$ eV cm^2 kg^{-1}. Paul and Warschauer[117] in work at lower pressures (8,000 kg cm^{-2}) found a coefficient of $1\cdot2\times10^{-5}$ eV cm^2 kg^{-1}. The difference is significant in that adoption by Ehrenreich of the coefficient found by the latter workers would alter his conclusions about the identification of the higher minima. Furthermore, Edwards et al. determine a maximum gap near 60,000 kg cm^{-2} whereas Ehrenreich's analysis predicts a maximum near 35,000 kg cm^{-2}.

We conclude that more experiments are necessary. It would be very informative if the higher minima could be identified positively through, say, elastoresistance or galvanomagnetic measurements at high pressures or on gallium arsenide–gallium phosphide alloys of low gallium phosphide content. The extra optical absorption found by Spitzer and Whelan near $0\cdot25$ eV should be examined under pressure since, if it is due to interband (phonon-aided) transitions, its pressure coefficient will help identify the minima involved. In gallium arsenide, it is possible that minima other than the three so far considered are of importance. Whatever the outcome of the proposed additional investigations, it is clear that the pressure measurements have contributed and can continue to contribute to the study of the band structure.

8. VOLUME AND TEMPERATURE COEFFICIENTS

In this Section we shall collect experimental data scattered through previous sections on the volume and temperature dependences of energy gaps, effective masses, and dielectric constants.

A selection of the data is displayed in Table 8 with the errors on the quantities omitted. In the first column is listed the pressure coefficient of the quantity; in the second the volume-dependent part of the temperature coefficient, calculated from the first column and the compressibility and thermal expansion coefficient; in the third the measured temperature coefficient is given. The difference between the second and third columns gives the explicit temperature coefficient.

It is immediately evident that there usually exists an explicit temperature

TABLE 8. DEPENDENCE OF PARAMETERS FOR GERMANIUM AND SILICON ON PRESSURE AND TEMPERATURE

Quantity	$\left(\dfrac{\partial X}{\partial P}\right)_T$	$-\dfrac{\alpha}{\beta}\left(\dfrac{\partial X}{\partial P}\right)_T$ (118)	$\left(\dfrac{\partial X}{\partial T}\right)_P$
Germanium			
Energy gap to (111) minima	$+5\times10^{-6}$ eV cm²kg⁻¹ (1)	-0.7×10^{-4} eV.deg.K⁻¹	$\sim -4\times10^{-4}$ eV.deg.K⁻¹ (88)
Energy gap to (000) minimum	$+1.3\times10^{-5}$ eV cm²kg⁻¹ (66)	-1.8×10^{-4} eV.deg.K⁻¹	$\sim -4\times10^{-4}$ eV.deg.K⁻¹ (119)
Average electron effective mass	$\left\|\dfrac{1}{m^*}\left(\dfrac{\partial m^*}{\partial P}\right)_T\right\| \sim 5\times10^{-6}$ cm²kg⁻¹ (21)	0.7×10^{-4} deg.K⁻¹	$\dfrac{1}{m^*}\left(\dfrac{\partial m^*}{\partial T}\right)_P = +3.5\times10^{-4}$ deg.K⁻¹ (39, 69)
Dielectric constant ($\epsilon_0 = 16$)	-19×10^{-6} cm²kg⁻¹ (39)	$+2.7\times10^{-4}$ eV.deg.K⁻¹	$+2.2\times10^{-3}$ deg.K⁻¹ (39)
Ionization energy gold impurity (0.18 eV below conduction band)	$+2.9\times10^{-6}$ eV cm²kg⁻¹ (20)	-0.4×10^{-4} eV.deg.K⁻¹	$\sim -1.5\times10^{-4}$ eV.deg.K⁻¹
Silicon			
Energy gap to (100) minima	-1.5×10^{-6} eV cm²kg⁻¹ (16)	$+0.19\times10^{-4}$ eV.deg.K⁻¹	$\sim -2.5\times10^{-4}$ eV.deg.K⁻¹ (88)
Average electron effective mass	$\left\|\dfrac{1}{m^*}\left(\dfrac{\partial m^*}{\partial P}\right)_T\right\| \sim 5\times10^{-6}$ cm²kg⁻¹ (30)	0.6×10^{-4} eV.deg.K⁻¹	$\dfrac{1}{m^*}\left(\dfrac{\partial m^*}{\partial T}\right)_P = +4.5\times10^{-4}$ deg.K⁻¹ (39, 69)
Dielectric constant ($\epsilon_0 = 12$)	-4.8×10^{-6} cm²kg⁻¹ (39)	$+0.6\times10^{-4}$ eV.deg.K⁻¹	$+1.0\times10^{-3}$ deg.K⁻¹ (39)

coefficient considerably larger than the implicit or volume-derived one. The two are connected thermodynamically to the measured temperature coefficient by the relation

$$\left(\frac{\mathrm{d}X}{\mathrm{d}T}\right)_P = \left(\frac{\partial X}{\partial T}\right)_V - \left(\frac{\partial X}{\partial P}\right)_T \left(\frac{\alpha}{\beta}\right)$$

where α, β are the thermal expansion coefficient and compressibility, respectively.

Relatively little work has been done on the theory of the explicit temperature effect, described by the first term on the right-hand side of the above equation. Radkowsky,[120] Fan,[121] and Muto and Oyama[122] have all considered its effect in changing the energy of the fundamental energy gap between valence and conduction bands or in shifting the fundamental absorption edge, which is a similar problem. James[123] and Brooks[124] have considered the ionization energies measured in electrical and optical experiments at temperatures greater than absolute zero, and have given formal expressions describing the explicit coefficient. There is, however, no theory that attempts to calculate the size of the effect, or to relate it to another measurable quantity as, for example, the deformation potential theory of Bardeen and Shockley relates carrier mobilities to the volume dependence of the gap under certain limiting approximations. Thus the data of Table 8 should be regarded simply as a demonstration that the electron–phonon interaction affects experimentally determinable quantities.

9. IMPURITIES IN GERMANIUM AND SILICON

9.1. INTRODUCTION

Substitutional impurities in germanium and silicon are conveniently classified into hydrogenic and deep-lying. The hydrogenic impurities are elements of Group III or Group V which, respectively, accept or donate one electron from or to the host crystal. The term 'hydrogenic' arises from the circumstance that the potential of the substitutional atom is so nearly the same as that of the host lattice, except for the extra charge, that the resulting discrete bound carrier energy levels are similar to those of a hydrogen atom and are separated from the valence or conduction band, respectively, by an energy gap which is very small compared with the separation between the bands themselves. The 'deep-lying' comprises all other impurities, for which energy levels are usually separated from the band edges by an amount which is not negligible compared with the band gap.

In host lattices having a high dielectric constant (such as germanium and silicon) the extra electron or hole is so loosely bound to the charged impurity that the bound wave functions cover many lattice cells. Under these

215

conditions the energy levels of the electron or hole are given by the simple expression

$$E_{\mathrm{I}n} = E_{\mathrm{H}}\left(\frac{m^*}{m}\right)\frac{1}{\epsilon^2 n^2} \qquad \ldots (48)$$

where $E_{\mathrm{I}n}$ is the energy of the bound charge relative to the nearest band edge, ϵ is a suitable low frequency dielectric constant, m^* is an appropriate average of the components of the effective mass tensor of the carrier, E_{H} is infinite mass Rydberg energy, and n is a principal quantum number. The ground state of the impurity corresponds to $n = 1$, and the corresponding energy is the ionization energy E_{I} of the impurity. This has been determined from resistivity and Hall effect studies as a function of temperature. The positions of the excited states ($n \neq 1$) have been extensively investigated by means of absorption spectra taken in the far infra-red at low temperatures. Apart from minor discrepancies, the correlation between theory and experiment is good.[125] The theory appears good enough to apply in the interpretation of the pressure experiments to be discussed shortly.

By contrast with the situation for hydrogenic impurities, our understanding of deep-lying impurities is very poor. There is a wealth of experimental information on the positions of the energy levels and on the electrical charge associated with various levels. There is also some information from spin resonance studies on the atomic configuration associated with various levels and some very crude evidence on the wave functions from the hyperfine splitting of the electron spin levels. However, very little is known about the details of the wave functions, and there is no theoretical explanation for the actual positions of the various levels. The closest approach to a theory is an examination by Brooks and Fletcher[126] of the matching of electronic wave functions in deep potential wells to wave functions in the forbidden gap constructed out of linear combinations of Bloch functions from the nearest band edges. This theory has so far been too complex for practical application. A cruder picture based on tetrahedral bonding has served as a useful heuristic guide in looking for new energy levels and in estimating their statistical properties. Progress in quantitative understanding of the deep-lying levels is inhibited not only by our inability to compute wave functions, but also by our lack of knowledge of atomic configurations. The recent experiments with spin resonance of transition group impurities have shown that the centres are frequently not isolated substitutional atoms but rather complex groups of atoms, often pairs. While this makes the calculation of energy levels, or the estimation of degeneracies, correspondingly more difficult, it means, at least, that a few well chosen single imperfections can be studied more confidently. Thus, for example, while it is known that manganese in silicon can occur as a single imperfection, or paired with a hydrogenic impurity, or in groups of four, it will be a simple matter to establish properties of the singly occurring manganese by proper choice of crystal and by monitoring the concentration of the other types of imperfection through spin resonance. There is, therefore, a fair expectation that singly occurring imperfections can be described in terms of their ionization energy, degeneracy, and lattice position; a less fair expectation of their excited state energy levels; and a poor expectation of a calculation from first principles of these parameters. For multiple defects, the description is clearly more complicated, but there seems to be no reason why a phenomenological description should not be found for those cases where only a few components are involved, and the particular multiple defect occurs predominantly over all other combinations of the component parts of the defect. That a very few combinations— whatever they are—predominate is clear for many of the impurities investigated, since the same ionization energies are found repeatedly and in different laboratories.

The systems investigated under pressure have been gold in germanium, gold in silicon, and manganese in silicon. We shall see that while the behaviour of the last of these is hard to describe, that of the first two systems is much easier. Explanations for the pressure coefficients of the ionization energies will not be apparent until some theory for the energy levels is established; however, the differences between the coefficients for the various levels are interesting, and may be of some use in constructing a theory of the impurity states.

9.2. Pressure Coefficients

(1) *Hydrogenic impurities*

Although the examination of changes in the absorption spectrum of the hydrogenic impurities with pressure is conceptually the simplest approach in determining shifts in the excited state energy levels, a rough calculation shows that this effect would be so small that optical methods would have inadequate resolution, and a brief consideration of the experimental difficulties suggests that other methods be tried. Holland has determined the changes in the resistivity of silicon crystals doped with aluminium, arsenic, and indium, at temperatures low enough so that the impurity is in its deionization range, and so that the free carrier density and the impurity ionization energy are related by a simple analytical formula. Silicon was chosen for this investigation because germanium would require temperatures so low as to complicate greatly the problem of applying high hydrostatic pressures. In silicon, well regulated temperatures of the order of $45°$ K were required. Holland[20, 101] used helium gas as pressure transmitting fluid, and immersed his pressure vessel, at the end of a length of thin stainless steel tubing, in a double Dewar vessel. By surrounding the pressure vessel with pumped solid nitrogen, and the vessel containing the solid nitrogen with a second nitrogen bath, and by the use of an ingenious temperature monitoring device (which employed a crystal identical to the

217

one under measurement, but outside the pressure vessel) Holland was able to achieve the equivalent of temperature regulation of $\pm 0\cdot002°$ K over extended periods. This proved to be necessary, since the changes observed with pressure were small. Briefly, Holland's method was based on the assumption that the temperatures outside and inside his pressure vessel were either the same, or were in some fixed relationship, when it was assembled in this cryostat system. The temperature of the silicon sample could then be monitored by a sensitive semiconductor crystal mounted on

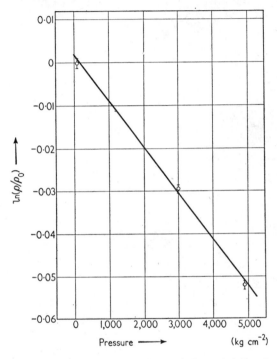

Figure 28. *Pressure dependence of the resistivity of arsenic-doped silicon at low temperatures* ($\rho_0 = 6\cdot11$ $\Omega cm \pm 5$ *per cent;* $T = 50°\,K \pm 1$ *per cent*)

the outside of the pressure vessel. At any pressure inside the vessel, the resistivity of the sample was measured over a small range of temperature, as indicated by the monitoring crystal. It was then a simple matter to find the resistivity change with pressure at a fixed temperature inside the scanning range. It was not necessary to know this temperature to better than, say, $0\cdot5°$ K, only to be assured that the resistivity readings were taken at the same temperature, as indicated by the monitoring sample. A typical curve found by Holland is shown in Figure 28. Such curves give the change in resistivity with pressure, which is clearly of the same order of magnitude as the mobility changes discussed in Section 3. Ideally, one

218

would like to measure a crystal sample of such low impurity density that there is no contribution from ionized impurity scattering at the temperature of measurement. Under this assumption a measurement of the resistivity changes with pressure at $150°$ K or $300°$ K should give the pressure coefficient of the lattice mobility, and assuming, as seems likely from Section 3, that this pressure coefficient is temperature independent and can, therefore, be used at $45°$ K, the resistivity changes at $45°$ K could be translated immediately into changes of impurity ionization energy. Unfortunately, no such pure crystal was available to Holland. An alternative, second-best procedure would be to measure a crystal so highly doped that impurity scattering would predominate at high temperatures, when a similar extrapolation could be made. Unfortunately, the doping required is then so high that impurity banding effects may be expected at $45°$ K. Holland, therefore, compromised, and made what corrections he could,[20] on the basis of calculation, for a relatively pure crystal. His estimate of the changes in ionization energies and, using the results of Section 5, of effective mass and dielectric constant are displayed in Table 9.

TABLE 9. PRESSURE COEFFICIENTS OF THE IONIZATION ENERGIES OF 'SHALLOW' IMPURITIES IN SILICON

Quantity	Ionization energy (eV)	Pressure coefficient (eV cm^{2}kg^{-1})
Energy gap	1·16	$-1·5 \times 10^{-6}$
Arsenic donor	0·049	-5×10^{-8}
Aluminium acceptor	0·057	0 to $+2 \times 10^{-8}$
Indium acceptor	0·16	$+4$ to $+6 \times 10^{-8}$
Gold donor	0·35	$< 5 \times 10^{-8}$
Gold acceptor	0·54 (w.r.t. E_g)	$-1·2 \times 10^{-6}$ (0–4,000 kg cm^{-2})

Dielectric constant	$\dfrac{\mathrm{d}\ln\epsilon}{\mathrm{d}P} = -0·4 \times 10^{-6}$ cm^{2}kg^{-1}
Effective mass	$\dfrac{\mathrm{d}\ln m^*}{\mathrm{d}P} = -2 \times 10^{-6}$ cm^{2}kg^{-1}

Despite the corrections involved, several definite conclusions can be drawn. In the first place, the changes in the ionization energy are very small. Equation (48) can be used to correlate changes in the ionization energy, effective mass, and dielectric constant, and the present results are entirely consistent with the changes discussed in Sections 3 and 5. It would not appear to be necessary to extend these measurements to the more difficult case of germanium. However, if the investigation of the truly hydrogenic impurities would seem to be closed, this is not so of those impurities that are only approximately hydrogenic. An example is indium-doped silicon, which has a much larger than hydrogenic ionization energy, but nevertheless shows surprisingly small changes in ionization energy with pressure. In general, changes in P-type germanium and silicon are usually smaller than in N-type, and changes in silicon smaller than in germanium (see below). Lithium in germanium has an ionization energy of only $0 \cdot 01$ eV, the most nearly hydrogenic of any impurity, and probably it deserves separate consideration. The changes of mass in the case of P-type silicon are not to be taken seriously as equation (48) does not apply for the degenerate valence band structure.

(2) *Deep-lying impurities*

The impurities investigated at Harvard were gold in germanium, gold in silicon, and manganese in silicon. The ionization energies of some of these impurities are shown in Table 10. The ionization energies are found either from photoconductivity spectra or from an analysis of Hall effect or resistivity data. Analysis of the carrier statistics for the latter effects requires a knowledge of the type of the impurity centre, and the spectrum of its ground state and excited state energy levels, as well as a knowledge of any other impurity centres in the crystal. In the absence of much of this information, the usual assumption is to suppose that the centre is described only by a non-degenerate ground state energy level and that there is probably some compensating impurity of the opposite type. In the case of gold in germanium, there are apparently four energy levels corresponding to different states of ionization, whose ground states are listed in the Table. If any one of these levels is to be investigated, it is preferable that the others be either completely ionized or completely deionized throughout the pressure range of the measurement. While it is not certain, *a priori*, that this will be possible, careful counterdoping usually permits a close approximation to the condition. Thus the lowest gold donor level in germanium, Au(1), can only be active when it is partially empty of electrons and is acting as a sink for electrons from the valence band. If N_d, N_a are the densities of donors and acceptors, and $N_a - N_d > N_{Au}$ the level Au(1) is emptied into the acceptor level at $0°$ K. As the temperature is raised, electrons are excited from the valence band, most easily into the remaining acceptor levels, but with increasing ease into the Au(1) levels. If $N_{Au} > N_a - N_d$, excitation of electrons occurs directly into the $N_a - N_d$ vacated gold levels. In either case, the gold donor states are entirely filled at $50°$ K and there remain $N_a - N_d$ holes in the valence band at this temperature; the crystal is P-type. If $N_d > N_a$, the gold donor level will not be active at any temperature.

The second gold level Au(2) is an acceptor nearer the valence band edge than the conduction band edge. It behaves similarly to a Group III acceptor, causing the sample to be P-type. If $N_{Au} > N_d - N_a > 0$, there will be $N_{Au} - (N_d - N_a)$ empty states in the level at $0°$ K; electrons from the valence band are thermally excited into these states until the states are all filled, at approximately $200°$ K, leaving conducting holes in the valence band.

220

TABLE 10. PRESSURE COEFFICIENTS OF THE IONIZATION ENERGIES OF 'DEEP' IMPURITIES IN GERMANIUM AND SILICON

Element	Impurity level	Ionization energy (eV)	Pressure coefficient (eV cm²kg⁻¹)	Implicit temperature coefficient (eV.deg.K⁻¹)
Germanium	Gold Au (1)	0·04 (w.r.t. E_v)	$+1 \times 10^{-7}$	-0.09×10^{-4}
	Au (2)	0·15 (w.r.t. E_v)	$+6 \times 10^{-7}$	-0.4×10^{-4}
	Au (3)	0·19 (w.r.t. E_g)	$+2.9 \times 10^{-6}$	
	Au (4)	0·04 (w.r.t. E_g)	$+2.1 \times 10^{-6}$	
Silicon	Gold Au (1)	0·35 (w.r.t. E_g)	$\leqslant 5 \times 10^{-8}$	
	Au (2)	0·54 (w.r.t. E_g)	-1.2×10^{-6} (0–4,000 kg cm⁻²) -1.5×10^{-6} (near 20,000 kg cm⁻²)	
	Au (2)	0·62 (w.r.t. E_v)	-3×10^{-7} (0–4,000 kg cm⁻²) -9×10^{-7} (near 20,000 kg cm⁻²)	

It is possible for the lower Au(1) level to influence this level. If $N_a - N_d > 0$, the Au(1) donor is filled as described above, and an electron will not be excited into the Au(2) level of a particular gold atom until the Au(1) level for that atom is filled. Thus a $\ln \rho$ versus $1/T$ curve will show, as T is increased, first a slope of $0 \cdot 04$ eV characteristic of the Au(1) level below about $50°$ K, and then a slope of $0 \cdot 15$ eV characteristic of the Au(2) level above about $80°$ K.

The third gold level Au(3) is an acceptor level nearer to the conduction band edge, and behaves as a source of electrons for the conduction band. If $2N_{Au} > N_d - N_a > N_{Au}$, the lower acceptor level Au(2) will be completely filled with electrons and the remaining $(N_d - N_a) - N_{Au}$ electrons will be in Au(3) at $0°$ K. Then, the electrons can be thermally excited into the conduction band and the material is N-type. The level is empty of electrons above $200°$ K.

The last of the gold levels Au(4) is an acceptor level very near the conduction band edge and it behaves similarly to Au(3), acting as a source of electrons in N-type material. If $3N_{Au} > N_d - N_a > 2N_{Au}$, the two lower acceptor levels Au(2) and Au(3) will be filled and the remaining $(N_d - N_a) - 2N_{Au}$ electrons will be in Au(4) at $0°$ K. These electrons are thermally excited into the conduction band, and the level is empty of electrons above $50°$ K. The $\ln \rho$ versus $1/T$ curve is very similar to the curve described for a sample with Au(1) and Au(2) both operative; from $200°$ K to $80°$ K the curve has a slope of $0 \cdot 19$ eV, characteristic of the Au(3) level, and below $50°$ K the slope is $0 \cdot 04$ eV, characteristic of the Au(4) level.

If $N_d - N_a > 3N_{Au}$, electrons are supplied to the conduction band from three different levels, the Group V donors with an ionization energy of $0 \cdot 01$ eV, the Au(4) level with an ionization energy of $0 \cdot 04$ eV, and the Au(3) level with an energy of $0 \cdot 19$ eV. These levels become successively fully ionized as the temperature is raised from $0°$ K, the Group V levels at $15°$ K, the Au(4) levels at $50°$ K, and the Au(3) levels at $200°$ K.

Holland,[20, 101] Khartsiev,[127] and Teitler and Wallis[128] (among others) have developed the statistics appropriate for multi-level impurity centres of this kind. The statistics are particularly simple when the counterdoping has been so arranged that, as previously explained, only one level is active in any particular experiment. Then the filling of a particular level is described by a Fermi factor of the form

$$f_i = \{1 + [g_i \exp (E_f - E_i)]^{-1}\}^{-1} \qquad \ldots (49)$$

where E_f is the Fermi level, E_i the energy of the level, and g_i a degeneracy factor that it seems best we obtain from a more sophisticated analysis.

If we assume that the lowest gold level can be filled in four ways, i.e. that the electronic state on a neutral gold atom has degeneracy 4, and that the three acceptor states have degeneracies 6, 4, and 1, i.e. that we can produce

222

singly, doubly, and triply ionized gold in six, four, and one ways, respectively, then the g_i in the above expression have the values 4, 3/2, 2/3, and 1/4.†

The equation of de Boer and van Geel[130] can then be modified to give the densities of free carriers when only one of the levels is 'operative' as

$$\left.\begin{aligned} \frac{p(p+N_{\text{Au}}+N_{\text{d}}-N_{\text{a}})}{N_{\text{a}}-N_{\text{d}}-p} &= g_1\phi_{1\text{p}} \\[2mm] \frac{p(p+N_{\text{d}}-N_{\text{a}})}{N_{\text{Au}}+N_{\text{a}}-N_{\text{d}}-p} &= g_2\phi_{2\text{p}} \\[2mm] \frac{n(n+2N_{\text{Au}}+N_{\text{a}}-N_{\text{d}})}{N_{\text{d}}-N_{\text{a}}-N_{\text{Au}}-n} &= g_3^{-1}\phi_{3\text{n}} \\[2mm] \frac{n(n+3N_{\text{Au}}+N_{\text{a}}-N_{\text{d}})}{N_{\text{d}}-N_{\text{a}}-2N_{\text{Au}}-n} &= g_4^{-1}\phi_{4\text{n}} \end{aligned}\right\} \quad \dots (50)$$

where $\qquad\qquad \phi_{i\text{p}} = C_{\text{v}}\exp\left[(E_{\text{v}}-E_i)/kT\right]$

and $\qquad\qquad \phi_{j\text{n}} = C_{\text{g}}\exp\left[(E_j-E_{\text{g}})/kT\right]$

and C_{g}, C_{v} are the density of states factors for conduction and valence bands.

Hall effect measurements are used to give estimates of the comparative magnitudes of $N_{\text{d}}-N_{\text{a}}$, N_{Au}, and n or p. These allow us to use more tractable expressions for n and p from the above equations, and so to deduce from measurements of the resistivity as a function of pressure the pressure coefficient of the ionization energy.

Thus, for example, for low temperatures the equation for level 3 can be rearranged: if we take the realized conditions $n < N_{\text{d}}-N_{\text{a}}-N_{\text{Au}}$ and $n < 2N_{\text{Au}}+N_{\text{a}}-N_{\text{d}}$, then the equation becomes

$$n = \left(\frac{N_{\text{d}}-N_{\text{a}}-N_{\text{Au}}}{2N_{\text{Au}}-N_{\text{d}}+N_{\text{a}}}\right)\left(\frac{\phi_{3\text{n}}}{g_3}\right)(1-\gamma_3) \qquad \dots (51)$$

where $\qquad\qquad \gamma_3 = \dfrac{N_{\text{Au}}\phi_{3\text{n}}}{g_3(2N_{\text{Au}}-N_{\text{d}}+N_{\text{a}})^2}$

From $1/\rho = nq\mu_{\text{n}}$ relating resistivity to mobility and carrier density, we obtain

$$\frac{\text{d}\ln\rho}{\text{d}P} = -\frac{\text{d}\ln\mu_{\text{n}}}{\text{d}P}+(\gamma_3-1)\left[\frac{\text{d}\ln C_{\text{g}}}{\text{d}P}+\frac{1}{kT}\frac{\text{d}}{\text{d}P}(E_3-E_{\text{g}})\right] \qquad \dots (52)$$

and

$$\frac{\text{d}\ln\rho}{\text{d}(1/kT)} = -\frac{\text{d}\ln\mu_{\text{n}}}{\text{d}(1/kT)}+(\gamma_3-1)\left[\frac{\text{d}\ln C_{\text{g}}}{\text{d}(1/kT)}+(E_3-E_{\text{g}})\right] +$$

$$+\frac{\gamma_3}{\gamma_3-1}\frac{1}{kT}\frac{\text{d}}{\text{d}(1/kT)}(E_3-E_{\text{g}}) \qquad \dots (53)$$

† Unfortunately, these values for the degeneracy factors are not very close to those that have been determined from an analysis of experimental data by Klein.[129] Until the matter is settled, the absolute values of the pressure coefficients are uncertain, but are no less well established than the energy levels themselves.

The terms in γ_3 are small correction terms we can ignore at low enough temperatures. Then, with suitable corrections applied, the slope of curves of $\ln \rho$ versus $1/T$ gives the $0°\,\mathrm{K}$ ionization energy; the temperature coefficient of this energy can be found in principle from the absolute value of the resistivity at any temperature, and the absolute value of the mobility. In practice, sufficient accuracy is seldom available for this determination. Equation (52) shows that, again in principle, γ_3 introduces a temperature dependence of the pressure coefficient of the ionization energy that may be used to evaluate γ_3, and thus $E_g - E_3$. In practice, the evaluation will be a very poor one, due to our lack of knowledge of the exact counter-doping and of the degeneracy factors.

The pressure coefficients of the mobility and the density of states factor are very small compared with that of the ionization energy, so that they can be omitted, or corrected for without serious fear of error. Thus the pressure coefficient of the ionization energy is simply found from the variation of the resistivity with pressure at fixed low temperature, according to equation (52).

Figure 29 shows a typical set of $\ln \rho$ versus P curves for one sample with level Au(3) active, and Figure 30 the temperature dependence of the pressure coefficients. From the latter the temperature coefficient of the level can also, in principle, be found. Similar considerations apply to the other three gold levels; the reader is referred to Holland's thesis[20] and to published papers[101] for the details of the approximations involved. In Table 10 are displayed the final pressure coefficients, and the implicit temperature coefficients.

We conclude, first of all, that these coefficients are considerably larger than those for the hydrogenic impurities.

Moreover, the pressure coefficients with respect to the conduction band are very much larger than with respect to the valence band. For the three acceptor levels the fractional change in the distance of the level from the valence band is almost constant, and very different from the change for the donor level. One might almost say that the level is tied to the valence band, even when its energy lies close to that of conduction band states.

Finally, despite the uncertainties involved, it seems probable that there exists an explicit temperature dependence of the ionization energy, which is hard to find in many experiments but might show up easily in optical experiments using magnetic fields, for in these there would exist fine structure on the absorption or photoconductive spectra which might be followed as the temperature was changed.

Gold in silicon produces only two levels, one an acceptor approximately $0\cdot54\,\mathrm{eV}$ below the bottom of the conduction band,[21] the other a donor about $0\cdot35\,\mathrm{eV}$ above the top of the valence band. Apparently these levels are comparable with levels 1 and 2 in the case of gold, and the corresponding acceptor levels 3 and 4 are absorbed into the conduction band. The statistics

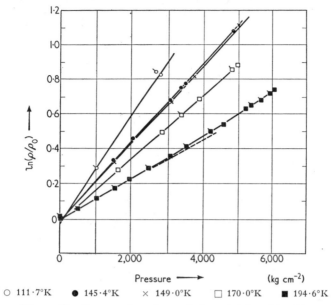

O 111·7°K   ● 145·4°K   × 149·0°K   □ 170·0°K   ■ 194·6°K

Figure 29. *Pressure dependence of the resistivity of a gold-doped germanium sample, level Au(3) active*

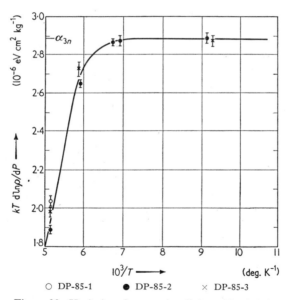

O DP-85-1   ● DP-85-2   × DP-85-3

Figure 30. *Variation of pressure coefficient of level Au(3) in germanium, with temperature*

for these cases are qualitatively different from the case of gold in germanium, mainly because the ionization energies are so high that the influence of intrinsic carriers cannot be neglected, and the pressure coefficients are also

225

so small that careful corrections for the effects of mobility change have to be estimated. All of these considerations are set out in Nathan's thesis and in a subsequent paper[100] and the final results are included in Table 10.

We observe, first of all, that, in contradistinction to germanium, the ionization energies decrease with pressure. We recall that the forbidden gap in silicon decreases with pressure, and the surmise that this is a fortuitous happening caused solely by the fact that the (100) minima are the lowest set in this element. It seems reasonable to link the negative coefficients for the ionization energies with the negative gap coefficient, and to draw the conclusion that the conduction band states in the (100) direction have a considerable influence on the properties of the level. No explicit temperature coefficients are derivable from the present pressure data.

We note, as in the case of germanium, that the pressure coefficients with respect to the conduction band edge are much larger than with respect to the valence band. An interesting situation occurs in the case of the acceptor level: As discussed in Sections 1 and 6, Nathan and Paul were able to obtain the pressure coefficient of the silicon gap from the sum of the pressure coefficients of two ionization energies, corresponding to the distance of one acceptor level from the two band edges. However, the pressure coefficients of ionization energies and total gap, determined in this way, increase at the highest pressure. The reason for this is not known, as was indicated at the conclusion of Section 6.

Holland[20] also investigated the manganese–silicon system, without obtaining conclusive results. The interpretation of his data was impeded by the presence of hysteresis, long-time effects of hours in duration, and irreproducibility on successive runs. Evidence from spin resonance indicates that manganese forms multiple defects in silicon of more than one configuration, and in view of this, Holland's suggestion that pressure causes slow rearrangement of impurity configurations seems plausible. Alternative explanations of his experiments such as surface effects and long-time pressure dependent trapping were effectively eliminated. It would seem that this would be one case where electron spin resonance experiments would clear up the difficulties by distinguishing between different configurations.

10. SUMMARY AND USES

10.1. INTRODUCTION

The pressure experiments on germanium and silicon have been useful in four main ways. (1) They have helped to establish the upper parts of the conduction band structure of these elements. (2) They have provided a basis for interpreting other physical properties by studying the effect of a simple variable, namely pressure. (3) They have given evidence of explicit temperature coefficients which theory has yet to explain satisfactorily.

(4) They have helped provide a basis for extrapolation from Group IV elements to intermetallic compounds.

While a wide range of further experiments is possible in germanium, silicon, and the intermetallics, only a small selection is worth the effort involved. The fact that the extra minima, active above 15,000 kg cm^{-2}, are indeed of (100) type, should be verified from magnetoconductivity or elastoresistivity measurements. When this is done, it is possible that most of the immediately useful information about the band structure changes with volume will be available. However, measurement under pressure of some of the reflection peaks that have been assigned to specific valence–conduction band transitions may also prove to be informative, both in checking the relative shifts of different states in the valence band and providing a further basis for examination of correlations of pressure coefficients in the Group IV and Group III–V semiconductors. Further changes at very much higher pressures are also possible, but of these we have no indication at all at the moment. Other marginal experiments might include a repetition of magnetoband experiments to obtain very precise energy gap changes.

10.2. Hot Electrons

The knowledge now available can, however, be used in the interpretation of theories for new physical effects following the second suggested application. As an example of this we quote the work of Koenig, Nathan, Paul, and Smith on changes with pressure of hot electron phenomena in germanium.[131] Since the hot electrons occupy portions of the conduction band structure as high as the (100) and (000) minima, changing the position of these minima with pressure is one way of investigating the laws governing the hot electrons. Figure 31 shows the variation of current density with electric field as a function of pressure at room temperature. At atmospheric pressure, Ohm's law holds up to fields of about 500 Vcm^{-1}. For higher fields, the conductivity gradually decreases and the current saturates for fields above 5,000 Vcm^{-1}. Reviews of the experimental and theoretical situation have been given by Gunn[132] and Conwell.[133]

Although the distribution in energy of the carriers in a conduction band when a field is applied may not be of the Maxwell–Boltzmann form, we can roughly represent the increase in the average energy of the carriers by a mean electron temperature. This electron temperature rises as the field strength is increased, and may be several times the lattice temperature. It has been suggested that electrons occupy portions of the conduction band as high as the (000) and (100) minima. We can then adopt one of two points of view. Either we accept that the electrons reach the energies of these minima, in which case their properties, such as mobility, to some extent reflect the properties of these minima; or else we do not accept this high electron temperature without question, and desire some proof that the electrons occupy the high energy minima. The measurements already described have established the pressure coefficients of the higher minima, and enabled us to estimate their position and state density. Thus the hot electron experiments, repeated at high pressures, test the thesis that the electrons reach the higher minima, and test the proposed effect of these minima on the current–voltage characteristic.

Under conditions of thermal equilibrium at atmospheric pressure and $300°$ K, only $\simeq 0\cdot3$ per cent of the electrons occupy the (100) minima. When the field is applied, this fraction increases and the amount of scattering of the 'hot' carriers also increases. At high pressures the carrier density in

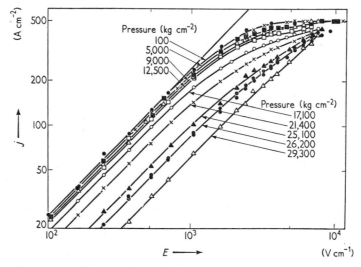

Figure 31. *Current–voltage characteristic for a germanium sample, oriented along a (100) axis, with pressure as a parameter.* $(\rho = 4 \ \Omega cm;$
$T = 297° K)$

the (100) minima and the scattering frequency, for a fixed field, are both increased; this should decrease the average drift velocity for the carriers.

The main features to be observed in Figure 31 are: (1) For the lower pressure range ($< 15,000 \ \mathrm{kg\,cm^{-2}}$), the pressure dependence of the conductivity is somewhat greater at intermediate fields than at low fields while the critical field E_c (the field at which deviations from Ohm's law set in) remains unchanged; (2) The sample remains 'ohmic' to higher fields at high pressure than it does at the low; (3) The saturation current is independent of pressure at least up to $10,000 \ \mathrm{V\,cm^{-1}}$ (electrical breakdown in the contacts leading into the pressure vessel prevented this study being extended to higher pressures).

The constancy of the critical field at low pressures can be explained as a balance between two opposing effects. As the pressure is increased, the

228

average mobility of the carriers decreases; it thus becomes harder for the field to 'heat' them, and E_c tends to increase. On the other hand, the decrease in mobility is caused by the decrease in the separation of the (111) and (100) minima, and this makes it easier for the applied field to spill carriers into the (100) minima where their mobility is reduced. This tends to decrease E_c. On balance, E_c will remain essentially constant at the lower pressures. This explanation, although not bolstered by (difficult) quantitative calculations, is rather plausible.

This balancing process does not go on indefinitely. At pressures higher than 25,000 $kg\,cm^{-2}$, there is substantial sharing of the electrons between the two types of minima and also very frequent scattering of electrons between the different minima, which causes a reduction of the mobility by a factor of 4 from its atmospheric pressure value. The electric field now finds it very hard to 'heat' the electron distribution, and Ohm's law is obeyed almost to the highest fields applied.

The details of further experiments of this general sort are to be found in the published paper, but this brief discussion may suffice to illustrate the use of the known pressure coefficients of the different minima in interpreting new effects.

10.3. TUNNEL DIODES

A second example of the use of the known pressure coefficients in investigating new phenomena can be seen in the work of Nathan, Miller, and Smith,[134] Nathan, Miller, and Finegold,[135] and of Nathan and Paul[136] on the effects of pressure on the properties of tunnel diodes.

The operation of these diodes depends on the fact that the material used on both sides of the junction is doped to degeneracy, so that the potential drop across the diode is greater than the energy gap. There are then empty states in the valence band on the P-side at the same energy as filled electron states on the N-side; since the junction is very heavily doped its width is small, and electrons can tunnel across the space charge layer. In equilibrium equal and opposite tunnelling currents flow. When a bias is applied, excess current gives the characteristic shown in the inset of Figure 32. The ordinary diode current, caused by carriers that are thermally activated over the potential barrier, passing from one conduction band to the other (or from and to valence bands), is negligible at these low voltages.

According to the theory of Keldysh[137] and of Price and Radcliffe[138] the current J can be written

$$J = A \exp(-\alpha E_G) \qquad \ldots (54)$$

The quantities A and α contain an average effective mass and dielectric constant. When pressure is applied α and A both change. The variation of the pre-exponential term can probably be neglected, but the mass variation in α may not, especially in narrow energy gap materials with the extrema in the conduction and valence band structures at the same point in **k**-space. However, in this case it is likely that the fractional changes in mass and energy gap will be equal, so that the mass change is easily incorporated. In the following, we shall neglect such changes, so that our discussion is more applicable to, say, phonon-induced indirect tunnelling in germanium than to direct tunnelling in indium antimonide.

The exponential change in J, and specifically of J_p, the peak current in the forward direction, which occurs at the same applied voltage at all pressures, is plotted in Figure 32 for diodes of silicon, germanium, gallium arsenide, and gallium antimonide. We notice immediately some qualitative

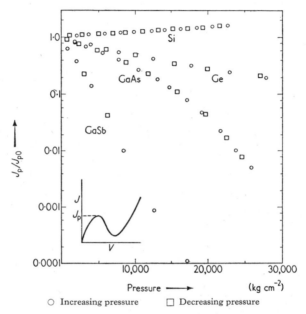

○ Increasing pressure   □ Decreasing pressure

Figure 32. *Variation with pressure of peak forward current in tunnel diodes of germanium, silicon, gallium arsenide, and gallium antimonide*

features that are easily explained from our knowledge of the pressure coefficients of E_G. The change for silicon is opposite in sign to that for the other materials, since the energy gap decreases with pressure only for silicon. The change for germanium is slightly decreased at the highest pressures, which probably reflects the influence of the (100) states. The changes for gallium arsenide and gallium antimonide are accelerated at high pressures. However, we know that at these pressures the electrons in the conduction bands of these substances change from the (000) symmetry to the (111) or (100). The probability of tunnelling into the (000) valence bands is reduced for these electrons because of a momentum selection rule. Thus at the top pressures the tunnelling current decreases not only because of the increase in gap but also because of the changeover in the symmetry of the conduction band electrons.

More quantitative information is, however, available. From equation (54) we find that

$$\ln J_p = \ln A + E_G(\mathrm{d}\ln J_p/\mathrm{d}P)/(\mathrm{d}E_G/\mathrm{d}P)$$

If several diodes of different J_p are measured, and $\ln J_p$ plotted against $(\mathrm{d}\ln J_p/\mathrm{d}P)$ the resultant straight line should have a slope of $E_G/(\mathrm{d}E_G/\mathrm{d}P)$. For germanium diodes, constructed by making P-type dots on N-type material and doped so that phonon-assisted tunnelling was dominant, Miller, Nathan, and Smith[134] found

$$E_G/(\mathrm{d}E_G/\mathrm{d}P) = 12\cdot4\times10^4 \qquad \mathrm{kg\,cm^{-2}}$$

If E_G is taken to be $0\cdot65$ eV and a pressure coefficient of $(\mathrm{d}E_G/\mathrm{d}P)_T = 5\times10^{-6}$ eV cm^2 kg^{-1} used, we calculate $E_G/(\mathrm{d}E_G/\mathrm{d}P) = 13\times10^4$ kg cm^{-2}.

The agreement is, therefore, rather good especially when we reconsider the inexactness of equation (54) and probably indicates that the theory and the interpretation of the experiment are at least qualitatively substantiated. Similar confirmation is afforded by experiments on a number of silicon diodes, but measurements on germanium diodes constructed by alloying N-type dots on P-type substrates[134] and also measurements on germanium diodes dominated by 'non-phonon-aided' tunnelling[134] have not yet been interpreted. The pressure measurements seem to indicate that the tunnelling laws are different in these two cases.

A striking feature of the current–voltage characteristic when a germanium diode is biased in the reverse direction is the occurrence of a sharp increase in the current at applied voltages $> 0\cdot1$ V.[139] This increase is caused by the onset of direct tunnelling from the valence band (000) states into the (000) states in the conduction band.

Usually this aspect of the current–voltage curve is observable only at low temperatures, when the phonon-assisted tunnelling that occurs for applied voltages $< 0\cdot1$ V is reduced. The changes under pressure can, however, be seen at room temperature. The effect of pressure is to increase the onset voltage at a rate precisely equal to the pressure coefficient of the separation in energy of the (000) and (111) conduction band states[135] thus confirming the original hypothesis of Morgan and Kane concerning the break in their characteristics, and our ideas on the behaviour under pressure of the band edges.

This cursory review of the effects in tunnel diodes may not convey the complexity of detail observed in pressure experiments on these devices, for which the interested reader is referred to the paper by Nathan and Paul. It may, however, serve as another example of the use of the known pressure coefficients in interpreting new phenomena.

10.4. OTHER EFFECTS

Holland's work on manganese impurities in silicon has made a start in the direction of investigating impurity diffusion as a function of pressure. His work on the effect of pressure on the ionization energies of deep-lying impurities hardly scratches the surface of this relatively unworked field.

The use of the pressure experiments in establishing the magnitude of explicit temperature coefficients has already been cited.

As we discussed in Section 7, the experiments on germanium and silicon provided a basis for extrapolation from Group IV semiconductors to inter-metallic Group III–V compounds such as indium antimonide. In these intermetallics the pressure experiments have been quite useful in helping to establish the band structure at atmospheric pressure. It is not yet known whether we can extrapolate to the Group II–VI compounds such as cadmium sulphide. Drickamer's measurements[140] suggest that qualitative extrapolation may be possible, but that it may not be made quantitative. Nevertheless, we can expect that correlations of the type discussed earlier will occur among the different Group II–VI compounds. Similar correlations may be expected in families such as sulphur, selenium, and tellurium, and lead sulphide, selenide, and telluride. Preliminary investigations on the latter trio have been reported from the Harvard[141] and the Westinghouse Laboratories,[142] which confirm that the pressure coefficients of the band gaps are similar and that complexity in the band structure can be expected.

As we have emphasized often, there are many difficult experiments whose repetition at high pressures is not worth while. However, we hope to have shown that a programme of selected measurements on a suitable semi-conductor can be both interesting and informative, and that such measurements should be kept in mind as providing a simple, convenient, and indeed fundamental, tool in further investigations.

REFERENCES

1. PAUL, W., and BROOKS, H. *Phys. Rev.* **94**, 1128 (1954)
2. BRIDGMAN, P. W. *Proc. Amer. Acad. Arts Sci.* **68**, 95 (1933); *Proc. Amer. Acad. Arts Sci.* **72**, 159 (1938)
3. BARDEEN, J. *Phys. Rev.* **75**, 1777 (1949)
4. *See, for example,* LONG, D. *Phys. Rev.* **101**, 1256 (1956); NEURINGER, L. J. *Phys. Rev.* **113**, 1495 (1959); KOZYREV, M. *Solid State Physics in U.S.S.R.*, Vol. 1, No. 1 (Pergamon, London, 1959) (Translation)
5. BRIDGMAN, P. W. *Proc. Amer. Acad. Arts Sci.* **79**, 129 (1951); *Proc. Amer. Acad. Arts Sci.* **81**, 221 (1952)
6. JOHNSON, E. R., and CHRISTIAN, S. M. *Phys. Rev.* **95**, 560 (1954)
7. HERMAN, F. *Rev. mod. Phys.* **30**, 102 (1958)
8. LANDWEHR, G. *Z. Naturf.* **11a**, 257 (1956)
9. NATHAN, M. I., PAUL, W., and BROOKS, H. *Phys. Rev.* **124**, 391 (1961)
10. BENEDEK, G. B., PAUL, W., and BROOKS, H. *Phys. Rev.* **100**, 1129 (1955)
11. HOWARD, W. E. *Thesis* (Harvard University, 1961). Available as Report HP-7 from the Division of Engineering and Applied Physics, Harvard University
12. BRIDGMAN, P. W., and PAUL, W. Unpublished measurements

13. FAN, H. Y., SHEPHERD, M. L., and SPITZER, W. *Photoconductivity Conference*, p. 184 (Eds. R. G. Breckenridge, B. R. Russell, and E. E. Hohn) (Wiley, New York, 1956)
14. NEURINGER, L. J. *Phys. Rev.* **113**, 1495 (1959)
15. SLYKHOUSE, T. E., and DRICKAMER, H. G. *J. Phys. Chem. Solids* **7**, 210 (1958)
16. PAUL, W., and PEARSON, G. L. *Phys. Rev.* **98**, 1755 (1955)
17. PAUL, W., and WARSCHAUER, D. M. *J. Phys. Chem. Solids* **5**, 102 (1958)
18. NATHAN, M. I., and PAUL, W. *Bull. Amer. phys. Soc.* **2**, 134 (1957)
19. LONG, D. *Phys. Rev.* **99**, 388 (1955); *Phys. Rev.* **101**, 1256 (1956); KEYES, R. W. *Phys. Rev.* **99**, 490 (1955)
20. HOLLAND, M. G. *Thesis* (Harvard University, 1958). Available as Report HP-4 from the Division of Engineering and Applied Physics, Harvard University
21. NATHAN, M. I. *Thesis* (Harvard University, 1958). Available as Report HP-1 from the Division of Engineering and Applied Physics, Harvard University
22. LAX, B. *Rev. mod. Phys.* **30**, 122 (1958)
23. HERMAN, F., and SKILLMAN, S. *Proceedings of the International Conference on Semiconductor Physics*, Prague (Czechoslovakian Academy of Sciences, 1960)
24. PHILLIPS, J. C. *Phys. Rev.* **125**, 1931 (1962)
25. BASSANI, F. Private communication; *See also* reference 102
26. PHILLIPS, J. C., and KLEINMAN, L. *Phys. Rev.* **116**, 287 (1959)
27. HALL, H. H., BARDEEN, J., and PEARSON, G. L. *Phys. Rev.* **84**, 129 (1951)
28. BRIDGMAN, P. W. *The Physics of High Pressures* (Bell, London, 1949)
29. BRIDGMAN, P. W. *Proc. Amer. Acad. Arts Sci.* **74**, 1 (1940)
30. SMITH, A. C. *Thesis* (Harvard University, 1958). Available as Report HP-2 from the Division of Engineering and Applied Physics, Harvard University
31. WARSCHAUER, D. M., and PAUL, W. *Rev. sci. Instrum.* **29**, 675 (1958)
32. PAUL, W., and WARSCHAUER, D. M. *J. Phys. Chem. Solids* **5**, 89 (1958)
33. PAUL, W., BENEDEK, G. B., and WARSCHAUER, D. M. *Rev. sci. Instrum.* **30**, 874 (1959); *See also* BENEDEK, G. B., PAUL, W., and BROOKS, H., reference 10, and HOWARD, W. E., reference 11
34. PAUL, W., and WARSCHAUER, D. M. *Rev. sci. Instrum.* **27**, 418 (1956); *Rev. sci. Instrum.* **28**, 62 (1957); *Rev. sci. Instrum.* **29**, 675 (1958)
35. BROOKS, H. *Advances in Electronics and Electron Physics*, Vol. 7 (Ed. L. Marton) (Academic, New York, 1955); HERRING, C., and VOGT, E. *Phys. Rev.* **101**, 944 (1956)
36. KEYES, R. W. *Advances in Solid State Physics*, Vol. 11 (Eds. F. Seitz and D. Turnbull) (Academic, New York, 1961)
37. WARSCHAUER, D. M., and PAUL, W. Unpublished optical absorption measurements
38. NATHAN, M. I., PAUL, W., and BROOKS, H. *Bull. Amer. phys. Soc.* **3**, 14 (1958); *See also* reference 9
39. CARDONA, M., PAUL, W., and BROOKS, H. *Solid State Physics in Electronics and Telecommunications*, Vol. 1 (Eds. Desirant and Michiels) (Academic, New York, 1960); *J. Phys. Chem. Solids* **8**, 204 (1959); CARDONA, M. *Thesis* (Harvard University, 1959). Available as Report HP-5 from the Division of Engineering and Applied Physics, Harvard University
40. BAILYN, M. Unpublished measurements; MCSKIMIN, H. J. *J. acoust. Soc. Amer.* **30**, 314 (1958); KOPPELMANN, J., and LANDWEHR, G. *Z. angew. Phys.* **11**, 164 (1959)
41. BRIDGMAN, P. W. *Proc. Amer. Acad. Arts Sci.* **77**, 208 (1949)
42. HAYNES, J. R., and SHOCKLEY, W. *Phys. Rev.* **81**, 835 (1951)
43. For a bibliography and review see, for example, reference 30
44. LAWRENCE, R., and GIBSON, A. F. *Proc. phys. Soc. Lond.* **B65**, 994 (1952)
45. An extensive account is to be found in Technical Report No. 181, H. Brooks, Division of Engineering and Applied Physics, Harvard University
46. BROOKS, H., and PAUL, W. *Bull. Amer. phys. Soc.* **1**, 48 (1956)
47. GOLDBERG, C. *Phys. Rev.* **109**, 331 (1958); *See also* reference 11
48. GLICKSMAN, M., and CHRISTIAN, S. M. *Phys. Rev.* **104**, 1278 (1956)
49. BAILYN, M. Unpublished measurements
50. KOPPELMANN, J., and LANDWEHR, G. Reference 40
51. MCSKIMMIN, H. J. *J. acoust. Soc. Amer.* **30**, 314 (1958)
52. DRESSELHAUS, G., KIP, A. F., and KITTEL, C. *Phys. Rev.* **100**, 1218 (1955)

53. ABELES, B., and MEIBOOM, S. *Phys. Rev.* **95**, 31 (1954)
54. SHIBUYA, M. *Phys. Rev.* **95**, 1385 (1954)
55. BROCKHOUSE, B. N. *Phys. Rev. Lett.* **2**, 256 (1959)
56. FEHER, G. *J. Phys. Chem. Solids* **8**, 846 (1959)
57. McLEAN, T. P. *Progress in Semiconductors 5*, p. 53 (Eds. Gibson, Kroger, and Burgess) (Heywood, London; Wiley, New York, 1960)
58. LAX, B., and ZWERDLING, S. *Progress in Semiconductors 5*, p. 221 (Eds. Gibson, Kroger, and Burgess) (Heywood, London; Wiley, New York, 1960)
59. MEYER, H. J. G. *J. Phys. Chem. Solids* **8**, 264 (1959)
60. ROSENBERG, R., and LAX, M. *Phys. Rev.* **112**, 843 (1958)
61. KAHN, A. H. *Phys. Rev.* **97**, 1647 (1955)
62. KANE, E. O. *J. Phys. Chem. Solids* **1**, 82 (1956)
63. BRAUNSTEIN, R. *J. Phys. Chem. Solids* **8**, 280 (1959)
64. See reference 58, p. 243, for a recent discussion and reference
65. LAX, M., and BURSTEIN, E. *Phys. Rev.* **97**, 39 (1955)
66. CARDONA, M., and PAUL, W. *J. Phys. Chem. Solids* **17**, 138 (1960)
67. PAUL, W. *J. Phys. Chem. Solids* **8**, 196 (1959)
68. MacFARLANE, G. G., McLEAN, T. P., QUARRINGTON, J. E., and ROBERTS, V. *J. Phys. Chem. Solids* **8**, 388 (1959)
69. CARDONA, M., PAUL, W., and BROOKS, H. *Helv. phys. acta* **33**, 329 (1960)
70. LUKES, F. *Czech. J. Phys.* **8**, 253, 423 (1958); LUKES, F. *J. Phys. Chem. Solids* **11**, 343 (1959)
71. BRIGGS, H. B., and KONKEL, W. H. Private communication
72. BENEDICT, T. R., and SHOCKLEY, W. *Phys. Rev.* **89**, 1152 (1953)
73. DUNLAP, W. C., and WATTERS, R. L. *Phys. Rev.* **92**, 1396 (1953)
74. LARK-HOROVITZ, K., and MEISSNER, K. W. *Phys. Rev.* **76**, 1530 (1949)
75. BRATTAIN, W. H., and BRIGGS, H. B. *Phys. Rev.* **75**, 1705 (1949)
76. BRIGGS, H. B. *Phys. Rev.* **77**, 287 (1950); SALZBERG, C. D., and VILLA, J. J. *J. opt. Soc. Amer.* **47**, 244 (1957)
77. ARCHER, R. J. *Phys. Rev.* **110**, 354 (1958)
78. SPITZER, W. G., and FAN, H. Y. *Phys. Rev.* **106**, 882 (1957)
79. CARDONA, M., and SOMMERS, H. S. *Phys. Rev.* **122**, 1382 (1961)
80. MOSS, T. S. *Optical Properties of Semiconductors* (Butterworths, London, 1959)
81. WEST, C. D., and MAKAS, A. S. *J. chem. Phys.* **16**, 427 (1948)
82. BURSTEIN, E., and SMITH, P. L. *Phys. Rev.* **74**, 229 (1948)
83. CARDONA, M. *Thesis* (Harvard University, 1959). Available as Report HP-5 from the Division of Engineering and Applied Physics, Harvard University
84. DASH, W. C., and NEWMAN, R. *Phys. Rev.* **99**, 1151 (1955)
85. RAMACHANDRAN, G. N. *Proc. Indian Acad. Sci.* **25**, 266 (1947)
86. ANTONCIK, E. *Czech. J. Phys.* **5**, 409 (1955)
87. FAN, H. Y. *Phys. Rev.* **82**, 900 (1951)
88. HAYNES, J. R., LAX, M., and FLOOD, W. F. *J. Phys. chem. Solids* **8**, 392 (1959)
89. LUKES, F. *Czech. J. Phys.* **8**, 423 (1958)
90. ANTONCIK, E. *Czech. J. Phys.* **6**, 209 (1956)
91. ARCHER, R. J. *Phys. Rev.* **110**, 354 (1958)
92. PHILIPP, H. R., and TAFT, E. A. *Phys. Rev.* **113**, 1002 (1959)
93. BOWERS, R. *J. Phys. chem. Solids* **8**, 210 (1959)
94. LAX, B. et al. *Phys. Rev.* **93**, 1418 (1954)
95. DRESSELHAUS, G., et al. *Phys. Rev.* **98**, 368 (1955)
96. KEESOM, P. H., and SEIDEL, G. *Phys. Rev.* **113**, 33 (1959)
97. STEVENS, P. K., CLELAND, J. W., CRAWFORD, J. H., and SCHWEINLER, H. C. *Phys. Rev.* **100**, 1084 (1955)
98. GEIST, D. *Naturwissenschaften* **45**, 33 (1958)
99. CARLSON, R. O., COLLINS, C. B., and GALLAGHER, C. J. *Bull. Amer. phys. Soc.* **1**, 128 (1956)
100. NATHAN, M. I., and PAUL, W. *Phys. Rev.* **128**, 38 (1962)
101. HOLLAND, M. G., and PAUL, W. *Phys. Rev.* **128**, 30, 43 (1962)
102. PAUL, W. 'Proceedings of the Intermetallic Semiconductor Conference at Schenectady, 1961'. *J. appl. Phys.* (Suppl.) S32, 2082 (1961)

103. 'Proceedings of the Intermetallic Semiconductor Conference at Schenectady, 1961'. *J. appl. Phys.* (Suppl.) S32 (1961)
104. HERMAN, F., GLICKSMAN, M., and PARMENTER, R. H. *Progress in Semiconductors 2* (Eds. Gibson, Aigrain, and Burgess) (Heywood, London; Wiley, New York, 1957)
105. EHRENREICH, H. *J. Phys. Chem. Solids* **12**, 97 (1957); *Phys. Rev.* **120**, 1951 (1960)
106. See, for example, WELKER, H., and WEISS, H. *Advances in Solid State Physics*, Vol. 3 (Eds. F. Seitz and D. Turnbull) (Academic, New York, 1956); FOLBERTH, O., and WELKER, H. *J. Phys. Chem. Solids* **8**, 14 (1959)
107. HERMAN, F. *J. Electron.* **1**, 103 (1955)
108. CALLAWAY, J. *J. Electron.* **2**, 330 (1956)
109. GLICKSMAN, M. *J. Phys. Chem. Solids* **8**, 511 (1959)
110. SPITZER, W. G., and FAN, H. Y. *Phys. Rev.* **106**, 882 (1957)
111. BARCUS, L. C., PERLMUTTER, A., and CALLAWAY, J. *Phys. Rev.* **111**, 167 (1958)
112. GRAY, P. V., and EHRENREICH, H. *Bull. Amer. phys. Soc.* **3**, 255 (1958)
113. SPITZER, W. G., and WHELAN, J. M. *Phys. Rev.* **114**, 59 (1959)
114. EHRENREICH, H. *Phys. Rev.* **120**, 1951 (1960)
115. HOWARD, W. E., and PAUL, W. Unpublished measurements
116. EDWARDS, A. L., SLYKHOUSE, T. E., and DRICKAMER, H. G. *J. Phys. Chem. Solids* **11**, 140 (1959)
117. PAUL, W., and WARSCHAUER, D. M. Unpublished measurements
118. STRAUMANIS, M. E., and AKA, E. J. *J. appl. Phys.* **23**, 330 (1952); BRIDGMAN, P. W. *Proc. Amer. Acad. Arts Sci.* **77**, 187 (1949)
119. ZWERDLING, S., ROTH, L., and LAX, B. *J. Phys. Chem. Solids* **8**, 397 (1959)
120. RADKOWSKY, A. *Phys. Rev.* **73**, 749 (1949)
121. FAN, H. Y. *Phys. Rev.* **78**, 808 (1950); *Phys. Rev.* **82**, 900 (1951)
122. MUTO, T., and OYAMA, S. *Progr. theor. Phys., Kyoto* **5**, 833 (1950)
123. JAMES, H. M. *Photoconductivity Conference*, p. 204 (Eds. R. G. Breckenridge, B. R. Russell, and E. E. Hahn) (Wiley, New York, 1956)
124. BROOKS, H. *Advances in Electronics and Electron Physics*, Vol. 7 (Ed. L. Marton) (Academic, New York, 1955)
125. KOHN, W. *Advances in Solid State Physics*, Vol. 5 (Eds. F. Seitz and D. Turnbull) (Academic, New York, 1957)
126. BROOKS, H., and FLETCHER, N. Unpublished work; FLETCHER, N. *Thesis* (Harvard University, 1956)
127. KHARTSIEV, V. E. *J. tech. Phys., Moscow* **28**, 1651 (1958)
128. TEITLER, S., and WALLIS, R. F. *J. Phys. Chem. Solids* **16**, 71 (1960)
129. KLEIN, C. *Proceedings of the International Conference on Semiconductor Physics*, Prague, p. 278 (Czechoslovakian Academy of Sciences, 1960)
130. DE BOER, J. H., and VAN GEEL, W. C. *Physica* **2**, 186 (1935)
131. KOENIG, S. H., NATHAN, M. I., PAUL, W., and SMITH, A. C. *Phys. Rev.* **118**, 1217 (1960)
132. GUNN, J. B. *Progress in Semiconductors 2* (Eds. Gibson, Aigrain, and Burgess) (Heywood, London; Wiley, New York, 1957)
133. CONWELL, E. M. *J. Phys. Chem. Solids* **8**, 234 (1959)
134. MILLER, S. L., NATHAN, M. I., and SMITH, A. C. *Phys. Rev. Lett.* **4**, 60 (1960)
135. NATHAN, M. I., MILLER, S. L., and FINEGOLD, L. *Bull. Amer. Phys. Soc.*, **5**, 265 (1960)
136. NATHAN, M. I., and PAUL, W. *Proceedings of the International Conference on Semiconductor Physics*, Prague, p. 209 (Czechoslovakian Academy of Sciences, 1960)
137. KELDYSH, L. V. *Soviet Phys. JETP* **34** (7), 665 (1958)
138. PRICE, P. J., and RADCLIFFE, J. M. *IBM J. Res. Dev.* **3**, 364 (1959)
139. MORGAN, J. V., and KANE, E. O. *Phys. Rev. Lett.* **3**, 466 (1959)
140. EDWARDS, A. L., and DRICKAMER, H. G. *Phys. Rev.* **122**, 1149 (1961)
141. PAUL, W. 'Proceedings of the Intermetallic Semiconductor Conference at Schenectady, 1961'. *J. appl. Phys.* (Suppl.) S32, 2082 (1961)
142. SAGAR, A. 'Proceedings of the Intermetallic Semiconductor Conference at Schenectady, 1961'. *J. appl. Phys.* (Suppl.) S32, 2073 (1961)

APPENDIX: LIST OF MAIN SYMBOLS

c	velocity of light
d	dilatation
f_i	Fermi factor, energy level i
g	(111) conduction band minima
g	degeneracy factor
i	square root of (-1)
j	current density
k	Boltzmann constant
k	wave vector
m	free electron mass
m^*	effective mass
m_{dx}	density of states mass, in x band
m_{lx}, m_{tx}	components of effective mass tensor in x band
n	electron density
n	real part of refractive index
n_0	equilibrium or zero pressure electron density
n_g	electron density in g band
n_i	intrinsic carrier density
n_s	electron density in s band
n_x	electron density in x band
n_{x0}	electron density in x band, at zero pressure
p	momentum or momentum operator
p	hole density
p_0	equilibrium or zero pressure hole density
p_1	excess hole density
q	electronic charge
s	(100) conduction band minima
y	= energy divided by kT
$(y)_N$	ratio, value of quantity at 10^4 kg cm^{-2} to value at zero pressure
A_x	intravalley scattering probability, valley x
B	interband scattering probability
$\mathscr{C}$	$= (C_s/C_g)\exp(-\Delta E/kT)$
C_0	$= 2(2\pi kT/h^2)^{3/2}$
C_g, C_s	density of states factors for g, s conduction bands
C_p	average elastic constant
C_v	density of states factors for valence band
C_x	$= m_{dx}^{3/2} v_x$
C_x'	$= (m_{lx}^{1/2} m_{tx})[4\sqrt{(2)}\pi]/h^3$
D_n, D_p	diffusion coefficients for electrons and holes
E_c	critical field

E_d	donor ionization energy
E_f	Fermi level
E_g	energy of g conduction band edge
E_{g0}	energy of (000) conduction band edge
E_G	energy gap, valence to conduction band
$E_{G,\,eff}$	effective energy gap
E_{Gg}	energy gap, valence band to g conduction band
E_H	ionization energy of hydrogen
E_i, E_j	impurity energy level
E_I	impurity ionization energy
E_k	energy level for wave vector $\mathbf{k}$
E_{lg}	deformation potential for g conduction band edge
E_s	energy of s conduction band edge
E_v	energy of valence band edge
E_x	energy of x conduction band edge
J	current
J_p	peak current
K	absorption constant
K_g	$= m_{lg}/m_{tg}$
K_s	$= m_{ls}/m_{ts}$
L	diffusion length
N	carrier density (Section 5)
N_0	oscillator density
N_a	acceptor impurity density
N_d	donor impurity density
R	reflectivity
R_H	Hall constant
S	$= BC_s' v_s / A_g C_g'$
S'	$= BC_g' v_g / A_s C_s$
T	absolute temperature
V	voltage
α	volume thermal expansion coefficient
β	volume compressibility
ϵ	real part of dielectric constant
ϵ'	imaginary part of dielectric constant
ϵ_0	intrinsic dielectric constant
θ_D	Debye temperature
λ	wavelength
μ	mobility
μ^*	mobility in absence of interband scattering
μ_{eff}	effective mobility
μ_n, μ_p	electron, hole mobilities
μ_x	mobility in x band, any pressure
μ_{x0}	mobility in x band, at zero pressure

ν	frequency
ν	extinction index
ν_x	number of minima in x band
ρ	resistivity
σ	conductivity
τ_l, τ_t	components of scattering time tensor
$\tau(E)$	scattering time, as a function of energy
χ	electric susceptibility
χ_0	intrinsic electric susceptibility
χ_c	free carrier electric susceptibility
ω	angular frequency
Δ	$= \Delta E / kT$
Δ_p	real part of dielectric constant
ΔE	energy difference between g and s bands
ΔE_0	energy difference between g and s bands, at zero pressure